The Taste of Scotland Guide 1995

Introduction

Scotland is renowned worldwide as a source for some of the world's finest food and drinks made from best quality, natural raw materials. As consumers from all over the world increasingly look for freshness and variety with quality, Scotland's reputation continues to grow.

Within the range and variety of Scottish produce, Scotch whisky stands out as the "flagship". However, other foods such as Scotch beef, fresh and smoked Scottish salmon, game – venison and grouse, shellfish, seafish – fresh and smoked, oats, shortbread, soups – such as Scotch Broth, Cullen Skink or Cock-a Leekie, all have the hallmark and reputation for being simple and natural quality.

While for centuries the country has been in the business of producing and exporting food, this has not taken place at the expense of supplying and satisfying the palate of people in Scotland, both residents and visitors. Through all sorts of establishments, such as those listed in the Taste of Scotland Guide, ranging from the grandest of hotels to the humblest of restaurants and cafes, consumers anywhere in Scotland can buy first class meals at whatever price suits them.

Furthermore, the country is not resting on its historical reputation and living in the past. In recent years Scotland's leading chefs have proved their worth on more than one occasion in the heat of international competition. In the Culinary Olympics in Frankfurt in 1993 and in the Salon Culinaire competition in Singapore in 1994, the small team of chefs from Scotland achieved a standard of success that puts them among the best in the world, alongside much larger teams from other countries.

In these competitions the team of young Scottish chefs demonstrated not only that they possess all the necessary basic culinary skills, but also that, using mainly traditional Scottish raw materials, they can apply these to making innovative, new, appetising dishes designed for the contemporary taste.

Through the Taste of Scotland scheme, and its annual Guide, consumers can easily find and enjoy the fruits of the skills of these artists and their colleagues, no matter where they are in Scotland.

Standing Stones, Machrie
(Isle of Arran Tourist Board)

"Over 400 establishments have been selected for the Taste of Scotland Guide 1995, making it an invaluable reference for anyone who values the eating experience.

Regardless of which part of Scotland you are in, you are sure to find something to suit.

Within the Taste of Scotland Guide there is a range of highly recommended eating places, large and small, from restaurants to hotels and country houses, guest and farm houses.

Taste of Scotland covers the whole spectrum because people have different requirements at different times and so a variety of price ranges and style of food are given to offer maximum choice.

It is important to know that hotels and restaurants etc cannot buy their way into this Guide. They have to be identified and selected as being of superior standard and pass a strict inspection system.

Each year there are changes as worthy newcomers appear on the scene and some others fail to meet the requirements and are no longer listed.

Quality is the watchword and Taste of Scotland continues with its role of uplifting the standard of food in Scotland and encouraging the best presentation of the fine produce this country has to offer.

Enjoy the tastes of Scotland! "

Nancy K Campbell

Editor

1

River Tweed/Eildon Hills (Scottish Borders Tourist Board)

THE TASTE OF SCOTLAND 1995

This is to certify that

Hawkcraig House

has been selected for membership of

The Taste of Scotland Scheme

in recognition of its commitment to the pursuit of excellence in food preparation and service

TASTE OF SCOTLAND

current members are identified by the 1995 Certificate of Membership which should be on display.

The Taste of Scotland Scheme Ltd acknowledges the support of:

Scottish Tourist Board
Scottish Enterprise
Scotch Quality Beef & Lamb Association
Scottish Salmon Board

and

Bain of Tarves
Matthew Algie
Walkers Shortbread
Baxters
Waverley Vintners
The Macallan

Contents

How to use this guide

Inverness

Address & Tel. No. etc ➤

Description ➤

Any seasonal limitations ➤

Specimen inclusive terms
quoted on per person per
night basis ➤

STB Grading & Classification ➤

Location 116

BUNCHREW HOUSE HOTEL
Bunchrew
Inverness IV3 6TA
Tel: 01463 234917
Fax: 01463 710620
*On A862 Inverness-Beauly, c. 10 minutes from
centre of Inverness.*

Bunchrew House is a very fine 17th century
mansion spectacularly situated on the shores of
the Beauly Firth, within 18 acres of landscaped
gardens and woodlands. Careful restoration and
refurbishment has been carried out over the
years to preserve the heritage of this historic old
building while providing the high standards of
accommodation and amenities expected by
guests today. Bedrooms and suites are
individually decorated, very comfortable and
luxuriously appointed, and some feature
canopied four poster or half tester beds. Log
fires blaze in winter in the charming wood-
panelled drawing room where guests relax over
drinks before dinner in the candlelit Mackenzie
Room with its view out over the Firth to the Black
Isle. The chef presents an interesting selection
of dishes on the thoughtfully compiled four
course dinner menus. A new bistro style
restaurant is due to open during 1995 which will
offer a more informal style of eating and
complement the existing dining room. In their
first two years at Bunchrew, Stewart and Lesley
Dykes have proved themselves caring and
friendly hosts who put a great deal of effort into
maintaining the high standards for which
Bunchrew House is renowned.

Open all year
Rooms: 11 with private facilities
Bar Lunch 12 – 2 pm (b)
*Dining Room/Restaurant Lunch 12 –
2 pm (b)*
Bar Supper 7 – 9 pm (b)
Dinner 7 – 9 pm (d)
Facilities for disabled visitors
No smoking in dining room
Bed & Breakfast £40 – £70
Dinner B & B £65 – £95
*• Highland game terrine served with a pear and
rosemary jelly. Home-made pies. Baked fillet of
wild salmon topped with a herb crust and served
with a tomato and basil sauce. Pan-fried fillet of
beef topped with wild mushrooms and finished
with a tomato and red wine jus. Bread and butter
pudding served with a light crème anglaise.*
STB Commended 4 Crowns
Credit cards: 1, 2, 3
Proprietors: Stewart & Lesley Dykes

◄ Map Reference

◄ How to find

◄ Accommodation
◄ Meal times & prices

◄ Specimen food specialities
   to show style of food

◄ Credit cards accepted

4

Entries

- Establishments selected by Taste of Scotland are listed in this Guide in alphabetical order under the nearest town or village.

- Island entries are shown alphabetically by island or island group, e.g. Skye, Orkney.

- A full list of hotels, restaurants etc is given in alphabetical order in the Index at the end of the Guide.

Special diets or requirements

- Although vegetarian meals are more readily available nowadays, we would advise that you mention this requirement when making your booking.

- Other special needs, such as diet or facilities for disabled guests, should also be arranged in advance.

Wines and spirits

- Except where otherwise stated, all hotels and restaurants are licensed for the service of wines, spirits, beers etc.

- Most unlicensed establishments – which tend to be small guest houses or farmhouses – will welcome your taking your own wine, but again please enquire in advance.

- Where an establishment is shown to have a 'restricted licence' it generally means that residents and diners may be served alcoholic beverages, but members of the public may not call in for a drink.

Lunches

- Nowadays lunchtime eating has become much less formal except in city centre hotels and restaurants. Bar snacks are more usual in some smaller establishments and rural hotels.

- To simplify the choice available, we specify Bar Lunch or Dining Room/Restaurant Lunch in this Guide.

Restrictions on smoking

- Within the information on each establishment, we have noted where there is no smoking permitted in the dining room or restaurant.

- Where an area is set aside for non-smokers, the entry will show 'No smoking area in dining room/ restaurant'.

- In addition we have highlighted where no smoking is permitted throughout an establishment or where there are restrictions on smoking in guest bedrooms.

- Entries which do not give any such information are taken to have no restriction on smoking.

Pets

- Pets are accepted in some hotels by arrangement.

  It is wise, however, to confirm this when booking as there may be a small charge and sometimes there is a restriction on the areas within the establishment where pets are permitted.

- Restaurants generally do not accept dogs.

Foreign Languages

- Where establishments have provided us with information on any foreign languages spoken, this has been incorporated within the descriptive paragraph about the establishment.

Meal Prices

- Prices are quoted as a **guideline only** and Guide readers are advised to check prevailing prices when making their reservation.

- These estimated prices for 1995 were provided by the establishments, based on a three course meal, excluding drinks.

- Where more courses are the norm, this is indicated next to the price band.

Key to Price Bands

(a) under £10

(b) £10 – £15

(c) £15 – £20

(d) £20 – £25

(e) £25 – £30

(f) over £30

- Times of food service are listed to show **first and last orders**, unless otherwise stated.

Accommodation Rates

- Specimen inclusive terms are listed, once again as a **guideline**.

- Where a price range is given, the **lower price** normally indicates the rate **per person sharing** a double room, and the **higher price** the rate for **single occupancy** or **per person** in a **higher quality room**.

- The price range may also reflect high and low season fluctuations.

- Where a **room rate** is offered, this information is shown in the entry.

- Some room rates include breakfast – check with establishment.

Culzean Castle (Ayrshire Tourist Board)

Credit/Charge Cards

- Where an establishment accepts credit/charge cards, those taken are listed under the following codes:

Key

1   Access/Mastercard/Eurocard

2   American Express

3   Visa

4   Carte Bleu

5   Diners Club

6   Mastercharge

   SWITCH and DELTA cards are listed by name where appropriate.

How To Avoid Disappointment

- Make an **advance reservation** whenever possible.

- Mention you are using the **Taste of Scotland Guide**.

- **Remember!** Many food items are seasonal and the specialities listed have been selected as an indication of the style of food on offer, but there is no guarantee of availability on any particular day.

- **Check** if any **price changes** have taken place since the publication of this Guide.

- **Confirm** that **credit cards** are accepted.

Comments

- Taste of Scotland welcomes comments – both good and bad.

- However, **if you have an unsatisfactory meal**, we would always advise that you **speak to the restaurant or hotel manager or proprietor <u>at the time</u>**.

- It gives an immediate opportunity for the situation to be rectified or explained.

- If this fails to solve the problem, do write to the Taste of Scotland Scheme about your experience. While we do not have operational control of any establishment listed, we will pass on your comments for investigation.

- But do let us hear of your good experiences too!

- We like to give our members feedback on comments from the public, so comment slips are provided at the end of this Guide for your use.

BY APPOINTMENT TO
HER MAJESTY THE QUEEN

FRUIT CANNERS
W.A. BAXTER & SONS LTD

Baxters ®

The family of fine foods

Discover the World of Baxters

Enjoy the Baxters Experience

- Free admission
- Free car and coach parking with facilities for the disabled
- Audio Visual show • Guided factory tour
- The Old Shop Museum - Where the Baxter Story began
- The George Baxter Cellar - speciality foods, wines & spirits
- Mrs Baxter's Victorian Kitchen - extensive international gifts & cookery utensils
- Additional quality retail outlet offering the "Best of Scotland" merchandise
- Spey Restaurant seating 130
- Herd of pedigreed Highland cattle
- Landscaped grounds and views of the magnificent River Spey
- Woodland walks and trails
- Family picnic area
- Toilet facilities for the disabled

Coach parties are requested to book in advance.

VISITOR FACILITIES

OPEN 7 DAYS A WEEK - January to December.
9.30 a.m. - 5 p.m. weekdays.
10.a.m. - 5p.m. weekends.

FACTORY TOURS - Weekdays only.
Guided tours of the factory from
9.30 a.m. - 11.30 a.m. and
12.30 p.m. - 4.00 p.m.
(last Factory tour 2.00 p.m. Friday)

Tours subject to availability.

**Parties greater than 10 people,
please book in advance
to avoid disappointment -
an enquiry prior to your visit
should confirm availability.**

FACTORY TOURS ARE NOT AVAILABLE
DURING FACTORY HOLIDAYS.

*All visitor facilities are suitable for the disabled
except for the factory tour.*

**Baxters of Speyside Ltd.,
Fochabers, Scotland, IV32 7LD.
Tel: (01343) 820393**

*Come and discover the world
of Baxters, part of Scotland's
proud heritage*

STB Grading & Classification Scheme

Since 1985, the Scottish Tourist Board has been systematically inspecting hotels, bed and breakfasts, and self catering accommodation, defining the standards that visitors expect and helping owners and operators meet those standards. Every establishment which is a member of the Grading and Classification Scheme – almost 6,000 – is visited each year.

In a two-tier scheme, accommodation all over the country – from the simplest to the most sophisticated – is GRADED for quality and CLASSIFIED for its facilities.

Grades are based on a wide ranging assessment of quality and service aspects. Each establishment is assessed on its own merits so that any type can achieve the highest grade.

DELUXE reflects an EXCELLENT overall standard
HIGHLY COMMENDED reflects a VERY GOOD overall standard
COMMENDED reflects a GOOD overall standard
APPROVED reflects an ACCEPTABLE overall standard

These GRADES are awarded by the STB inspectors once they have checked all the important factors that contribute to quality in an establishment. Just as you would, they look for clean, attractive surroundings, well furnished and heated. They sample meals, sleep in the beds, and talk to the staff. Like you, they know that quality should be assessed irrespective of the range of facilities on offer and, of course, they know the value of a warm and welcoming smile.

The CROWN CLASSIFICATION denotes the range of facilities on offer - things such as private bathrooms, lounges, meal provision and so on.

From a basic LISTED classification up to FIVE CROWNS can be added. So more crowns mean more facilities.

The distinctive blue plaques show the awards made by the STB inspectors as a result of their independent annual assessment.

For more information about Grading and Classification of accommodation in Scotland contact :

Scottish Tourist Board, 23 Ravelston Terrace, Edinburgh EH4 3EU

Sunset on Glenfinnan Monument & Loch Shiel
(Alex Gillespie Photography, Fort William)

Berneray, North Uist (Western Isles Tourist Board)

Glen Affric (Inverness, Loch Ness & Nairn Tourist Board)

Harrow Inn Close (Moray Tourist Board/Anne Burgess)

Grippy.

ONE OF the differences between greatness and mere eccentricity, is an ability in the truly great *to draw out the genius* in another.

So it was with some smacking of the lips that we heard of a recent tasting organized by Decanter Magazine.

Three of Scotland's MOST LAUDED malt whiskies were to be rated in terms of 'partnership appeal' with that other great Scottish contribution to world gastronomy~ SMOKED SPEYSIDE SALMON.

And which one emerged with commendations such as 'a real corker...', 'full, strong, dry *grippy flavours*' and 'the perfect partner'?

Yes, you have *smoked it out*. ' I love it and would recommend it.'

The Macallan. The Malt.

Easter Elchies House, Home of The Macallan

The Macallan Taste Of Scotland Awards

1994 was an exciting year for the Taste of Scotland welcoming The Macallan as the new sponsor of the prestigious awards scheme.

Now in their eighth year the Awards were set up to encourage the pursuit of excellence and by so doing to encourage others to emulate the winners.

Each year we invite you, the customer, to nominate establishments in which you have received outstanding standards. You can be instrumental in deciding those worthy of the awards.

The Macallan single malt is known for its unique character and unrivalled quality and the marriage of these standards makes The Macallan the perfect partner for the Taste of Scotland Awards.

Awards are restricted to establishments which are listed in the Taste of Scotland Guide and thus are already highlighted as leaders in their particular category.

The 1994 winners of The Macallan Taste of Scotland Awards are:

Hotel of the Year	~	**Isle of Eriska Hotel, nr Oban**
Restaurant of the Year	~	**The Courtyard on the Lane, Aberdeen**
Country House Hotel of the Year	~	**Ballathie House Hotel, nr Perth**
Special Merit Award for Outstanding Hospitality	~	**Lynwilg House, by Aviemore**
Special Merit Award for Enterprise	~	**Chatters, Dunoon**
The Macallan Personality of the Year	~	**Andrew Radford, Atrium, Edinburgh**

The Macallan Personality of the Year is a new Award which is awarded by the judges for the first time this year. This award recognises an individual or memorable character within the Taste of Scotland establishments.

The 1994 winners have been highlighted in the listings with this symbol:

During 1995 the judges will be considering nominations once again. Please use the coupons on pages 195 and 197. Nomination cards are available at Taste of Scotland member establishments, and letters or postcards are equally welcome. We value your feedback from Taste of Scotland establishments.

Closing date for entries 31 August 1995.

1995 AWARDS

The categories for the 1995 Awards will be:

Hotel of the Year
Restaurant of the Year
Country House Hotel of the Year
The Macallan Personality of the Year
Special Merit Awards

As in the past, the categories for the Special Merit Awards will be decided based upon the recommendations received.

We welcome your nominations for all categories and in particular for the Personality of the Year with your reasons for the nomination.

Achray House Hotel

Stunning Lochside position in St Fillans – an area of outstanding natural beauty.
Well established, family run hotel, known for its wide selection of good food, service and a caring attitude that brings people back year after year.
The perfect base for sightseeing, golf, walking, field and watersports.
From £22.00/night, en-suite, B & B per night.

Contact: Tony or Jane Ross
Achray House Hotel
St Fillans, Crieff PH6 2NF
Tel 01764 685231
Fax 01764 685320

 E G O N RONAY'S GUIDES AA ★★ ❀

see entry page 133

Alba Smokehouse

SUPERIOR QUALITY SMOKED SEAFOOD
Direct to hotels by 24 hour delivery
Available to personal callers
Mail-order service

SCOTTISH FOOD AWARDS WINNER 1994
Scottish Food Newcomer of the Year
Scottish Food Product of the Year:
Smoked Queen Scallops

Nominated Supplier MacDonalds Hotels Ltd

Contact: Michael or Karen Leng
Kilmory, Lochgilphead,
Argyll PA31 8RR
Tel/Fax: 01546 606400

𝒜N OLD FRIEND INVITES YOU TO DINNER.

It's not often you get to eat out at a landmark. Stonehenge may have many attractions, but a Loch Fyne Oyster Soup isn't one of them. Nor is St.Paul's famed for its Prime Fillet of Angus Beef. Yet, you can get both these dishes at The Grill, No 1 Princes Street at another national treasure, The Balmoral Hotel. Enjoy Chef Campbell's daily changing 5-course dinner menu or choose from an extensive à la Carte menu.

THE GRILL

No. 1 Princes Street

For a copy of our menu please call 0131 556 2414

THE BALMORAL
EDINBURGH

FORTE GRAND

see entry page 92

The Best Malt Whisky?
by Charles MacLean

It has been said "there is no bad malt whisky – just good and better malt". And the best malt whisky of all? This is for you to find out while you travel round Scotland. It is a matter of personal preference, and even your own preferences will change with the occasion, the time of day, your mood. The first principle of malt whisky appreciation is to trust your own reactions.

There are three distinct styles of Scotch: malt whisky, grain whisky (there are only two of these generally available – Cameron Brig and Invergordon) and blended whisky. Over 95% of whisky drunk is in the latter category – a mix of grain and malt whiskies – including such household names as Bells, The Famous Grouse, Johnny Walker and Cutty Sark.

However it is the malts we are concerned with here. These exhibit the true character of Scotch whisky and display the greatest diversity of flavours, and they are as worthy of study as fine wines. Each is the product of a single distillery and, as with fine wine, each has both individual and regional characteristics.

The traditional regional divisions are Lowland, Highland (with Speyside as a sub-division) Islay and Campbeltown.

Lowland Malts tend to be pale in colour, light and dry in flavour. The malted barley used is generally unpeated, which makes for a grassy or hay-like aroma, often with cereal notes. They make excellent aperitifs. Names to look out for are Auchentoshan, Rosebank and Glenkinchie.

Campbeltown, on the Kintyre peninsula, used to have the greatest concentration of distilleries in Scotland – 32 at the height of its fame. Today there are only two: Springbank and Glen Scotia. They are medium-bodied and famous for their slightly smoky or misty scent, with a trace of salt on the palate.

Islay is the most southern of the Western Isles and produces the most aromatic whiskies of all, noted for their peatiness and seaweedy pungency. There are eight distilleries on the 25 mile-long island; their products vary widely – from the oily Laphroaig and aromatic Bowmore, to the complex Lagavulin, and the gentle Bunnahabhain.

It is more difficult to generalise about the characteristics of Highland malts.

From the far north come the classics Highland Park, Glenmorangie (the best selling malt whisky in Scotland) and Clynelish: medium-bodied, with spicy, heathery, fruity aromas. Whiskies from the Western Isles – Mull (where Ledaig is made), Skye (Talisker)

Kinnoull Hill, Perth (Perthshire Tourist Board)

and Jura (Jura) – have traces of peat, with a whiff of smoke and some spicy fire (especially Talisker). Those from the south and east

Highlands range from the gentle and flowery (such as Edradour; Old Fettercairn or Glengoyne) to the big flavoured and nutty (Royal Lochnagar and Glenturret, are examples).

Speyside is the heartland of malt whisky distilling, its products long prized by connoisseurs for their elegance, complexity and diversity.

At one end of the scale, Speysides are light-bodied and easily drunk, with fresh flowery scents and sweet flavours (try Tamdhu, Cardhu or Glenfiddich – the best selling malt whisky in the world). Others are big-bodied, rich, rounded and sherried, the finest digestifs imaginable (the classic is the Macallan, the most popular malt on Speyside itself). Still others fall between the two extremes, with great finesse and plenty of body (the world famous The Glenlivet is in this category, also Aberlour, Knockando and Glenfarclas).

There is a malt whisky for every occasion and every mood – whether you are looking for a mid-morning warmer, a pre-lunch aperitif, a post-prandial consideration, an after dinner digestif or a profound late night contemplation by a roaring log fire. All the bars and restaurants in Scotland offer a selection (ranging from half a dozen of the most popular names, to over a hundred 'expressions' or vintages). Bar staff, and other customers will all have their views and their favourites.

Initiating a discussion about malt whisky is a great way to break the ice; discovering your favourites is a wonderfully rewarding quest, and if you take some of your favourite malts home with you, you'll be able to savour your memories of Scotland as you savour the dram.

Charles MacLean
Author of The Mitchell Beazley
Pocket Whisky Book

Duffus Castle (Moray Tourist Board/Anne Burgess)

Balmoral

SET IN A BEAUTIFUL FORESTED AREA OF DEESIDE

From the proceeds of public access, donations are made to various charities.

CAR PARKING IS IN THE GRAMPIAN REGIONAL CAR PARK

ADMISSION: Adults £2.50, Senior Citizens £2.00, Accompanied Children under 16 Free

Enquire at the main gate for facilities for the disabled.

The Grounds, Gardens and an Exhibition of Paintings and Works of Art in the Castle Ballroom, and a Carriage Exhibition, are open to the public from May 1st to July 31st, Monday to Saturday, 10am~5pm daily.

REFRESHMENTS ROOM, GIFT SHOPS, COUNTRY WALKS, PONY TREKKING, PONY CART RIDES (WHEN PONIES AVAILABLE)

FOR FURTHER INFORMATION TELEPHONE CRATHIE (03397) 42334/5

see entry page 137

BURTS HOTEL

Melrose   Roxburghshire

Distinguished family-run town Hotel built in 1722. Tastefully furnished with 21 en suite bedrooms all with modern facilities including colour televisions, direct-dial telephones, Tea/Coffee facilities, etc.

Recently refurbished elegant restaurant offering both à la carte and table d'hôte menus where the emphasis is on the abundance of local game and fresh fish imaginatively prepared and beautifully presented by our chef, Gary Moore, who was a regional finalist in Taste of Scotland Scotch Lamb Challenge. Lounge bar serving light lunches and suppers daily, billiards room, two lounges, private carpark and extensive gardens.

Burts Hotel is the ideal centre for touring the beautiful Border country and enjoying traditional Scottish hospitality. Several golf courses are within easy reach and salmon and trout fishing can be arranged. Game shooting on local estates also available with prior notice.

 AA ★★★ **RAC**★★★   E G O N RONAY'S **GUIDES**   Michelin   Les Routiers

recommended

For brochure write to Graham and Anne Henderson, Proprietors. Tel 01896 822285 Fax 01896 822285

THE BUTTERY

Leave modern Glasgow behind as you cross the threshold. The Buttery is a dining out experience not to be missed. Good food delightfully prepared by Chef Johnson and his enthusiastic brigade, served in gracious Victorian surroundings by Manager Jim Wilson and his staff.

THE BUTTERY, 652 ARGYLL STREET, GLASGOW.
RESERVATIONS: 0141-221 8188.
FAX: 0141-204 4639.

Open for lunch and dinner every weekday and dinner on Saturday (closed on Sunday).

see entry page 107
see entry page 135

Sample Menu.

Terrine of Wild Salmon Waverley
served with Drambuie and fresh tarragon.
Haggis Land o'Burns
pan sauté with a dash of local whisky and garnished with oatcakes.
Loch Leven Mussels
lightly braised in garlic, white wine and cream.

Fillets of Lemon Sole Solway Bay
poached in lemon and presented in a prawn and leek sauce.

Shellfish Corryvrechan
*scampi, prawns, mussels and queen scallops
poached in a white wine and leek sauce with a dash of coriander.*
Aberdeen Angus Sirloin Steak Auld Alliance
pan sauté and served with an onion and brandy cream sauce.
Breast of Chicken Bannockburn
filled with a vegetable and haggis stuffing and sauté in basil butter.
Roast Haunch of Venison Ben Vorlich
presented in a rich red wine sauce.

Homemade Peach Cheesecake.
Apple and Ginger Charlotte with Cream.
The 'Other' Macallan
shortbread sandwich filled with soft fruit, ice cream and cream.
Scottish Cheeses
Dunsyre Blue and Ingles Smoked Cheddar with Biscuits.

Clachan Cottage Hotel
Lochside, Lochearnhead, Perthshire FK19 8PU
Tel (Lochearnhead) 01567-830247

La
POMPADOUR
RESTAURANT

COMFORT AND ELEGANCE IN EVERY DETAIL

Established in 1925 La Pompadour has been a leading exponent of fine cuisine in Scotland ever since. It is attention to detail that distinguishes La Pompadour's style and level of service.

Under the direction of Executive Chef Tony Binks, La Pompadour's menus feature the very best of Scottish produce. The menus are composed to coincide with the seasonality of Scotland's produce offering our guests an exciting combination of excellence in both culinary skills and produce.

La Pompadour, Macallan/Decanter Restaurant of the Year 1988, Taste of Scotland Restaurant of the Year 1992.

Telephone: 0131 225 2433 to make your reservation.

★★★★★

see entry page 93

Taste Of Scotland

Taste of Scotland is delighted to welcome the following prestigious companies as Corporate Members of the scheme.

Bain Of Tarves

*B*ain of Tarves is a Specialist Butchery and Game Meat Suppliers.

Founded in 1955 by John Christie Bain, the business began as a local butcher's shop in the Aberdeenshire village of Tarves and is still thriving to this day.

The requirements of this successful and quickly growing enterprise lead to the construction of new factory facilities in 1974. The addition of game processing facilities in 1978, followed by coldstore, chill and garage facilities in 1988, has resulted in a modern and fully EC approved processing plant which today sends a wide range of high quality Scottish produce to both domestic and export markets alike.

Matthew Algie

*I*n 1864, a Greenock born grocer called Matthew Algie began importing tea directly to the Clyde and distributing it by the chest to other grocers in the area.

Matthew Algie's Glasgow factory is run, to this day, by the founder's family. In recent years, the company has built its reputation on supplying fine blends of tea and coffee to top hotels and restaurants, as far apart as Portree and Park Lane.

Tea drinkers can enjoy one of Matthew Algie's finest blends at any time; their Scottish Choice Tea Bags are available in shops throughout Scotland.

Walkers Shortbread

*W*alkers Shortbread was founded by Joseph Walker in 1898 as a village bakery and is situated in the picturesque village of Aberlour in Speyside.

Walkers remains to this day a completely independent company run by the grandchildren of the founder.

The firm produces goods of the highest possible standard. Its wide range of pure butter shortbread, oatcakes, cakes and biscuits are ideally packaged for the quality minded caterer.

Taste of Scotland wishes to thank

CORPORATE MEMBERS

CORPORATE
MEMBER

Baxters

For over 125 years, Baxters Ltd has been producing a range of the finest quality foods enjoyed in markets at home and overseas.

An independent Scottish family owned and managed company, Baxters holds three Royal Warrants of Appointment and is known worldwide for innovation and quality.

Situated on the banks of the River Spey, Baxters' visitors centre is now one of Scotland's major tourist attractions.

Waverley Vintners

Waverley Vintners have been supplying fine wines to hotels and restaurants for many years.

A Wine Development Manager with extensive specialist wine knowledge, Norman Barr, is based in Perth and is available to advise any Taste of Scotland establishment on the choice of their wines and construction of their wine list.

Waverley Vintners also run a successful Wine Club which allows members of the public to enjoy their wide range of wines, choosing them in the comfort of their own home and having them delivered straight to the door.

The Macallan

The Macallan Distillery was one of the first Scottish Distilleries to take out a licence in 1824.

Located on the banks of the River Spey, the distillery was purchased by Roderick Kemp in 1892 and during the next 100 years the Company and family prospered.

The family link continues to this day with the present Chairman, Allan Shiach, direct descendant of Roderick Kemp, taking a very active role.

The Macallan was already a favourite among blenders – who to this day continue to use it as a "top dressing" – and was available in the 1960s as a single malt only on Speyside. In 1980, the decision was taken to launch The Macallan nationally in Britain as a single bottled malt whisky.

And the rest, as they say, is history !

these companies for their support.

Local Tourist Information

For specific information on a particular part of Scotland contact the following:

Angus Tourist Board
Tel: Arbroath (01241) 872609/876680

Aviemore & Spey Valley Tourist Board
Tel: Aviemore (01479) 810363

Ayrshire Tourist Board
Tel: Ayr (01292) 288688

Banff & Buchan Tourist Board
Tel: Banff (01261) 812419

Bute and Cowal Tourist Board
Tel: Dunoon (01369) 3785

Caithness Tourist Board
Tel: Wick (01955) 2596

City of Aberdeen Tourist Board
Tel: Aberdeen (01224) 632727

City of Dundee Tourist Board
Tel: Dundee (01382) 434664

Clyde Valley Tourist Board
Tel: Lanark (01555) 662544

Dunfermline District Council
Tel: Dunfermline (01383) 726262

Dumfries & Galloway Tourist Board
Tel: Dumfries (01387) 50434

East Lothian Tourist Board
Tel: Dunbar (01368) 63353

Edinburgh Tourist Board
Tel: Edinburgh (0131) 557 1700

Fort William & Lochaber Tourist Board
Tel: Fort William (01397) 70 3781

Forth Valley Tourist Board
Tel: Linlithgow (01506) 84 4600

Gordon District Tourist Board
Tel: Aberdeen (01224) 276276

Greater Glasgow Tourist Board
Tel: Glasgow (0141) 204 4400

Inverness, Loch Ness & Nairn Tourist Board
Tel: Inverness (01463) 234353

Isle of Arran Tourist Board
Tel: Brodick (01770) 302140

Isle of Skye & South West Ross Tourist Board
Tel: Portree (01478) 612137

Kincardine & Deeside Tourist Board
Tel: Banchory (0133 082) 2066

Kirkcaldy District Council
Tel: Leven (01333) 429464

Loch Lomond, Stirling & Trossachs Tourist Board
Tel: Stirling (01786) 475019

Midlothian Tourism Association
Tel: (0131) 440 2210 (Roslin)

Moray Tourist Board
Tel: Elgin (01343) 542666

Orkney Tourist Board
Tel: Kirkwall (01856) 872856

Perthshire Tourist Board
Tel: Perth (01738) 627958

Ross & Cromarty Tourist Board
Tel: Kessock (01463 73) 1505

St Andrews & North East Fife Tourist Board
Tel: St Andrews (01334) 472021

Scottish Borders Tourist Board
Tel: Jedburgh (01835) 63435/63688

Shetland Islands Tourism
Tel: Lerwick (01595) 3434

Sutherland Tourist Board
Tel: Dornoch (01862) 810400

Western Isles Tourist Board
Tel: Stornoway (01851) 70 3088

West Highlands & Islands of Argyll Tourist Board
Tel: Oban (01631) 63122

Coul House Hotel

Our views are breathtaking. The ancient 'Mackenzies of Coul' picked a wonderful situation for their lovely home. Today, Ann and Martyn will give you a warm Highland welcome. You'll enjoy the 'Taste of Scotland' food of chef Bentley, log fires, summer evening piper and 'Skye' and 'Raasay', the hotel's lovable labradors. Why not use our 'Highland Passport' to cruise on Loch Ness, visit Cawdor Castle, sail to the Summer Isles... or follow our 'Highland Heritage' trail to Glenfiddich Distillery, the Wildlife Park, Culloden Battlefield... for golfers, there's a 5-course holiday including championship Royal Dornoch... for anglers, we have our own salmon and trout fishing... there's pony trekking too.

Ring or write for our colour brochure.

**Coul House Hotel
By Strathpeffer,
Ross-shire
Tel 01997-421487
Fax 01997-421945**

see entry page 79

see entry page 142

THE Columba Hotel

Tranquil Lochside position with stunning views over Loch Fyne.

Log fired bars with local Malt Whiskies.

Local produce imaginatively prepared.

Extensive, but not expensive, Wine List.

STB
♛♛♛
Commended

Logis
of
Great Britain

**Tarbert, Kintyre,
Argyll PA29 6UF
Tel 01880-820 808**

see entry page 166

see entry page 88

Creebridge House Hotel

Galloway, South West Scotland

Built in 1760 this former shooting lodge to the Earl of Galloway is now an elegant 20 bedroom Country Hotel set in Newton Stewart in 3 acres of private gardens and woodland. 18 hole Golf course 400 yards from the front door. Private Salmon and Trout fishing on the Cree & Bladnoch rivers.

Choose from either the Garden Restaurant or our friendly local Bar where renowned Chef Proprietor Chris Walker and his team cook some of their Taste of Scotland Award winning dishes using fresh local produce. All rooms en suite with colour TV, direct dial phone etc.

*Prices from £27.50 bed and breakfast each
Phone or Fax for our brochure
Tel: 01671 402121 Fax: 01671 403258*

CROMLIX HOUSE

"A Taste of Cromlix is a Taste of Serenity"

The true traditions of Country House Hospitality are perfectly exemplified at Cromlix House, set within its own 5,000 acre estate.

Informal and welcoming, the essential feeling is that of a much loved home.

Recently refurbished our 6 unique guest-rooms and 8 spacious suites are furnished throughout with period fabrics and fine antique furniture.

Dining at Cromlix is, quite simply, an experience to be savoured.

Private Chapel, Sportings, Trout Lochs, Golf nearby.

AA★★★ (red), STB 4 Crown De Luxe
AA 2 Rosettes Cuisine Award
(See Major Guides)
(Red Stars - denotes consistently outstanding quality, ambience & hospitality)

Your hosts: David and Ailsa Assenti
(4 miles north of Dunblane (Stirling) off A9)

**Kinbuck by Dunblane, Perthshire FK15 9JT
Telephone 01786 822125 Facsimile 01786 825450**

Cuisine
FOODSERVICE

Unit E, Fallside Road, Bothwell,
Lanarkshire G71 8HB
Telephone 01698-817326

Suppliers of:

CHEESE, BUTTER, OTHER
CHILLED DAIRY PRODUCTS
TO CATERERS,
CASH & CARRY
& WHOLESALERS

see entry page 94

Dungallan Country House

Under the ownership of the Allan family, the feeling of being welcomed to their private home has been continued throughout Dungallan. From the moment guests arrive at reception, they receive genuine Highland Hospitality in elegant surroundings, from the rich decor furnishings of the lounge bar to the quiet intimacy of the reading room. There are traditional coal fires throughout the house for those cooler days and evenings and a wide selection of Scottish Malts to warm the weary traveller.

Bedrooms are cosy and welcoming. All are en suite with complimentary tea/coffee tray, bowl of fruit and colour television. The Bridal Suite has an idyllic sea view, four poster and champagne and flowers on arrival.

Gallanach Road, Oban, Argyll
Tel: 01631 63799 Fax: 01631 66711

see entry page 144

THE PENTLAND RESTAURANT

Inspirational Cuisine

Splendid Surroundings

Quality Assured

Par for the Course really....

Part of the Country Club Hotel group

DALMAHOY HOTEL
Country Club Resort

KIRKNEWTON MIDLOTHIAN EH27 8EB
TELEPHONE: 0131 333 1845

Scotland's Cheeses

The geography and climate of Scotland are well suited to cheese-making, with numerous breeds of cattle and sheep raised on terrain ranging from fertile lowlands and straths to exposed highland moorland.

At one time nearly every county in Scotland had its own cheese, but dairy industrialisation in the last century, wartime restrictions and ongoing rationalisation have taken a heavy toll on farmhouse cheesemaking.

However, the handful of cheddar cheesemakers remaining nurtured Scotland's reputation for excellent quality cheddar, and in recent years there has been a re-awakening in artisan cheesemaking in a dozen small dairies and farms across the country. For the first time there are now available genuinely Scottish speciality cheeses and superb local versions of internationally popular fine cheeses, such as brie, camembert and gruyere.

Scottish cheddar still accounts for over 80% of the total output and the main creameries are located in the milk producing areas of Galloway, Lockerbie, Mull of Kintyre (Campbeltown), and on the islands of Bute, Arran, Islay and, of course, the Isles of Orkney with their own distinctive and popular variety of cheddar.

Production of Dunlop cheese takes place in Ayrshire, Arran and Islay. Production of mozzarella has been introduced near Edinburgh and in Fife. The longer established artisan cheesemakers are located near Dundee, Lanark and Inverness and on the Isles of Orkney and Mull.

Scottish cheddar is widely available but farmhouse and speciality cheeses are sometimes available only locally. However, these are generally well featured by Taste of Scotland members. There are several excellent Scottish cheesemongers in and around Edinburgh and Perth and tucked away in unexpected corners across Scotland.

Some of the fine cheeses to look out for include:

Bishop Kennedy : a style of cheese made for hundreds of years in the monasteries of France but still relatively unknown in Scotland. Full fat soft cheese, rind washed in malt whisky to produce a distinctive orangy red crust and a strong creamy taste. Runny when ripe.

Bonchester : small coulommier-style cheese made with unpasteurised Jersey milk. Available mainly March to December.

Bonnet : mild, pressed goatsmilk cheese from small Ayrshire dairy. Similar to Inverloch (Isle of Gigha) and Sanday (the Isles of Orkney).

Brie : Howgate Scottish Brie, traditionally made, matures to a runny sticky texture. Also Howgate Camembert.

Brodick Blue : ewes milk blue cheese from Brodick. Arran Blue is the cows milk version.

Caboc : (see cream cheese)

Cream Cheese : several versions, mostly based on revived traditional Highland recipes and rolled in oatmeal, including Caboc (Ross-shire), Howgate (Tayside) and Lochaber-smoked. Available plain or with peppercorns, garlic or herbs.

Crowdie : a soft fresh cheese, several versions, mainly available only locally. An ancient Highland crofters cheese originally made using milk left after the cream had separated naturally. Plain or flavoured with peppercorns, garlic or herbs. (Hrasma, Crannog, Gruth Dhu etc).

Dunlop : closely resembling Scottish cheddar with soft texture. Mostly creamery-made in blocks on Arran and Islay but also traditionally in Ayrshire (Burns), near Dumfries and at Perth (Gowrie).

Dunsyre Blue : cows milk farmhouse blue cheese made on the same farm as Lanark Blue, with vegetarian rennet and unpasteurised milk.

Ettrick : traditional pressed cheese of Borders origin slightly crumbly and sharp tasting. Bound in cheesecloth and matured over six to nine months.

Howgate : established artisan cheesemaker, originally from Howgate near Edinburgh, now located near Dundee. Pioneered the making in Scotland of continental cheeses including Howgate Brie, Camembert and Pentland. Other cheeses include St Andrews, Ettrick, Bishop Kennedy, Strathkinness and Howgate Highland Cream Cheese.

Inverloch : pasteurised pressed goats cheese from Isle of Gigha. Coated in red wax.

Isle of Mull : traditional unpasteurised farmhouse cheddar from Tobermory. Cloth-bound.

Kelsae : unpasteurised pressed cheese made near Kelso from Jersey milk. Similar to Wensleydale but creamier in texture and taste.

Lanark Blue : unpasteurised ewes milk cheese in the style of Roquefort.

Loch Arthur : traditional farmhouse organic cheddar from Loch Arthur creamery near Dumfries.

Mull of Kintyre : small truckle of mature Scottish cheddar coated in black wax. A smoked version is also available.

Orkney : distinctive cheddar whose history goes back nearly two centuries, made in two creameries on Orkney

Pentland : traditional unpasteurised brie made in small quantities and not widely available (see Howgate)

Perthshire : fine traditional (cloth bound) truckle cheese. Full creamy flavour. Limited availability.

St Andrews : award winning full fat, washed rind soft cheese, mild creamy, full flavoured with characteristic golden, orangy rind. (See Howgate)

Scottish Cheddar : creamery produced cheddar now made in Galloway (Stranraer), Lockerbie, Rothesay and Campbeltown.

Stichill : unpasteurised creamy Jersey milk Cheshire-style cheese from the Scottish Borders.

Strathkinness : superb Scottish version of gruyere, nearly 50 gallons of milk goes into a cheese! Matured 6-12 months. (see Howgate) Limited availability.

Swinzie : pasteurised, pressed ewes milk cheese from Ayrshire.

Teviotdate : vignotte style, white moulded unpasteurised cheese.

Established in 1966 Howgate is one of the few British makers of washed rind cheeses, having gained awards in 1993 at both the London and Nantwich International Shows.

**St Andrews • Bishop Kennedy • Strathkinness
Pentland • Ettrick • Howgate Brie • Camembert
Highland Cream Cheese**

Howgate, Camperdown Creamery, Faraday Street, Dundee, DD2 3QQ. Tel: 01382 811622, Fax: 01382 8993

DESIGN ON A PLATE

DAVID FRAME CREATIVE

Graphic Design · Illustration · Copywriting · Print Management

1-3 South East Circus Place, Edinburgh EH3 6TJ
Tel 0131 225 6540 · Fax 0131 225 6779

see entry page 156

Fernie Castle Hotel

Set in 25 acres of mature grounds with its own loch, Fernie Castle offers
a warm and friendly welcome and provides a perfect base for touring,
golfing or a relaxing break.

Enjoy the atmosphere of the 14th century candlelit Keep Bar, or the
elegance of the 1st floor Castle Restaurant, where you can sample the
best of fresh local and Scottish produce.

We are a family run hotel and open all year round. Special interest
packages, including golfing, fishing and shooting can be arranged.
Please contact us for a brochure and tariff.

 AA ★★★ RAC★★★
STB Commended

Letham · Nr. Cupar · Fife KY7 7RU
Tel 01337-810381 · Fax 01337-810422

see entry page 132
see entry page 118

Gartwhinzean Hotel & Restaurants

Powmill, by Dollar, Clackmannanshire.
Tel: 01577 840595 Fax: 01577 840595

The Gartwhinzean Hotel and Restaurant now owned and
run by the Brown Family, who will ensure you of the very
best traditions and standards of inn keeping.

Diane and Paul extended to you a warm welcome and hope
you will visit the "Gart" and find out for yourself.

THE COFFEE SHOP
Informal, open all day, serving light meals

THE FONDUE AND GRILL ROOM
Inexpensive quality food in atmospheric natural surroundings

TASTE OF SCOTLAND RESTAURANT
Serving Sunday Lunch, High Teas and Dinner,
all in Taste of Scotland style

CAMERON SUITE AND BALLROOM
With the capacity of up to 250 people for Conference, Weddings,
Dinner Dances and Private Parties: ample private parking. The
Gartwhinzean is fully licensed. Open all year including the Festive
Season and other Holiday periods.

Glenmoriston Arms Hotel

LOCH NESS AREA
We have the perfect location for a
holiday in the Highlands.
This family run Hotel offers peace &
tranquillity, woodlands & forest
walks, many species of birds &
wildlife, & spectacular drives
through some of Scotland's most
beautiful Glens.
Return for a relaxing dinner in our
widely acclaimed restaurant &
maybe a dram from our selection of
over 100 malts.
All rooms en-suite.

*Brochure & tariff & sample menus
telephone or write to:*
**Glenmoriston Arms Hotel
Invermoriston
Highland IV3 6YA.
Tel 01320 351206
Fax 01320 351206**

EGON RONAY
www
STB Commended

AA ★★
RAC★★

26

Lochranza (Isle of Arran Tourist Board)

Highland Games (Bute & Cowal Tourist Board)

Scottish Salmon

Scotch whisky and Robert Burns – two of Scotland's finest ; but without a doubt Scottish salmon, the magnificent "King of Fish", is also part of Scottish folklore.

Once, Scottish rivers held such abundant stocks of wild salmon that rich and poor alike could feast on them at will. Poached in vast copper kettles, they graced the Laird's table. The sea captain dined on salmon – pickled, smoked and salted – during long voyages under sail. In fact, so common was it, that historical sources note a clause in Perth apprentices' indentures, limiting the number of salmon meals to not more than three times per week !

Sadly, stocks of wild Scottish salmon have become so depleted that it is not only a seasonal delicacy, but an expensive one too, affordable to relatively few people.

In contrast, the work of the Scottish Salmon farming industry which is a mere 25 years old, has meant that this majestic fish can once again be seen at many a table, and all year round too! Scottish salmon reared in the clear, unpolluted inshore waters of Scottish lochs ensure the myth is preserved.

While classic poached salmon will always remain special, the widespread availability of the fish has challenged modern chefs to combine it with imaginative and often exotic ingredients with surprising results. Salmon's distinctive, fresh flavour is as delicious with ginger and soy sauce as it is with lemon and dill.
Experimentation with different cooking methods also yields surprising results. Try it poached, grilled, baked, pan-fried, microwaved or even barbecued. Whichever you choose, an evening meal using Scottish salmon can be ready in less than 20 minutes.

Scottish salmon is also the healthy option, winning increasing favour with busy, health conscious families, and for good reason.

It is literally packed with goodness, providing a rich source of protein and essential nutrients such as calcium and iron without the large amounts of saturated fat found in other high protein food such as cheese and meat. Less fat also means fewer calories – a 4 oz portion contains only 197 calories when steamed or poached.

Scottish salmon also contains two particular polyunsaturates known as the Omega fatty acids which are believed to have many beneficial effects including blood cholesterol levels.

So armed with the facts on salmon's undisputed convenience, versatility and nutritional values, how does one choose the very best salmon available?

The answer is to look for the Scottish Salmon Board's Tartan Quality Mark which may be found either as a gill tag attached to a whole fish or as a label on prepacked fresh cuts or smoked salmon.

The mark can only be applied to fish which have met the stringent standards of the Scottish Quality Salmon scheme and is an assurance that the fish is both genuinely Scottish and reaches the highest standards of freshness, firmness and flavour. In the UK, Tartan Quality Mark Scottish salmon is widely available from fishmongers and leading supermarkets.

The quality of Tartan Quality Mark Salmon has also been recognised in France, with the award of the prestigious Label Rouge mark to Scottish Salmon Board members' fish - the very first time a product outside France has achieved such an accolade. Salmon carrying these labels can be found in leading French supermarkets and fishmongers.

Make one of Scotland's finest products a regular feature of your menus. Enjoy Scottish salmon !

Tartan Quality Mark

SCOTTISH SALMON

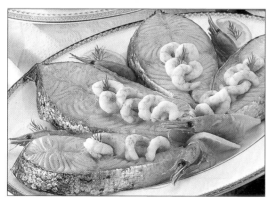

It's delicious and so easy to prepare.
For details of your local stockists or recipes contact:
The Scottish Salmon Bureau – 0131-229 8411.

see entry page 160

"The Taste of Scotland Island Experience"

Taste of Scotland and Scotsell, the Scottish Islands Holiday specialist, are pleased to present this unique car touring island holiday to the west coast and Hebridean Islands of Scotland.

Enjoy the splendid coastal scenery of Wester Ross with your first night at the Dundonnell Hotel near Ullapool, before sailing from Ullapool to Stornoway on the Isle of Lewis, where three nights evening meal, bed and breakfast is arranged for you at one of the comfortable Taste of Scotland guest houses.

Collectively known as the 'Long Island', remarkable examples of stone antiquity are to be found in Lewis, while in its more mountainous neighbour of Harris, the ancient crafts of hand spinning and weaving are still practised.

Sail from Tarbert to Lochmaddy in North Uist, drive over the causeway to Benbecula and enjoy sampling the extensive menu at the Dark Island Hotel during your two nights here.

Discover the contrasting scenery of the Uists, from a crofting and machair landscape, home to many wild flowers, to the magnificent beaches of the west.

From Lochmaddy, sail over the sea to the magical island of Skye, where two nights of comfortable hotel accommodation and fine dining complement your explorations of this fascinating island.

Be enchanted by the dramatic scenery and legends of the Cuillin Mountains, the castles of the Clans MacDonald and MacLeod, visitor centres and croft house museums, with even a distillery to tempt you!

In such magnificent surroundings, this is a wonderful way in which to sample a 'Taste of Scotland'.

Details of this unique holiday and other Taste of Scotland holidays will be found in Scotsell's Scottish Island Brochure. Friendly and knowledgeable experts arrange your ferries and accommodation, leaving you peace of mind to look forward to and enjoy your 'Taste of Scotland' Holiday.

Discover the Western Isles the easy way this year!

For your Scottish Islands brochure, please telephone Scotsell on 0141 772 5928, or send the coupon below to:

SCOTSELL,
SUITE 2D CHURCHILL WAY,
BISHOPBRIGGS,
GLASGOW G64 2RH
TEL (0141) 772 5928 FAX (0141) 762 0297

NAME ....

ADDRESS ....

....

....

POSTCODE..

REF TOFS95

*Glasgow University from Kelvingrove
(Greater Glasgow Tourist Board)*

The artists' colony, Kirkcudbright (Dumfries & Galloway Tourist Board)

Hopetoun House (Forth Valley Tourist Board)

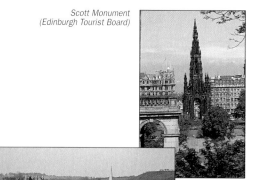

Borthwick Castle (James Gardiner Associates/
Midlothian Tourism Association)

Tinto Hill, near Biggar (Clyde Valley Tourist Board)

Tay Rail Bridge and The Law (Dundee Tourist Board)

It's been pouring in Scotland since 1864.
MATTHEW ALGIE
SCOTTISH CHOICE
PREMIUM ROUND TEA BAGS
88 TEA BAGS
ESTABLISHED 1864
MATTHEW ALGIE
Tea & Coffee Merchants
THERE'S ONLY ONE SCOTTISH CHOICE

Crovie (Grampian Highland & Aberdeen Tourism)

Autumn Ring of Mist on Ben Nevis from Corpach (Alex Gillespie Photography, Fort William)

KILFINAN
H O T E L

Discover the true flavour of the West Highlands at this 100 year old coaching Inn on the East Coast of Loch Fyne. Set amidst thousands of acres of unspoilt countryside, it is an ideal base for all outdoor activities and peaceful relaxation. Chef/Manager Rolf Mueller creates exquisite meals using seasonal produce from the adjoining estate and loch.

Luxury and comfort amidst rugged Highland scenery – and all within two hours scenic drive from Glasgow.

A warm welcome awaits you.

AA ❋ ❋ **Food Award**

E G O N RONAY'S **GUIDES**

STB Highly Commended ♛♛♛

Kilfinan, Nr. Tighnabruaich, Argyll, PA21 2EP
Tel: 01700 821 201 Fax: 01700 821 205

see entry page 124
see entry page 57

KINLOCH CASTLE
ISLE OF RUM
NATIONAL NATURE RESERVE

Kinloch Castle is one of Scotland's remarkable hotels. Situated on an island of spectacular wildness and beauty, the hotel offers the guests a chance to experience living history in the Edwardian Castle rooms which have changed little since the turn of the century. Your hosts Kathleen and Iain MacArthur will ensure a warm welcome with good food complemented by fine wines.

The island and castle are owned by Scottish Natural Heritage, which manages Rum as a National Nature Reserve renowned for its wildlife and scenery.

RUM – A UNIQUE EXPERIENCE

If you would prefer a more informal arrangement, why not stay in the hostel accommodation at the back of the Castle? You can opt for self-catering or buy your meals in the Castle Bistro.

For brochure, tariff and reservation please contact:
Kinloch Castle
Isle of Rum PH43 4RR
Tel 01687 2037

SCOTTISH NATURAL HERITAGE

see entry page 156
see entry page 130

Loch Melfort Hotel

The finest location on the West Coast of Scotland right beside Arduaine Gardens

For comfort and that mouthwatering "Taste of Scotland" amidst magnificent surroundings

Open End February ~ January 2nd

Spring and Autumn Breaks ~ Christmas and New Year Holidays

♛♛♛
AA ★★★ **STB Commended**

AA **Selected Hotel of the Year Scotland**

Scotland's Commended

and recommended by leading Hotel Guides

Loch Melfort Hotel, Arduaine,
by Oban, Argyll. PA34 4XG

Tel: 01852 200233 Fax: 01852 200214

The Log Cabin Hotel
& Edelweiss Restaurant

Uniquely built of solid pine logs in a unique setting with open log fires. Sample the delights of Scotland's larder in our Edelweiss Restaurant complemented by a superb wine cellar. Relax in the well-stocked Maltings Bar with over 100 malt whiskies. Enjoy Bar Suppers and Bar Lunches each day. For Sunday Lunch choose from our Scandinavian style cold table. All cuisine is prepared in our kitchens using the freshest of local produce. Non-residents always welcome. Open all day for coffees and teas with homemade shortbread. Visit our craft gallery specialising in turned wood.

E G O N RONAY'S **GUIDES**   ♛♛♛ **STB Commended**   **AA** ★★ **RAC**★★

KIRKMICHAEL PERTHSHIRE PH10 7NB
TEL 01250-881288 FAX 01250-881402

MAXWELTON HOUSE

*Visit the birthplace of
Annie Laurie made famous by
the well loved ballad.*

OPEN TIMES:

Easter – End of September
Daily • 10.30am – 5.30pm

House, Gardens, Museum, Chapel, Lunch/Tea Room: Taste
of Scotland Award 1993, Gift Shop and Craft Shops

Parking FREE for coaches and Cars

Visitors coming for lunch or tea are welcome to enjoy the
extensive gardens and greenhouses, with a varied
collection of trees, shrubs and plants.

The Museum, restored from its ruinous state and part of a
charming collection of buildings situated about a
courtyard, houses early domestic tools and implements of
kitchen, dairy, farm and garden, and is well worth a visit.

**Tel: 0184 82 385
or write to: Maxwelton House Trust,
Moniaive, Thornhill, Dumfriesshire, DG3 4DX**

see entry page 139
see entry page 74

Monachyle Mhor Hotel/Farmhouse

Small family run, 18th Century
award winning hotel/farmhouse is set
in its own 2000 acres.

All bedrooms, en-suite with the
most magnificent views overlooking
Lochs Voil & Doine.

The hotel is delightfully furnished with
family period furniture & country fabrics.

Robert & Jean Lewis invite you to dine in our
restaurant with delicious dishes including game
and fresh herbs from our own estate. The
farmhouse is fully licensed & non-residents are
most welcome to dine with us. We serve
unusual bar meals all day. Glasgow/Edinburgh 1
hour. Private fishing & stalking to guests.
Open all year.

STB *Commended*

AA ★★

Please write or telephone for bookings or further details.

Balquhidder, Lochearnhead, Perthshire FK19 8PQ
Tel 01877-384 622 • Fax 01877-384 305

see entry page 69
see entry page 160

THE ROMAN CAMP
COUNTRY HOUSE HOTEL

Nestling in the heart of the beautiful Trossachs, the Roman
Camp Hotel offers a magical mixture of gracious living and
historic atmosphere.

Surrounded by 20 acres of superb gardens on the banks of
the River Teith, the hotel's picturesque interior reflects the
original charm of this 17th century building.

All bedrooms have private bathrooms, and facilities which
make for a welcoming, comfortable stay. Guests can enjoy
peace and tranquillity in a truly unique style.

Fresh produce and fine wines will tempt the most discerning
diner and friendly personal service creates an atmosphere
of leisured living.

The Roman Camp invites you to relax and enjoy the warmest
of welcomes and the greatest of pleasure.

For brochure, tariff and reservations write, telephone or fax.

**The Roman Camp Hotel
Callander FK17 8BG
Telephone 01877-330003 Fax 01877-331533**

ROSEDALE HOTEL

**Portree, Isle of Skye
Tel: 01478 613131 Fax: 01478 612531**

Long established hotel in unrivalled waterfront
situation. All bedrooms are en suite and individual in
style and character with tv, radio and tea/coffee
making facilities. Most rooms face the water. Public
rooms include two lounges, one bar and a restaurant
with an A.A.Rosette.

Egon Ronay, Ashley Courtenay, Signpost, Les
Routiers, Taste of Scotland

AA ★★ ❀   RAC★★   **STB** *Commended*

THE SANDFORD

COUNTRY HOUSE
HOTEL

The Sandford Hotel, one of the Kingdom of Fife's most picturesque, listed, country house hotels, is renowned for its fine Scottish and European cuisine and comfortable accommodation.

Seasonal dishes in particular, served in the oak beamed restaurant, are the hallmark of Head Chef, Steven Johnstone. An extensive wine list has been carefully chosen in order to complement the variety of dishes on the extensive table d'hôte menu.

The Sandford is located near to both St Andrews and Dundee, and provides an ideal venue for those touring, fishing, golfing or shooting in this region of Scotland.

Bar Lunch 12.00 to 2.00 pm
Bar Supper and Dinner 6.00 to 9.30 pm
Open January to December (inclusive)
Languages: French, German, Italian

The Sandford Country House Hotel
Newton Hill, Wormit, nr Dundee, Fife DD6 8RG
Tel 01382-541802 • Fax 01382-542136

see entry page 88

Somerton House Hotel

A handsome Victorian mansion, Somerton House is distinguished by unusual Kauri timber panelling from New Zealand and its 'Taste of Scotland' restaurant.

An interesting menu opens with flaked salmon and shrimps in a peppery seafood sauce served with tortilla chips, followed by dishes such as lamb with yoghurt and apricots, and oak-smoked trout with a hot horseradish sauce. Desserts include Ecclefechan Flan and Atholl Brose.

Hours: Open for coffee, lunch, tea and dinner.
Average Prices: A la Carte £10.50; Sunday Lunch £8.25; Snacks £3.40

Proprietors: Mr & Mrs A. Arthur
Somerton House Hotel, Carlisle Road,
Lockerbie, Dumfriesshire DG11 2DR
Tel 01576-202583/202384

RAC★★
AA ★★

see entry page 136

A Recipe for Success

Cookery writer Elizabeth Luard and
Wine Connoisseur Rose Murray-Brown are essential
reading as you prepare for that special occasion.
From recipes with a difference to advice
on the right wines to serve, the result can only
be the perfect taste of Scotland.

THE SCOTSMAN
The Newspaper for all Tastes

When quality counts - only Scotch Beef and Lamb will do

Prime quality beef and lamb from Scotland

Taste of Scotland
Scotch Lamb Challenge 1994

Scotch Lamb
Naturally, One Of The Traditional Tastes Of Scotland

Today's chefs are as appreciative of the fine quality and delicate flavour of naturally-reared Scotch Lamb as were their predecessors. Backed by the guarantees which Quality Assured Scotch Lamb – and the complementary Farm Assured Scotch Lamb – schemes can offer, caterers can have every confidence that Scotch Lamb is one of Scotland's finest products.

The Taste of Quality

For the third consecutive year the Scotch Quality Beef and Lamb Association has worked with the Taste of Scotland Scheme to provide a showcase for Taste of Scotland members' skills.

Open to all chefs and cooks employed by Taste of Scotland members, the Scotch Lamb Challenge demands the creation of a new Scotch Lamb dish and its presentation as the centrepiece of a three course meal.

As in 1993, entries were invited under two categories –
Category 1 (Gourmet) or Category 2 (Classic).

Winner: Category 1 and
Overall Winner of the 1994 Taste of Scotland Scotch Lamb Challenge

Gary Bates, Executive Chef,
Dalmahoy Hotel & Country Club, by Edinburgh

Winner: Category 2

Martin Hollis, Chef/Proprietor,
The Loft Restaurant, Blair Atholl

The great response in entries for the 1994 Challenge and the high standards of innovation, preparation and presentation of the dishes, were a compliment to all the finalists, to the principles of the Taste of Scotland Scheme – and to Scotch Lamb.

The Scotch Lamb recipes from the two winners follow and the four finalists' recipes introduce the Recipe Section which starts on page 173.

Why not try Scotch Lamb dishes the next time you visit a Taste of Scotland restaurant and experience for yourself the Taste of Quality?

At the final of the 1994 SQBLA Scotch Lamb Challenge to Taste of Scotland member Chefs (left to right): Charles Kelso of the Butchers Supply Company of Edinburgh presents a set of Geisser chefs' knives to Gary Bates (Executive Chef at Dalmahoy Hotel & Country Club, by Edinburgh), Winner of the Gourmet Section and Overall Winner of the competition, with Vic Prow, UK Promotions Manager of SQBLA, and Kaye Gardiner, 1994 Miss Scotch Lamb.

Martin Hollis at work – Martin, Chef/Proprietor of The Loft Restaurant, Blair Atholl, 1994 SQBLA Scotch Lamb Challenge Classic Category Winner.

Best End of Scotch Lamb
*served beside a Gâteau of Sweet Basil Stovies, topped with a
Crust of Skirlie and garnished with Leek and Haggis Boudin*

Winner: Category 1 and Overall Winner
1994 Taste of Scotland Scotch Lamb Challenge
Gary Bates, Executive Chef, The Dalmahoy Hotel

Ingredients

4 lb best end of lamb	1 large leek	12 basil leaves
8 oz chicken flesh	1 carrot	4 tablespoons honey
4 oz haggis	2 medium sized onions	sprig of chervil
1 egg white	2 sheets caul fat	salt and pepper
¼ pint whipping cream	2 oz rolled oats	

(Serves four)

Method

1. Take the best end of lamb. Remove all fat, bone and sinew, except from the rib bone. Take out 8 cutlets with the bone nicely attached. Take any fat from the best end and render down to make the skirlie. Place the cutlets in the refrigerator until required.

2. Take the chicken flesh and mince or blend in a food processor. Add the egg white and a little salt. Crumble up the haggis and mix in a bowl with the chicken pulp. Add a little cream just to lighten and enrich it.

3. Remove the cutlets from the refrigerator and place a spoon full of mousse on to each cutlet and wrap in a caul fat. Return to refrigerator.

4. Take the potatoes, peel and cut into a cylindrical shape. Slice very thinly and season with salt and pepper. Take 4 individual gâteau rings and cover one end with tin foil. Place on an oven tray, foil side down. Take the potato, sliced onion and basil leaves and make alternate layers with butter between each layer. When the rings are full, cover with foil and bake in a moderate oven until tender. Take the leeks and cut into 5 inch lengths. Gently steam for one minute. Carefully pull off tubes of leek one at a time. Fill the tube with the haggis mixture using a piping bag. Wrap each one in cling film and gently steam until the mousse is set.

5. Take an iron frying pan with a little olive oil and heat. Place the cutlets, mousse side down and gently fry. Turn the cutlets over and place the pan in the oven for 4–5 minutes.

6. Whilst the lamb is cooking, remove the stovies from the ring and place in the centre of the plate. Take the boudin and slice into 5 and arrange around the plate. Quickly fry a little chopped onion in the lamb dripping and the oats. Season and place on top of the stovies.

7. Remove the lamb from the oven and place up against the stovies. Pour a little lamb jus on the plate, garnish with a sprig of fresh chervil and serve.

A Roulade of Scotch Lamb
with a Fennel, Mushroom and Basil Filling

Winner: Category 2
1994 Taste of Scotland Scotch Lamb Challenge
Martin Hollis, Chef/Proprietor, The Loft Restaurant, Blair Atholl

Ingredients

1 double best end of Scotch lamb (4-4½ lb)
7 oz bulb fennel
5 oz mushrooms
7 oz onion
1 tablespoon fresh basil
3 cloves garlic

7 oz mirepoix (celery, onion, carrot, leeks)
1½ lb potatoes
2 fl oz red wine
2 tablespoons tomato puree
7 oz carrots
4 oz turnips

4 oz courgettes
4 oz swede
2 oz butter
2 tablespoons oil
seasoning

(Serves four)

Method

1. Remove bones from lamb and retain for sauce.

2. Take the eye of the lamb, trim all sinews and fat from the meat.

3. Make an incision along the eye of the meat. Bat out to form an even rectangle.

4. Slice mushrooms and onion finely. Chop basil and cut fennel into a julienne. Season the lamb with salt and pepper then cover the lamb with chopped fennel, mushrooms, basil and onion spreading evenly over the surface. Roll the lamb and secure the string.

5. Brown the bones in the oven with tomato puree and mirepoix. Place the bones in a pot, barely cover with water, bring to the boil and reduce by half. Pass through a fine chinois, reduce by half again.

6. Shape carrots, turnips, courgettes and swede into small barrels. Grate the potatoes, rinse under cold water, then dry.

7. Seal lamb in hot oil and cook in oven GM8 / 225°C / 440°F for 7-10 minutes.

8. Blanch vegetables in boiling water.

9. Whilst lamb is cooking prepare gallettes by grating potatoes and shape into 4 evenly sized rounds. Prepare a pan of hot oil and insert pastry cutters. Press potatoes into shape.

10. Cook until golden brown. Remove rings and turn over potatoes and cook until second side is golden brown. Remove and keep warm in oven.

11. Remove lamb from oven and allow to rest. Deglaze the pan with red wine, basil and garlic, reduce. Add reduced stock, check seasoning. Finish the sauce with butter and pass through a fine chinois.

12. To serve, flood 4 hot plates with sauce, place a gallette potato in the centre of each plate. Arrange turned vegetables around the potato. Slice lamb into 12 slices (each roulade) and arrange 6 slices on top of each potato, then serve.

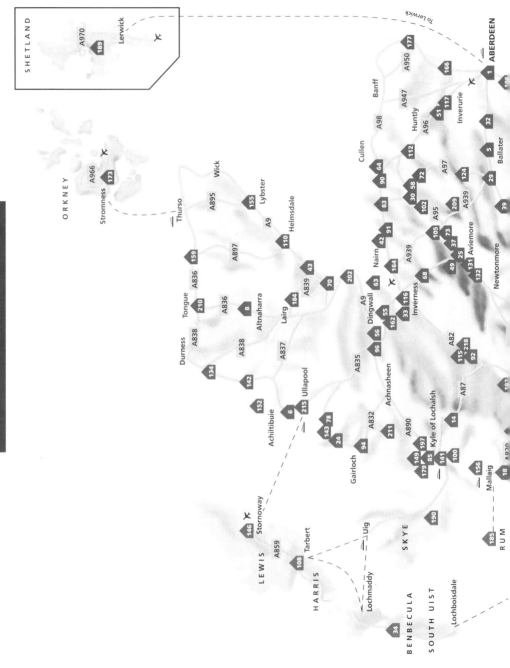

Taste of Scotland

SHETLAND

A970
189 Lerwick

To Lerwick

ORKNEY

A966
173 Stromness

Wick

A895
155 Lybster

Thurso

A897

159
A836

Tongue
210
A836

Durness
A838

A838

134

142

152

Achiltibuie

6 **215** Ullapool

143 **78**
24

94

Gairloch

179 **85** **141**
149 **197**

145 Stornoway

LEWIS
A859
Tarbert
108
HARRIS

Uig

SKYE

190

Lochmaddy

BENBECULA
SOUTH UIST
Lochboisdale
34

Helmsdale
110

A9

43
A839
70

202

184
Lairg

8
Altnaharra

A837

A835

Achnasheen

A832
211
A890

Kyle of Lochalsh
100
14
A87

156
Mallaig
18

RUM
185

63
Nairn
42 **91**
164
A939
Dingwall
55
162 **33** **116**
Inverness
96 **56**

68

Banff
A950 **177**
166

ABERDEEN
1

A947
Huntly
A98 **51** **117**
A96 Inverurie
Cullen
112 **32**
A97 **5** Ballater
64 **124**
90 **72** **29**
83 **30** **58** A95 **209** A939
102 **105** **39**
73
37 Aviemore
25
49 **131**
132
Newtonmore

A82
115 **218**
92

A87

EDINBURGH Cities
St Andrews Other towns

123 Taste of Scotland
member establishments

✈ Airports

Ferries

A1 Major roads

0 miles 35
0 kilometres 50

47

THE TASTE OF SCOTLAND

Listings '95

Aberdeen

Location 1

ARDOE HOUSE HOTEL
Blairs, South Deeside Road
Aberdeen AB1 5YP
Tel: 01224 867355 • Telex: 739413
Fax: 01224 861283

B9077, 3 miles west of Aberdeen.
Ardoe House is a traditional Scottish baronial-style granite mansion which stands in its own grounds and wooded parkland on the South Deeside Road. Originally built in 1898 by Soapie Ogston, the local soap manufacturer, for his wife, the house has been refurbished and restored to its former elegance. Over recent years Ardoe has been sympathetically extended, yet still retains the style and charm of a country mansion. The grand hall and public rooms in the original house feature ornate wood panelling and carvings, and there are also magnificent fireplaces. Of particular note are the stained glass windows on the main staircase. In the newer part of the hotel is the Garden Room, where breakfast is served, and a modern function suite with superb views across the River Dee. The wood-panelled dining room is within the original house and still has its large ornately carved mantlepiece. The imaginative menus created by Chef Paul Bergin give great attention to the flavour and presentation of the best of local produce.

Open all year
Rooms: 71 with private facilities
Bar Lunch 12 – 2.30 pm (a)
Dining Room/Restaurant Lunch 12 – 2 pm except Sat (a)
Bar Supper 6.30 – 10 pm (a)
Dinner 6.30 – 9.30 pm (d) 4 course menu
Dogs accepted at Manager's discretion
Bed & Breakfast £66.50 – £149.50
Dinner B & B £55 – £172
Room Rate £55 – £150
Special Weekend Rates available
• Terrine of pheasant and pigeon on a bed of seasonal leaves. Stew of Scottish seafood – salmon, sole, king scallops and prawns – bound in a saffron cream. Tournedos of prime Angus beef with a shallot and red wine jus.
STB Highly Commended 5 Crowns
Credit cards: 1, 2, 3, 5 + SWITCH

CALEDONIAN THISTLE HOTEL
Union Terrace
Aberdeen AB9 1HE
Tel: 01224 640233 • Telex: 73758
Fax: 01224 641627

City centre.
Set right in the heart of Aberdeen, this large city centre hotel overlooks Union Terrace Gardens and is just 100 yards or so from the Granite City's main shopping street, Union Street, and His Majesty's Theatre. The hotel was built over 100 years ago and, although not evident from the ground floor, has a magnificent staircase with a wooden banister rail and wrought iron supports and beautiful stained glass windows featuring the City Arms of Aberdeen and Scottish emblems. A programme of re-decoration and refurbishment of the bedroom accommodation was in progress during 1994. There is a choice in restaurant styles within the hotel. An interesting range of light meals is available in Elrond's Cafe which is a spacious bar restaurant, or you may choose the more formal atmosphere of The Restaurant on the Terrace. Head Chef Ian Green believes in using, where possible, only quality fresh produce from the Grampian region, to create interesting menus displaying his own international experience and the best of Scottish cuisine.

Open all year except Boxing Day + 27 Dec, 2 + 3 Jan
Rooms: 80 with private facilities
Cafe Bar open all day (b)
Bar Lunch 11 am – 2 pm except Sun Sat (a)
Dining Room/Restaurant Lunch 12 – 2 pm except Sun Sat (b)
Dinner 6.30 – 10 pm (d)
Bed & Breakfast £40 – £108
Dinner B & B £52 – £123
Room Rate £40 – £138
Special Weekend Rates available
• Sauté scallops baked in filo pastry, on a chive cream and coulis of tomato. Salmon roses laced with a Chablis butter and keta caviar sauce. Loin of Scotch lamb pot-roasted with thyme, port and oranges, glazed with a rosemary meringue.
STB Commended 5 Crowns
Credit cards: 1, 2, 3, 5

THE COURTYARD ON THE LANE
No 1 Alford Lane
Aberdeen AB1 1YD
Tel: 01224 213795

In Aberdeen's west end, between Holburn Street and Albyn Place, just round the corner from Union Street.
This quaint little old stone building with shutters at the windows is quite a find in the middle of Aberdeen. It is situated down a newly cobbled and renovated lane at the west end of the city, not far from the bustle of Union Street. The Courtyard on the Lane is in fact two restaurants in one. On the ground floor is Martha's Vineyard Bistro where simple bistro-style food is offered in a 'fun' atmosphere. The Courtyard Restaurant itself is on the first floor and specialises in more 'serious' food from short menus based on fresh local ingredients. Those devotees of The Courtyard who have followed from its previous location at Elrick and those who now discover it in its new city centre form, will be equally delighted by the experience.

Open all year except Christmas + Boxing Days, 1 Jan + 2 wks summer
Bistro Lunch 12 – 2.30 pm except Sun Mon (b)
Dining Room/Restaurant Lunch 12 – 2 pm except Sun Mon Sat (c)
Bistro Supper 6.30 – 10 pm except Sun Mon (b)
Dinner 7 – 9.30 pm except Sun Mon (e)
Closed Sun Mon
• Terrine of west coast scallops and langoustines with a shellfish dressing. Grilled fillets of turbot, brill and halibut with a dill and mustard hollandaise. Loin of local lamb with a gratin of tomatoes and potatoes cooked in stock. Caramelised apple tart with caramel ice-cream and toffee sauce. Bistro – chargrilled John Dory on a red pepper sauce. Smoked haddock and tomato omelette. Grilled goat's cheese on a croûton with salad.
Credit cards: 1, 2, 3, 6 + SWITCH, DELTA
Proprietors: Tony Heath & Shona Drysdale, Vic Booth

CRAIGHAAR HOTEL
Waterton Road, Bucksburn
Aberdeen AB2 9HS
Tel: 01224 712275
Fax: 01224 716362

Turn off A96 roundabout at Bankhead Avenue. Follow to end then turn left along Bankhead Road. Straight ahead at crossroads.

The Craighaar Hotel is set in a quiet wooded residential area, five minutes from Aberdeen Airport and ten minutes from the city centre. It is not only the convenience of its situation that appeals to guests of this popular privately run hotel, which enjoys a good reputation with both the business community and local residents. It boasts a number of distinctive features, not the least of which are its attractive gallery suites with comfortable sitting room and an upstairs bedroom, providing ideal business or family accommodation. The traditional lounge bar has an open log fire and there are function rooms for conferences, seminars or private dining. There is a choice of restaurants and the menus are created around the prime local produce and excellent seafood for which Aberdeen is renowned.

Open all year
Note: Christmas Day accommodation by request
Rooms: 55 with private facilities
Bar Lunch 12 – 2 pm except Sun Sat (a)
Dining Room/Restaurant Lunch 12 – 2 pm except Sun Sat (a-b)
Carvery Lunch 12 – 2.30 pm Sun only (a)
Bar Supper 6.30 – 10 pm (a-b)

Dinner 7 – 9.30 pm except Sun (b-d)
No dogs
Bed & Breakfast £25 – £95
Dinner B & B from £40
• *Scottish smoked salmon and watercress terrine with a tomato and basil coulis. Loin of lamb stuffed with a basil mousse, on a wild rowan and mint jelly sauce. Escalope of salmon with fresh chervil and julienne of vegetables baked in filo pastry, served with a cream sauce flavoured with Chablis, garlic and chervil. STB Highly Commended 3 Crowns*
Credit cards: 1, 2, 3, 5, 6 + SWITCH, DELTA

CRAIGLYNN HOTEL
36 Fonthill Road
Aberdeen AB1 2UJ
Tel: 01224 584050
Fax: 01224 584050

On corner of Fonthill Road and Bon Accord Street, midway between Union Street and King George VI Bridge. Car park access from Bon Accord Street.

Craiglynn is an impressive granite Victorian house once owned by an Aberdeen merchant. It is now a very comfortable small hotel personally run by Chris and Hazel Mann who are most welcoming hosts and whose theme is Victorian elegance with modern comforts. Lovely rosewood panelling and a corniced ceiling feature in the dining room that was originally the billiard room of this fine house, which also has large stained glass windows and parquet flooring. Bedrooms are tastefully furnished and decorated, and all have direct dial telephones and colour TV. There are two elegant lounges to relax in, one of which has an open fire burning during the winter evenings. The dinner menus are decided upon daily and offer an interesting choice of dishes carefully cooked, using fresh local produce as available.

Open all year except Christmas + Boxing Days
Rooms: 9, 7 with private facilities
Dinner at 7 pm (b)

Reservations required for non-residents
No smoking in dining room + bedrooms
Restricted Licence
No dogs
Bed & Breakfast £34 – £53.50
Dinner B & B £46.20 – £68.45
Special Weekend Rates available
• *Home-made soups. Suprême of chicken with a fresh orange, tarragon and cream sauce. Lamb cobbler. Fillet of trout with almonds. Black cherry crumble. Sticky toffee pudding.*
STB Commended 3 Crowns
Credit cards: 1, 2, 3, 5
Proprietors: Chris & Hazel Mann

FARADAY'S RESTAURANT
2 Kirk Brae, Cults
Aberdeen AB1 9SQ
Tel: 01224 869666
Fax: 01224 869666

4 miles from city centre on North Deeside Road. On reaching Cults, turn right at traffic lights – Faraday's 100 yards on right.

This restaurant takes its name from a Victorian engineer, Michael Faraday who is now considered to be the father of electrical engineering. The building, which has been carefully restored, used to be an electric pump station for the area of Cults. A minstrel's gallery overlooks the wood-panelled restaurant, which is decorated in dusky pink and grape colours. It is an intimate and relaxed setting in which to enjoy the innovative menus created by John Inches, which change weekly to take best advantage of the quality fresh produce available. The cuisine reflects John's background of traditional Scottish cooking carefully combined with extensive travel through France.

Open all year except 26 Dec to 8 Jan
Restaurant/Bar Lunch 12 – 1.30 pm except Sun Mon (b)
Dinner 7 – 9.30 pm except Sun (c-d)
Closed Sun
Facilities for disabled visitors
• *Smoked salmon and leek tart accompanied by a light red pepper and cardamom cream. Rosemary scented venison fillet with spiced kumquats and a rich red wine gravy. Oven-roasted rock turbot roasted with ginger and yoghurt complemented by a light lime hollandaise. Spring cherry rhubarb and apple crumbly with a hazelnut crunch and crème chantilly.*
Credit cards: 1, 3
Proprietor: John Inches

Credit Card Code		Meal Price Range	
1.	Access/Mastercard/Eurocard	(a)	under £10
2.	American Express	(b)	£10 – £15
3.	Visa	(c)	£15 – £20
4.	Carte Bleu	(d)	£20 – £25
5.	Diners Club	(e)	£25 – £30
6.	Mastercharge	(f)	over £30

THE MARCLIFFE AT PITFODELS

North Deeside Road, Pitfodels
Aberdeen AB1 9PN
Tel: 01224 861000
Fax: 01224 868860

At the west end of Aberdeen, 2 miles from city centre on A93 Aberdeen-Braemar.

The Marcliffe at Pitfodels is a delightful combination of old and new which blend harmoniously to give a feeling of luxury and opulence in this hotel which opened in November 1993. The original old house was carefully restored and skilfully designed extensions were created, providing high quality bedroom accommodation and two function rooms – the Grand Ballroom and the Courtyard Suite. In the older building bedrooms are named after Scottish castles and have antique furnishings. The spacious foyer has a flagstone floor, comfortable sofas and the glow of an open fire. A team of chefs prepares the menus for the restaurants, based on the best of Scottish and local produce. The Conservatory Restaurant offers an informal style of dining whereas The Invery Room with its opulent furnishings and silverware is a more formal restaurant and conveys the atmosphere of a country house. It is open in the evenings only and in keeping with the surroundings gentlemen are requested to wear jacket and tie. The hotel takes pride in its selection of 200 wines, 100 malt whiskies and 50 Cognacs. During 1994 an interior courtyard was being glass-roofed to create the Atrium Courtyard, due to open October 1994.

Open all year
Rooms: 42 with private facilities
Dining Room/Restaurant Lunch 12 – 2.15 pm (b)
Dinner 6.30 – 10 pm (c)
No smoking area in restaurant
Bed & Breakfast £65 – £145
Dinner B & B £85 – £165
Special Weekend Rates available
• Home-made soup served with crusty bread. Baked black pudding with creamed potatoes and shallot sauce. Suprême of chicken stuffed and baked with Gruyere cheese on creamy spinach sauce. Traditional roast beef with Yorkshire pudding and its own juices. Selection of chargrilled steaks. Chocolate torte with orange anglaise. Sticky toffee pudding with fudge sauce.
STB Highly Commended 5 Crowns
Credit cards: 1, 2, 3, 5, 6 + SWITCH
Proprietors: Stewart & Sheila Spence

MARYCULTER HOUSE HOTEL

South Deeside Road
Aberdeen AB1 0BB
Tel: 01224 732124
Fax: 01224 733510

B9077 Banchory-Aberdeen (South Deeside Road) c 5 miles from Aberdeen, 1 mile west of B979 and B9077 junction. Signposted.

The origins of Maryculter House go back to the 13th century when a community of Knights Templars was founded on the south bank of the River Dee. It is therefore no surprise to discover many of the original features within the older parts of the hotel. A prime example is the Cocktail Bar with its vaulted ceiling and huge open hearth fireplace, built above cellars dating from 1255. The hotel is set in five acres of private grounds on the banks of the river. Each of the bedrooms has been individually furnished and decorated in a style in keeping with the character of the place. In the informal atmosphere of the bar – The Poachers Pocket – there is a good range of interesting dishes on the menu both for lunch and dinner. The Priory is the setting for more formal dining, where the four course dinner menus display to the full the skills and talents of the kitchen brigade led by Head Chef Alfie Murray.

Open all year except 26 + 27 Dec
Rooms: 22 with private facilities
Bar Lunch 12 – 2 pm (b)
Bar Supper 6.30 – 9.30 pm (b)
Dinner 6.30 – 9.30 pm except Sun (e)
4 course menu
Facilities for disabled visitors
No smoking in restaurant
Bed & Breakfast £85 – £110
Special Weekend Rate from £65
• Locally smoked salmon on a bed of seasonal leaves accompanied by a black peppercorn dressing. Roast best end of

Border lamb set on a spicy raspberry glaze. Breast of pheasant filled with a mushroom duxelle wrapped in smoked bacon, baked and served with a creamed oyster mushroom sauce. Poached suprême of Scottish salmon with a tomato, mushroom and mustard sauce.*
STB Commended 4 Crowns
Credit cards: 1, 2, 3, 5

Aberdour

Location 2

HAWKCRAIG HOUSE

Hawkcraig Point, Aberdour
Fife KY3 0TZ
Tel: 01383 860335

From centre of Aberdour, take Hawkcraig Road (signed 'Silver Sands') through large car park, then to right down very steep access to Hawkcraig Point.

Wind your way down the very steep hill and be prepared to be bowled over by the view from this charming 19th century white-washed old ferryman's house. It sits at the water's edge, next to the old harbour, with unspoilt views of Aberdour Bay with its seals and seabirds and the island of Inchcolm's 12th century abbey. In this idyllic spot you would hardly imagine that you were only half an hour from Edinburgh by road or rail. Within a pleasant hour's drive is Gleneagles, St Andrews and the East Neuk of Fife, with its charming little fishing villages. Elma Barrie has earned renown for her high standard of food, hospitality and comfort, borne out by the fact that guests return again and again to enjoy the pleasure of staying at Hawkcraig House. Children over eight years welcome.

Open mid Mar to 30 Oct
Rooms: 2 with private facilities
Dinner 7 – 8.30 pm (c)
Open to non-residents – booked meals only
Unlicensed – guests welcome to take own wine
No smoking throughout
No dogs
Bed & Breakfast £19 – £26
Dinner B & B £37 – £44
• Home-made soups. Scotch salmon mayonnaise. Goujons of Pittenweem lemon sole with tartare sauce. Roast sirloin of Scotch beef. Pavlova with fresh strawberries. Bramble fool. Scottish cheeses.
STB Highly Commended 3 Crowns
No credit cards
Proprietor: Elma Barrie

Aberfeldy

GUINACH HOUSE

by The Birks, Aberfeldy
Perthshire PH15 2ET
Tel: 01887 820251
Fax: 01887 829607

On A826, south-west outskirts of
Aberfeldy, on road to 'The Birks',
Guinach is signposted from Urlar Road.
Guinach House is situated in three acres
of secluded garden grounds with
magnificent views across the valley. It
was built at the turn of the century as a
private country house and is now the
home of Bert and Marian MacKay who
are attentive hosts, helping create a
relaxed friendly atmosphere for their
guests. Bert is a Master Chef and makes
full use of local produce to create
interesting and imaginative four course
dinner menus.

Open all year except Christmas Day
Rooms: 7 with private facilities
Bar Lunch 12 – 2 pm (a)
Dining Room/Restaurant Lunch 12 –
2 pm (b)
Dinner 7 – 9.30 pm (d) 4 course menu
No smoking in dining room
Bed & Breakfast from £37.50
Dinner B & B from £58.50
• *West coast mussels cooked in white*
wine with onions and herbs. Local oak-
smoked venison. Grilled halibut steak
with a lemon and prawn butter, set on
braised sorrel. Fillet of beef topped with
diced chicken liver with capsicums
masked in a Madeira wine sauce. Layers
of shortcake with strawberries.
Profiteroles with hot chocolate sauce.
STB Highly Commended 3 Crowns
Credit cards: 1, 3
Proprietor: Albert MacKay

Aberfoyle

THE SCOTTISH WOOL CENTRE

Riverside Car Park, Aberfoyle
Stirlingshire FK8 3UG
Tel: 01877 382850
Fax: 01877 382854

Adjacent to main car park in Aberfoyle,
southern gateway to the Trossachs.
Within The Scottish Wool Centre is a self-
selection restaurant and coffee shop
where visitors to the complex can relax
over coffee or a leisurely lunch and
appreciate the views of The Trossachs
and Ben Lomond. The restaurant is

pleasant and spacious set out with pine
tables and chairs. Meals are served
throughout the day and families are most
welcome. The items range from delicious
home-baking and snacks to a selection
of freshly cooked dishes featuring local
produce and vegetarian options. It is a
most interesting visitor centre where in
summer you can see 'The Story of
Scottish Wool' which covers the 2,000
year history of sheep in Scotland and in
winter a year in a shepherd's life is
recounted in 'The Shepherd's Way'. The
centre's spinners and weavers invite
visitors to try making wool into yarn and
cloth in the old fashioned way. A
selection of woven garments, knitwear
etc is available in the shop, and outside
there is a Kids Farm where children can
meet the lambs and goats.

Open all year except Christmas Day +
1 Jan
Food available 9.30 am – 5.30 pm
summer: 10 am – 4 pm winter (a)
Unlicensed
Facilities for disabled visitors
No smoking area in restaurant
• *Home-made soup e.g. leek and potato,*
cauliflower and black pepper, feather
fowlie. Scotch lamb hot pot. Beef
casserole with chunky vegetables and
dumplings. Garden vegetable crumble.
Weekend roasts e.g. pork with a herb
and apple crust, honey roast ham with
orange and ginger sauce, leg of lamb
with rosemary and garlic. Home-made
steak pies. Wide selection of home-
baking.
No credit cards

Aboyne

HAZLEHURST LODGE

Ballater Road, Aboyne
Aberdeenshire AB34 5HY
Tel: 013398 86921

On A93 on western side of Aboyne.
Imaginative, highly regarded cooking by
Chef Anne Strachan in the intimate
atmosphere of this attractive rose
granite former coachman's lodge on
Aboyne Castle. With creative use of
herbs and fresh vegetables Anne brings
traditional cooking to today's table.
Wines are personally selected from top
growers and the prices are friendly. The
accommodation within the Lodge is in
three individually designed bedrooms, all
with full private facilities, and the other
two rooms are in the Hazlehurst Cottage.

Each bedroom is of a high standard
reflecting the owners' artistic background
and the specially commissioned furniture
exemplifies the best of Scottish craft
design. Hazlehurst makes an ideal base
for a relaxing stay on beautiful unspoilt
Royal Deeside.

Open Feb to Dec
Rooms: 5, 4 with private facilities
Dining Room Lunch available for special
bookings
Dinner 7.30 – 9.30 pm (d)
No smoking in dining room + bedrooms
Bed & Breakfast from £25
• *Spring vegetable soup with a shank of*
lamb stuffed with basil pesto. Gamebird
terrine with ceps served with a
chanterelle sauce. Brill with dill, tarragon
and Chardonnay butter served with crab
soufflé, in a bisque sauce. Layers of
vegetables and herb pancakes en
brioche, with a red pepper sauce.
Floating caramelised meringue on a
custard cream accompanied by brandied
peach.
STB Deluxe 3 Crowns
Credit cards: 1, 2, 3, 5
Proprietors: Anne & Eddie Strachan

THE WHITE COTTAGE RESTAURANT

Craigwell, Aboyne
Aberdeenshire AB34 5BP
Tel: 013398 86265

On main A93 Aberdeen-Braemar,
2½ miles east of Aboyne.
When Laurie and Josephine Mill bought
the 150 year old 'White Cottage' in
1986, it was indeed white. However
when beautiful pink granite was revealed
after all the whitewash was removed,
they decided to keep it that way but
retain the White Cottage name. After a
year of major renovations, they opened
for business. Low ceilings, wooden floor
and a real log fire at either end of the
restaurant make for a cosy intimate
dining experience. There is a beautiful
conservatory with French doors leading
on to the garden where guests can enjoy
an aperitif before their meal – or indeed
have lunch or supper. Laurie's style of

cooking is honest and unpretentious: he genuinely enjoys preparing his stocks and sauces and, being from the west coast, particularly relishes cooking shellfish. Josephine presides over the restaurant together with a happy young team. The Mills take great delight in seeing their guests really enjoy the food they present. Standards are high and they work hard to keep them so. Last year they launched a new side to the business aptly titled 'Hampers', providing picnics small and great to all kinds of people. The guest accommodation is simple but very comfortable and has lovely views.

Open all year except 24 to 29 Dec +
31 Dec to 4 Jan
Rooms: 2 , 1 with private facilities
Bar Lunch 12 – 3 pm except Mon (a)
Dining Room/Restaurant Lunch 12 –
3 pm except Mon (b)
Bar Supper 6 – 9 pm except Mon (a-b)
Dinner 7 – 9 pm except Mon (d)
Closed Mon
Restaurant Licence
No dogs
Facilities for disabled visitors
No smoking in restaurant
Bed & Breakfast £18.50 – £25
Dinner B & B £26.50 – £39.50
Special Rates available
• Welsh rarebit. Moules marinières.
Carrot and lovage soup. Fisherman's pie.
Balmoral venison sausages. Smoked
salmon and scrambled eggs. Saffron
sea-cakes. Roasted haunch of Balmoral
venison with garlic and red wine. Baked
River Dee wild salmon with lemon and
tarragon. Home-made puddings. Gigha
cheeses.
Credit cards: 1, 3
Proprietors: Laurie & Josephine Mill

Achiltibuie

Location 6

SUMMER ISLES HOTEL
Achiltibuie
Ross-shire IV26 2YG
Tel: 01854 622282
Fax: 01854 622251

Prestige Award Winner 1991

Ten miles north of Ullapool turn west off
A835 and continue for 15 miles along
single track road.

Leaving the main road is like leaving one world and moving into another, and the terrain to Achiltibuie is primitive, enchanting and hauntingly beautiful. The village itself is a haphazard layout of cottages, but its pièce de resistance is the Summer Isles Hotel, a haven of civilised comfort and culinary standards of astonishingly high level. Mark and Geraldine Irvine are utterly charming hosts, bent on ensuring that in this remote corner of Ross-shire you will want for nothing – and indeed you won't. There is everything here, and overlying it is the sheer tranquillity and beauty of the place. You will feed on the finest harvest of seafish, shellfish and the freshest of fresh locally grown vegetables, fruit and farm produce all prepared with skill and presented with flair. Like everyone else who has been there, you will leave reluctantly, determined to return.

Open 12 Apr to 9 Oct
Rooms: 11 with private facilities
Bar Lunch (Achiltibuie Cafe) 12 –
2.30 pm (b)
Bar Supper (Achiltibuie Cafe) 5 –
9 pm (b)
Dinner at 8 pm (f) 5 course set menu –
booking essential for non-residents
Note: Lunch is not served in the hotel,
but is available in the adjoining
Achiltibuie Cafe
No smoking in restaurant
Bed & Breakfast £32.50 – £62
Dinner B & B £65 – £95
• Cream of spinach soup with garlic
croûtons. Home-made breads. Stilton
soufflé served with mixed salad leaves.
Turbot and sole in a cream sauce.
Lemon flan and orange and ginger
sorbet. Hazelnut gâteau with summer
fruit. Superb cheese trolley.
STB Highly Commended 3 Crowns
No credit cards
Proprietors: Mark & Geraldine Irvine

Alloa

Location 7

THE GEAN HOUSE
Gean Park
Tullibody Road, Alloa
Clackmannanshire
FK10 2HS
Tel: 01259 219275
Fax: 01259 213827

Prestige Award Winner 1992

A907 from Kincardine Bridge or Stirling.
Park entrance on B9096 Tullibody, less
than 5 minutes from Alloa Town Hall
roundabout.

This luxurious country house hotel stands in its own grounds with parks, woodlands, lawns and a lovely rose garden. A great deal of care has been taken in the restoration of the building and in its refurbishment. The interior decor and furnishings exude elegance and impeccable good taste. Ranking high in the many architectural features are the minstrel gallery and the inglenook fireplace in the oak-panelled reception hall. The bedrooms are superb and beautifully furnished with many delightful personal touches. Everything about this magnificent house is outstanding and the food is of the same standard of excellence and perfection so obvious throughout the building.

Open 4 Jan to 31 Dec
Rooms: 7 with private facilities
Dining Room/Restaurant Lunch 12 –
2 pm (b)
Dinner 7 – 9 pm (e)
No dogs
Facilities for disabled visitors
No smoking in dining room
Bed & Breakfast from £70
Dinner B & B from £95
Special Weekend Rates available
• Game terrine served with a redcurrant
and apple jelly. Shetland Salmon with an
orange and vermouth cream and
garnished with fresh herbs. Scotch lamb
pan-fried and served with a mushroom
and herb sauce. Perthshire pork layered
with Dunsyre Blue cheese topped with a
basil essence. Gean House bread and
butter pudding.
STB Deluxe 4 Crowns
Credit cards: 1, 2, 3, 5, 6
Proprietors: Sandra & Paul Frost

Altnaharra
by Lairg
Location 8
ALTNAHARRA HOTEL
Altnaharra
Sutherland IV27 4UE
Tel: 01549 411 222
Fax: 01549 411 222
A836, 21 miles north of Lairg.
Splendid isolation and tranquillity could
be the theme of this famous fishing
hotel, located deep in the heart of
beautiful Sutherland and well remote
from the hurly burly of the modern world
and main traffic routes. This is a hotel
for lovers of outdoor pursuits, and
though anglers form a fair proportion of
its clientele there are lots of other things
to do. The accommodation is
comfortable and the cuisine will satisfy
the hungriest of hunters returning from
the hills.
Open 1 Mar to end Oct
Rooms: 20 with private facilities
Bar Lunch 12 – 2.15 pm (b)
Bar Supper 6 – 9 pm (b)
Dinner 7.30 – 8.30 pm: cold buffet
Sun (c)
No smoking in dining room
Bed & Breakfast £35 – £45
Dinner B & B £48 – £60
Special Rates available
• Home-made soups. Smoked salmon.
King prawns in filo pastry. Seafood
platter. Roast leg of Sutherland lamb
with mint sauce. Rainbow trout with
lemon butter and flaked almonds.
Credit cards: 1, 3

Alyth
Location 9
DRUMNACREE HOUSE
St Ninians Road, Alyth
Perthshire PH11 8AP
Tel: 0182 83 2194
Turn off A926 Blairgowrie-Kirriemuir to
Alyth. Take first turning on left after
Clydesdale Bank – 300 yards on right.
A traditional stone-built country house of
character at the foot of Glenisla in the
old market town of Alyth. High standards
are obvious throughout and the
proprietors, Allan and Eleanor Cull, pay
particular attention to making their
guests feel welcome and comfortable.
Eleanor takes care of the front of the
house while Allan is chef and calls on his
wide experience of overseas travel and

international cuisine to produce
imaginative menus with that little bit of
extra in flavour and presentation. Many
of the organic vegetables and herbs
come from the hotel's own garden and
dinner in the relaxed atmosphere of the
candlelit dining room can be a splendid
way to round off the day.
Open 1 Apr to 23 Dec
Rooms: 6 with private facilities
Dinner 7 – 9.30 pm except Sun Mon (c)
Restricted Licence
Facilities for disabled visitors
No smoking in dining room + bedrooms
Bed & Breakfast from £31
Dinner B & B from £49.50
Special Weekly Rates
• Home-cured salmon gravadlax. Warm
Arbroath smokie mousse. Pan-fried fillet
of seatrout with a beurre blanc and chive
sauce. Suprême of chicken on a bed of
couscous with a spicy cream sauce.
Bacon wrapped fillet of pork stuffed with
prunes, with a port wine sauce. Home-
made truffles.
STB Highly Commended 3 Crowns
Credit cards: 3, 6
Proprietors: Allan & Eleanor Cull

Annan
Location 10
NORTHFIELD HOUSE
Eaglesfield Road, Annan
Dumfriesshire DG12 5LL
Tel: 01461 202851
Northfield House is situated approx one
mile north of Annan on B722 Eaglesfield
Road.
Approached through its own leafy and
well kept grounds, this secluded country
house is a joy to discover. Northfield
House is set in an elevated position
overlooking the River Annan, with private
fishing for salmon and seatrout. This is
the home of James and Mary Airey who
are charming hosts and have put much
thought into every aspect of their guests'
comfort. The period features of the
rooms are enhanced by the sumptuous
and elegant furnishings. From the dining
room there is a lovely outlook over lawns

and shrubs to mature trees. In the seven
years since the Aireys opened their
house to guests, many have returned
time and time again, doubtless in no
small measure due to the high standards
of hospitality and food. Mary Airey has
earned a good reputation for her
outstanding cuisine utilising only the
finest of fresh ingredients including
vegetables, herbs and fruit from the
kitchen garden. The set menu at dinner
is carefully balanced and interesting both
in content and presentation. Children
over 12 years welcome.
Open Feb to Dec except Christmas/New
Year
Rooms: 3 with private facilities
Dinner 7 for 7.30 pm (d) 5 course menu
Non-residents by arrangement only
Unlicensed – guests welcome to take
own wine
No dogs
All rooms on ground floor
No smoking in dining room + bedrooms
Bed & Breakfast £40 – £50
Dinner B & B £62 – £72
• Watercress roulade with a fromage
frais and fresh herb filling. Fresh young
Solway salmon served on a bed of fresh
spinach with a dill sauce. Monkfish tail
with scallops in a saffron sauce. Roast
wild duck with morello cherry sauce.
Fillet of prime Scotch beef with
horseradish, crème fraîche and mustard
sauce. Blueberry shortcake with a fruit
coulis.
No credit cards
Proprietors: James & Mary Airey

Anstruther
Location 11
THE CELLAR RESTAURANT
24 East Green, Anstruther
Fife KY10 3AA
Tel: 01333 310378

Prestige Award Winner 1993

Peter Jukes has long had a reputation as
one of the country's leading chefs and
his skills are demonstrated at their finest
in his masterly treatment of seafood. It
is little wonder that he attracts
discerning diners from all over the
country. The Cellar is full of character
with an interior of stone walls, beamed
ceilings and open fires, and approached
through a walled courtyard that helps to
prepare the atmosphere of the place.
Though fish and shellfish are the
specialities there is almost always

excellent lamb and beef on the menu, prepared and presented with the same care and attention that is the hallmark of the proprietor. There is a distinguished wine list to complement the food. The restaurant is deservedly popular so to avoid disappointment it is best to make a table reservation in advance.

Open all year except Christmas/New Year
Dining Room/Restaurant Lunch 12.30 – 1.30 pm Tue to Sat (b)
Dinner 7 – 9.30 pm Tue to Sat (e)
4 course menu
Closed Sun Mon
Facilities for disabled visitors
No smoking in restaurant
• Crayfish and mussel bisque. Monkfish roasted on the bone with herb and garlic butter. Grilled suprême of East Neuk halibut flavoured with citrus juices, served with hollandaise sauce. Turbot and Western Isles scallops braised in Chardonnay and enriched with cream. Medallion of beef fillet with oyster mushrooms and Dijon mustard sauce. Strawberries with a warm caraway sauce anglaise.
Credit cards: 1, 2, 3
Proprietor: Peter Jukes

Appin
Location 12
INVERCRERAN COUNTRY HOUSE HOTEL
Glen Creran, Appin
Argyll PA38 4BJ
Tel: 0163 173 414/456
Fax: 0163 173 532

Just off A828 Oban-Fort William at head of Loch Creran, 14 miles north of Connel Bridge.

The first thing that strikes one about Invercreran is the superb location. It is perched on a hillside with really magnificent panoramic views over glens and hills. The house itself is strikingly different, a stylish modern mansion house, yet not in the slightest out of place in this remote and lovely glen. Splendid public rooms with spacious terraces, and large comfortable bedrooms, contribute to the overall feeling of luxury. John and Marie Kersley with their family have created a really special place which offers total relaxation and enjoyment. There are lots of interesting walks locally – and don't be surprised if you come across the odd herd of red deer. The food lives up to the high standards that mark this place and is served with courtesy and charm in the delightful dining room. Children over five years are welcome.

Open 1 Mar to 31 Oct
Rooms: 9 with private facilities
Bar Lunch 12 – 2 pm (b)
Dining Room/Restaurant Lunch 12 – 2 pm except Mon (c)
Dinner 7 – 8 pm (e) 4 course menu
No dogs
No smoking in dining room
Bed & Breakfast £44 – £69
Dinner B & B £71 – £96
Special Rates available
• Mallaig landed haddock terrine with a light tarragon cream dressing. Poached fillet of salmon with a lime and mint butter dressing. Pan-fried collops of Highland venison with a rowanberry and red wine sauce. Crêpes filled with oranges, butterscotch sauce and toasted almonds. Blairgowrie raspberry cranachan.
STB Deluxe 4 Crowns
Credit cards: 1, 3
Proprietor: John Kersley

THE STEWART HOTEL
Glen Duror, Appin
Argyll PA38 4BW
Tel: 0163 174 268
Fax: 0163 174 328

A828 – Fort William 17 miles; Glencoe 10 miles; Oban 30 miles.

In a delightful setting of five acres of tranquil landscaped gardens overlooking Loch Linnhe, and a mere ten miles from Glencoe, The Stewart Hotel makes a very good base for touring this spectacular area of the country. The original building goes back over a century and was designed as as hunting lodge with the generous internal proportions associated with the period. The dining room, bar and public rooms are in this part while the modern well equipped bedrooms are in a newer wing. With ready access to plentiful supplies of the delicious fish and shellfish for which the west coast is renowned, the chefs create well balanced menus which change daily and are presented with finesse.

Open 1 Apr to 15 Oct
Rooms: 19 with private facilities
Bar Lunch 12 – 2 pm (a)
Bar Supper 6 – 7 pm (a)
Dinner 7 – 9 pm (d) 4 course menu
No smoking in dining room
Bed & Breakfast £35 – £40
Dinner B & B £48 – £65
• Loch Linnhe prawns served with garlic

butter on a bed of samphire. Tail of monkfish encased in filo pastry served on a light spinach sauce. Pan-fried suprême of chicken on an onion confit. Fresh fruit brûlée.*
STB Commended 4 Crowns
Credit cards: 1, 2, 3, 5
Proprietors: The Lacy Family

Arbroath
Location 13
BYRE FARM RESTAURANT
Redford, Carmyllie
Arbroath DD11 2QZ
Tel: 01241 860245

On B961 Dundee-Brechin. From Forfar, take Carnoustie road to turn off for Redford. From Arbroath, turn off at Condor and follow Redford sign.

This old stone building constructed from local stone and slates used to be a cottage with a byre at the end. It is now a popular venue for people passing through the area as well as for locals who go to enjoy the home-baking and wholesome cooking in a peaceful rustic atmosphere. The food is straightforward and unpretentious yet introduces some interesting speciality dishes and makes provision for vegetarians.

Open all year except New Year/ first wk Jan
Restaurant Lunch 12 – 2.30 pm (a)
Supper 6 – 7 pm (a)
Dinner 6.30 – 8 pm (b) except Sun Mon – reservations only
Facilities for disabled visitors
No smoking in restaurant
• Farmhouse soup with home-made brown rolls. Potted smoked fish pâté with bannocks. Home-made steak pie with light puff pastry. Angus Glen venison in rich gravy. Lamb wrapped in pastry parcel with redcurrant sauce. Arbroath smokie warmed in lemon butter.
Credit cards: 1, 3
Proprietor: Anne Law

Ardelve

LOCH DUICH HOTEL
Ardelve
by Kyle of Lochalsh IV40 8DY
Tel: 0159 985 213
Fax: 0159 985 214

*Off A87 from Fort William and Inverness
(via Loch Ness), 7 miles from Kyle of
Lochalsh/Skye ferry.*

Originally built over 300 years ago as a
drovers inn, the Loch Duich Hotel
overlooks Eilean Donan Castle, the seat
of Clan MacRae and one of the most
photographed ancient monuments in
Scotland. The present building was built
in 1896 and was owned by Farquhar
MacRae who was responsible for the
rebuilding of the Castle. Since their
arrival Iain Fraser and Sonia Moore have
done a great deal to upgrade the hotel
providing all the comforts and modern
facilities required for guests today. The
dining room is a long low ceilinged room
with several windows looking over the
famous castle. Local chef, Stephen
Crockett, and the proprietors have
combined their expertise to produce
excellent menus using fresh local
produce. Naturally there is a strong
emphasis on the splendid fish and
shellfish for which the west coast is so
renowned, but beef, heather lamb and
venison etc also feature.

*Open 21 Mar to 19 Dec + 28 Dec to 2
Jan*
Rooms: 18, 5 with private facilities
Bar Lunch 12 – 2 pm (a)
*Dining Room/Restaurant Lunch 12.30 –
2 pm Sun only (a)*
Bar Supper 6 – 9 pm (b)
Dinner 7 – 9 pm (c) 4 course menu
No smoking in dining room
Bed & Breakfast £22 – £28.50
Dinner B & B £37 – £43.50
Special New Year Rates
*• Smoked salmon mousse. Casserole of
venison with red wine. Honey glazed rack
of lamb with fresh mint. Fresh prawns in
a creamy Pernod sauce. Baked rainbow
trout with leek and Stilton filling.*
STB Commended 2 Crowns
Credit cards: 1, 3, 6
Proprietors: Iain Fraser & Sonia Moore

Ardentinny

ARDENTINNY HOTEL
Ardentinny
Loch Long, nr Dunoon
Argyll PA23 8TR
Tel: 01369 810 209
Fax: 01369 810 345

*12 miles north of Dunoon. From Gourock-
Dunoon ferry, take A815 then A880. Or
scenic drive round Loch Lomond A82 and
A83 then A815 to Strachur, taking left
turn halfway along Loch Eck.*

The Ardentinny is an enchanting old
droving inn, dating from the early 1700s
which sits on a small promontory in Loch
Long, surrounded by the Argyll Forest
Park. The hotel has lovely gardens
stretching down to the sea loch where a
new pier has been added to supplement
the moorings which are available for
diners arriving by yacht. Many guests
choose the Ardentinny just to relish the
food, the peace and the quiet, but equally
there are many others who make it their
base to take advantage of the outdoor
pursuits available, such as golf, hill-
walking, boating, fishing and yachting.
Many distinctive features of the old inn
are retained yet every modern comfort is
provided in the well equipped en suite
bedrooms which have splendid views out
over loch and mountain. For the dining
room the chefs prepare delicious dinners
to a very high standard and will happily
cater for all diets. Lunches feature
seafood and other local delicacies and
are available either in the Patio Garden or
the Buttery, where supper is also served.

Open 15 Mar to 1 Nov
Rooms: 11 with private facilities
*Bar Lunch (Patio Garden/Buttery) 12 –
2.30 pm*
Mon to Sat: 12 – 5.30 pm Sun (b)
Bar Supper (Buttery) 6 – 10 pm (c)
Dinner 7.30 – 9 pm (d)
No smoking in dining room
Bed & Breakfast £20 – £45
Dinner B & B £39 – £75
Special Rates available
*• Local venison marinated and served
with juniper and gin. Ardentinny clam
chowder. Breast of Solway duck with
honey and chives. Crab cakes with
cracked mustard sauce. Variety of
shellfish dishes.*
STB Commended 4 Crowns
*Credit cards: 1, 2, 3, 5, 6 + SWITCH,
DELTA*
*Proprietors: John & Thyrza Horn,
Hazel Hall*

Ardnamurchan

MEALL MO CHRIDHE
COUNTRY HOUSE
Kilchoan, Ardnamurchan
Argyll PH36 4LH
Tel: 01972 510238
Fax: 01972 510238

*From Corran Ferry by A861, then along
B8007 by the side of Loch Sunart.*

Meall mo Chridhe (pronounced Me-al-mo-
cree) is an elegant listed Georgian
country house, built around 1790, and a
former Church of Scotland manse. The
Gaelic name means 'little hill of my
heart'. This is the home of Roy and Janet
Smith and it sits amidst 45 acres of
private grounds with spectacular views
over Kilchoan Bay and the Sound of Mull,
near the most westerly point of the UK
mainland – the Ardnamurchan
lighthouse. It is a good stop-over location
for those touring the Western Highlands
and Hebridean Islands, and is
convenient for the Kilchoan-Tobermory
(Isle of Mull) ferry. Situated in an area
renowned for its beauty and remoteness,
Meall mo Chridhe makes a wonderful
place to stay and appreciate the quieter
pace of life. Comfortably appointed
rooms, beds draped in patchwork quilts,
and fine old furniture complete the
restful scene. In the historic dining room,
once the 'Marriage Room' of the manse,
guests enjoy dinners by candlelight at
the huge mahogany table. Janet
prepares appetising and imaginative
dinner menus from the fine harvest of
local seafood, game etc, complemented
by home-grown fresh seasonal
vegetables, herbs and soft fruits from
the walled garden. Many of the home-
made specialities of the house – from
bread and preserves to ice-creams, even
patchwork – are on sale in the adjoining
farm shop and craft studio.

Children over 12 years welcome.

Open 1 Apr to 31 Oct + 31 Dec to 5 Jan
Rooms: 3 with private facilities
Dinner at 7.30 pm (d) 4 course menu
*Unlicensed – guests welcome to take
own wine + spirits*
No smoking throughout
Bed & Breakfast £34 – £39
Dinner B & B £56 – £66
Special Rates for 3/5/7 day breaks
*• Home-made breads. Ardnamurchan
fish soup. Loch Sunart langoustines in
garlic butter. Local dived king scallops in
white wine sauce. Medallions of Highland
venison with bramble sauce. Baked*

Tobermory trout with mushrooms and herbs. Bread and butter pudding. Home-made ice-creams and fresh fruit sorbets.
STB Highly Commended 3 Crowns
No credit cards
Proprietors: Roy & Janet Smith

Arduaine

Location 17

LOCH MELFORT HOTEL
Arduaine, by Oban
Argyll PA34 4XG
Tel: 01852 200233
Fax: 01852 200214
On A816, 19 miles south of Oban.
The reputation of the Loch Melfort continues to grow as Philip and Rosalind Lewis keep improving standards. The location is quite outstanding with dramatic views to the islands across Asknish Bay. Originally the home of the Campbells of Arduaine it has been extended to take full advantage of the outlook and give bedrooms and dining room the maximum opportunity to enjoy landscape and seascape. Adjacent to the hotel and with access directly from it are Arduaine Gardens which are superbly maintained by The National Trust for Scotland and are open all year. There are few who will not revel in a morning or afternoon wandering through these delightful grounds.
Open 24 Feb to 4 Jan
Rooms: 26 with private facilities
Morning coffee + afternoon teas 10 am – 6 pm
Bar Lunch 12 – 2.30 pm (a-c)
Bar Supper 6 – 9 pm (a-c)

Dinner 7.30 – 9 pm (e)
No smoking in dining room
Facilities for disabled visitors
Bed & Breakfast £30 – £47.50
Dinner B & B £37.50 – £65
Special Spring/Autumn Breaks available
• Omelette roulade with mushroom and tomato filling. Own gravadlax with a dill and sweet mustard dressing. Langoustine from Luing with home-made mayonnaise. Whole plaice marinated in yoghurt and spices and grilled. Roast free-range turkey with celery and pineapple stuffing. Charcoal grilled sirloin steak with parsley butter. Chocolate and walnut tart. Raspberry and lemon pavlova.
STB Commended 4 Crowns
Credit cards: 1, 3, 6 + SWITCH
Proprietors: Philip & Rosalind Lewis

Arisaig

Location 18

ARISAIG HOUSE
Beasdale, by Arisaig
Inverness-shire PH39 4NR
Tel: 01687 450622
Fax: 01687 450626

Prestige Award Winner 1991

Just off A830 Fort William-Mallaig, 3 miles east of Arisaig.
Arisaig House continues to attract the attention and earn the plaudits of connoisseurs – and rightly so. This fine old building stands on a commanding site surrounded by lovely gardens and woodlands through which you can wander down to the seashore and enjoy the beaches or rock cliffs. It is one of those special country houses emanating an immediate air of elegant and luxurious living. The high standards of Ruth and John Smither and their family are apparent throughout the building. Public rooms and bedrooms are furnished with good taste, and the staff are trained to a high degree and polite well mannered service comes naturally. The chefs make full use of the excellent fresh seafood so readily available but menus are carefully compiled to ensure sufficient variety of choice. Arisaig House is an experience to be savoured and one to which you will want to return. Children over 10 years welcome.
Open 31 Mar to 30 Nov
Rooms: 12 + 2 suites with private facilities
Bar Lunch 12.30 – 2 pm (a-b)

Dining Room/Restaurant Lunch 12.30 – 2 pm (d)
Dinner 7.30 – 8.30 pm (f) 4 course menu – booking essential
Restricted Licence
No dogs
Bed & Breakfast £71 – £102.50
• Loch nan Uamh prawns and scallops with fresh basil and coriander. Smoked quail mousseline. Lobster and langoustine bisque. Roast prime Scotch sirloin with Yorkshire pudding. Noisettes of spring lamb with fresh herb jus. Monkfish collops with parsley and garlic. Marinated venison loin with green lentils.
STB Deluxe 4 Crowns
Credit cards: 1, 2, 3, 6 + SWITCH
Proprietors: Ruth, John &
Andrew Smither

THE OLD LIBRARY LODGE & RESTAURANT
High Street, Arisaig
Inverness-shire PH39 4NH
Tel: 01687 450 651
Fax: 01687 450 219
In centre of village on seafront.
Overlooking the sea, with views to the small isles, The Old Library Lodge is a 200 year old stone-built stable which has been tastefully converted into a charming restaurant with good accommodation. Alan Broadhurst's creative cooking makes full use of local shellfish, fish and meat and he has built up a fine reputation for his restaurant with both locals and visitors. A carefully selected wine list complements the food which includes garden produce from the village and herbs from the Broadhursts' own herb garden.
Open Easter to end Oct
Rooms: 6 with private facilities
Restaurant Lunch 11.30 am – 2.30 pm (a)
Dinner 6.30 – 9.30 pm (c)
Restricted Licence
Bed & Breakfast from £30
Dinner B & B from £50
Special Rates for 3+ nights
• Mussel and fennel soup with home-made bread. Rolled local sole filled with salmon served with a cream and chive sauce. Fillet of venison with a rowanberry and red wine sauce. Grilled Mallaig scallops on a vegetable ragoût. Apple fudge crumble. Creme brûlée.
STB Commended 3 Crowns
Credit cards: 1, 3 + SWITCH, DELTA
Proprietors: Alan & Angela Broadhurst

Isle of
Arran

Location 19

AUCHRANNIE COUNTRY HOUSE HOTEL

Auchrannie Road, Brodick
Isle of Arran KA27 8BZ
Tel: 01770 302234
Fax: 01770 302812

One mile north of Brodick Ferry Terminal and 400 yards from Brodick Golf Club.
Auchrannie is a red sandstone old Scottish mansion, once the home of the Dowager Duchess of Hamilton, now a comfortable hotel with a leisure club, indoor swimming pool and a popular Bistro. It is the renowned Garden Restaurant in particular that is recommended by Taste of Scotland. Varied menus are presented with particular emphasis on fresh local produce including seafood. The hotel enjoys a unique situation from which to explore Arran's magnificent scenery – 56 miles of varied coastline and its seven golf courses. In addition to the luxuriously appointed bedrooms and family suites, there are spacious lodges sleeping up to six persons.
Open all year
Rooms: 28 with private facilities
Lunch (Brambles Bistro) 12 – 2.30 pm (a)
Dinner (Brambles Bistro) 5 – 9.30 pm (b)
Dinner (Garden Restaurant) 6.30 – 9.30 pm (d)
No smoking in Garden Restaurant
No dogs, except in lodges
Bed & Breakfast £40.50 – £46.50
Dinner B & B £59 – £64.50
Special Rates for 3+/7+ nights
• Roast loin of spring lamb set on a bed of creamed spinach with Madeira essence. Pan-fried medallions of monkfish tails on a spring onion and fresh ginger butter sauce. Baked suprême of Guinea fowl on a wild mushroom and hazelnut stuffing, with a fresh thyme scented sauce. Rendezvous of west coast seafood with a fresh dill and cucumber cream sauce.
STB Highly Commended 5 Crowns
Credit cards: 1, 3 + SWITCH
Proprietor: Iain Johnston

CREELERS SEAFOOD RESTAURANT

The Home Farm, Brodick
Isle of Arran KA27 8DD
Tel: 01770 302810
Fax: 01770 302797

Prestige Award Winner 1993

From Brodick Pier, go north following coast road towards Brodick Castle and Corrie for 1½ miles. Restaurant on right.
Set in the Arran Visitors Centre, the restaurant, formerly the bothy to the old home farm of Brodick Castle, has been established by Tim and Fran James as a seafood bistro. The decor like the food is simple, but colourful, the atmosphere almost continental and the service is quite charming. Tim, formerly a trawlerman on the west coast, still creels for a majority of the shellfish and catches the wild salmon and sea trout. The remainder of the fish is bought fresh off the quays of Kintyre. However the meat and vegetarian dishes are an excellent alternative to eating fish. There is an extensive starter choice to accompany both the lunch and dinner menus. Their seafood shop and smokehouse attached to the restaurant enables you to purchase some of the produce you may have sampled in the restaurant. A mail order service for Arran Smoked Products is also available.
Open 15 Mar to 31 Oct
Restaurant Lunch 12.30 – 2.30 pm except Mon (b)
Dinner 7 – 10 pm except Mon (e)
Closed Mon except Bank Holidays + during Jul/Aug
Facilities for disabled visitors
• Rendezvous of local sea and shellfish with Pernod and dill sauce. Fillet of hake with fresh crab and fish mousse on chive bisque. Delice of Kintyre salmon with lemon and chive fumet. Tournedos of black Angus beef on celeriac and potato rosti with red wine jus. Sika venison steak on a light scented liquorice reduction. Cranachan cheese cake.
Credit cards: 1, 3
Proprietors: Tim & Fran James

DUNVEGAN HOUSE

Shore Road
Brodick
Isle of Arran KA27 8AJ
Tel: 01770 302811

Turn right from ferry into Brodick, c 500 yards – on sea front.
Once a substantial family home, this traditional red sandstone house has been carefully restored and skilfully extended in keeping with the original design. It is set back from the main promenade in its own garden where guests can sit out and enjoy the views across the bay to Brodick Castle and Goatfell. A lovely relaxing atmosphere prevails inside. Naomi and David Spencer are a friendly young couple who look after their guests well and make them feel at home. Bedrooms are comfortable and tastefully appointed, and most are en suite. There are delightful views from the dining room which overlooks the garden. The table d'hôte dinner menu changes daily and guests are invited to make their selection from several alternatives by mid afternoon. Table appointments are impeccable and the food is good traditional cooking served up very tastefully and represents excellent value for money. The breakfasts are particularly good with high quality produce and interesting additions to the norm. For most people Dunvegan will prove to be an enjoyable and satisfying experience.
Open all year
Rooms: 10, 7 with private facilities
Dinner 7 – 7.30 pm (b)
Residents only
Restricted Licence
No dogs
No smoking in bedrooms
Bed & breakfast £18.50 – £25
Dinner B & B £30.50 – £37
Special Rates for 4+ nights
• Home-made soups. Baked salmon in a prawn and lemon sauce. Arran lamb cutlets in rosemary gravy with fresh mint sauce. Guinness and steak pie with traditional suet crust. Baked trout stuffed with almonds and herbs. Traditional hot puddings with creamy custard. Breakfast – haggis or fruit pudding, locally smoked kippers.
STB Highly Commended 3 Crowns
No credit cards
Proprietors: David & Naomi Spencer

GLEN CLOY FARMHOUSE

Glencloy, Brodick
Isle of Arran KA27 8DA
Tel: 01770 302351

1½ miles from Brodick Pier on road
towards Brodick Castle. Sign at post box
in wall.

Glen Cloy Farmhouse is a beautiful
century old sandstone house, situated in
a peaceful glen just outside Brodick. The
bedrooms are individually furnished and
are cosy and warm. Two of the five
bedrooms have en suite facilities and
there are two other bathrooms. The
chef/proprietor and his wife bake their
own bread, and vegetables and herbs
come from the kitchen garden. The
farmhouse is ideally located to explore
the island's attractions, being close to
golf, castle, and the mountains.

Open 1 Mar to 7 Nov + restaurant only
Fri Sat Sun Nov to Mar
except Christmas + New Year
Rooms: 5, 2 with private facilities
Dinner 7 – 7.30 pm (b)
Residents only 1 Mar to 7 Nov
Unlicensed – guests welcome to take
own wine
No smoking in dining room
Bed & Breakfast £20 – £27
Dinner B & B £32 – £37
Special Rates for 3+ nights
• *Home-made bread, soups and*
desserts. Cream of cauliflower soup.
Chicken suprême in a ginger cream
sauce. Home-made orange trifle with
fresh oranges. Scottish cheeses.
STB Commended 2 Crowns
No credit cards
Proprietors: Mark & Vicki Padfield

GLENISLE HOTEL

Shore Road, Lamlash
Isle of Arran KA27 8LS
Tel: 01770 600 559/258

On main street of Lamlash.

The Glenisle is a traditional Scottish
whitewashed hotel, with hanging baskets
and awnings, set in neatly kept gardens
overlooking the bay. A programme of
internal refurbishment has been carried
out, including some extension to the
restaurant. Many of the attractively
furnished bedrooms enjoy splendid sea
views towards Holy Isle. There is a
friendly and relaxed atmosphere about
the place enhanced by the comfortable
surroundings. In the cocktail lounge a
feature has been made of wooden
carvings from the famous old Clyde
steamer, the Talisman. The restaurant
menus offer quite a range of dishes

reflecting the Scottish and local Arran
produce available.

Open all year except 4 to 15 Feb
Rooms: 13 with private facilities
Bar Lunch: 12 – 2 pm (a)
Dining Room/Restaurant Lunch 12 –
2 pm (a)
Dinner 7 – 8.45 pm (b)
Bed & Breakfast from £33.50
Dinner B & B from £44
• *Home-made soups and pâtés. Trout*
grilled in lemon butter, served with a
coating of flaked almonds. Chicken
suprême stuffed with haggis, with a
cream and whisky sauce. Prime Scotch
fillet of beef in a Guinness and mussel
sauce. Smoked fish layer – whiting,
haddock and trout served with a lemon
and lime glaze.
STB Commended 4 Crowns
Credit cards: 1, 3 + SWITCH
Proprietor: Fred Wood

KILMICHAEL COUNTRY HOUSE HOTEL

Glen Cloy, by Brodick
Isle of Arran KA27 8BY
Tel: 01770 302219

1½ miles from Brodick Pier, turning
inland at golf course (signposted). In own
grounds at end of long private drive.

Kilmichael is believed to be the oldest
house on Arran and it has been lovingly
transformed to a splendour it could
never have known in the past. This is a
small country house of a special
standard enriched with antique furniture,
oriental rugs, Chinese porcelain and
objets d'art, and the only hotel on Arran
graded 'Deluxe' by the Scottish Tourist
Board. Elegance is sometimes an over-
worked word, but not here. The decor,
furnishings, style and quality of the
place demonstrate impeccable good
taste and the same care and attention
go into the planning of meals. The rich
harvest of the island's seas together
with its game and agricultural produce
are incorporated in appealing menus
and complemented by a well chosen
wine list. This is a wonderful restful
hideaway from the hustle and bustle of
ordinary life.

Open all year except Christmas wk
Rooms: 6 with private facilities
Dinner 7.30 – 8.30 pm except Mon (d)
5 course menu
Dinner for non-residents – booking
essential
Children over 12 years welcome
No smoking in dining room + bedrooms
Bed & Breakfast £32 – £50

Dinner B & B £52 – £75
Special Rates for 3+/7+ nights
• *Warm mushroom pâté in a pastry box.*
Salad of avocado, tomatoes and Arran
goats cheese. Apple and parsnip soup.
Scottish salmon with saffron and yellow
pepper sauce. Fillet of Scotch beef
Wellington with wild mushroom sauce.
Roast saddle of hare with rosemary and
redcurrant sauce. Strawberry cream fool.
Mousse of two chocolates with raspberry
coulis.
STB Deluxe 4 Crowns
Credit cards: 1, 3
Proprietors: Geoffrey Botterill
                & Antony Butterworth

LILYBANK HOTEL

Shore Road, Lamlash
Isle of Arran KA27 8LS
Tel: 01770 600230

On main street in Lamlash, 4 miles from
ferry terminal (Brodick).

Built in the late 18th century, Lilybank is
a charming whitewashed small family
run hotel which has been lovingly
restored and refurbished by its present
owners, Clive and Carol Berry. The
Berrys have tastefully renovated the
hotel to a high standard to provide
quality accommodation throughout. In
this relaxed and comfortable
atmosphere guests may experience
some of the finest views over the bay
and Holy Isle while enjoying the food
prepared by Carol based on the
abundant local produce available such
as locally smoked fish and shellfish,
island cheeses, Arran beef and lamb,
and free range eggs. Such caring and
attentive hosts make this a delightful
place to stay.

Open all year
Rooms: 6 , 5 with private facilities
Dinner 7 – 8 pm (b)
Restricted Hotel Licence
Facilities for disabled visitors
No smoking in restaurant + bedrooms
Bed & Breakfast £18.50 – £27.50
Dinner B & B £31 – £40
Special Rates for 3+ nights
• *Home-made bread, soups, pâtés and*
desserts. Smoked trout mousse. Collops
of Arran lamb with a bramble sauce.
Poached fillet of salmon with a lemon
and chive sauce. Carbonnade of beef.
Prime Arran sirloin steak. Apricot and
Drambuie oaty crumble. Brodick Blue
cheese and oatcakes.
STB Highly Commended 3 Crowns
No credit cards
Proprietors: Clive & Carol Berry

Auchencairn

Location 20

BALCARY BAY HOTEL

Auchencairn, nr Castle Douglas
Kirkcudbrightshire DG7 1QZ
Tel: 01556 640217/640311
Fax: 01556 640272

*A711 Dalbeattie-Kirkcudbright to
Auchencairn. Then take 'no through road'
signposted Balcary (single track) for 2
miles.*

In a quiet and idyllic setting on the shore
at Balcary Point stands this lovely old
country house dating from 1625. It has a
fascinating history, having been the
headquarters for a smuggling operation
during the 17th century. The building
retains much of the old character and
charm but is now an elegant and very
comfortable hotel. During the past year
the restaurant, cocktail bar and reception
lounge have all been tastefully
refurbished and a new conservatory was
in progress to extend the dining facilities.
The restaurant menus show a good
balance of interesting dishes making use
of the quality produce of the area. With
the combination of excellent hospitality,
good food and a superb setting this is a
wonderful place to 'get away from it all'.

Open 3 Mar to 11 Nov
Rooms: 17 with private facilities
Bar Lunch 12 – 2 pm (a)
Dining Room/Restaurant Lunch 12 –
1.45 pm Sun only (a): à la carte lunch by
reservation only Mon to Sat (c)
Dinner 7 – 9 pm high season: 7 –
8.30 pm low season (c)
Bed & Breakfast £44 – £50
Dinner B & B £44 – £68
Special Rates for 2+ nights
Spring/Autumn: for 3 + 7 nights
Jun to Sep
*• Smoked haddock and spinach
pancake. Grilled trout fillets cooked in an
orange butter. Saddle of venison roasted
on a bed of hazelnuts, with a rich red
wine sauce. Grilled halibut with ginger.
Noisettes of lamb with a gin and juniper
berry sauce.*
STB Highly Commended 4 Crowns
Credit cards: 1, 3
*Proprietors: Ronald & Joan Lamb,
Graeme & Clare Lamb*

COLLIN HOUSE

Auchencairn, Castle Douglas
Dumfries & Galloway DG7 1QN
Tel: 01556 640292
Fax: 01556 640276

*Turn off A711 east of Auchencairn,
signposted.*

This charmingly proportioned country
house, with its distinctive Suffolk pink
exterior, is set in 20 acres of grounds
with neatly kept mature gardens and
terraces. A Listed building, Collin House
overlooks the beautiful Galloway
coastline, Auchencairn Bay and Hestan
Island. On a clear day the Cumbrian Hills
can be seen across the Solway Firth. The
house was built around 1750 and has
recently been superbly restored and
sympathetically extended, and now
affords guests every luxury and comfort.
Many period pieces of furniture enhance
the spacious rooms. Guests can relax in
the very comfortable drawing room over
drinks before dinner. The dining room is
an elegant room with windows to the
front overlooking the gardens while those
to the rear of the house look across the
bay to Hestan Island. There is a
delightful feeling of discreet opulence. At
dinner a small choice menu is offered
and this changes daily making extensive
use of excellent fresh local produce
including fish and game in season. Collin
House has been awarded three AA
Rosettes in respect of the high standard
of food, plus two Red Stars for the hotel.
There is a carefully selected small but
interesting wine list. Christmas and New
Year house parties are a speciality.

Open Mar to Jan
Rooms: 6 with private facilities
Dinner 7.30 – 8 pm (e) 4/5 course menu
*Dinner for non-residents by reservation
only*
Table Licence
No smoking in dining room
*Children over 11 years welcome in dining
room*
Dogs by arrangement
Bed & Breakfast £39 – £42
Dinner B & B £68 – £70
Special Rates for 3+ nights
*• Lobster bisque. Crab soup with rouille.
Risotto of smoked venison with cèpes.
Hot kipper pâté with shallot butter sauce.
Noisettes of Scottish lamb on a bed of
spinach with port wine sauce. Escalope of
sea bass filled with its own mousseline
and served with basil scented juices.*
STB Deluxe 3 Crowns
Credit cards: 1, 3
Proprietors: Pam Hall & John Wood

Location 21

AUCHTERARDER HOUSE

Auchterarder
Perthshire PH3 1DZ
Tel: 01764 663646/7
Fax: 01764 662939

Prestige Award Winner 1989

*Off B8062 Auchterarder-Crieff, 1 mile
from village.*

Auchterarder House is superb in every
way and Ian and Audrey Brown are
constantly striving to raise standards
even higher. This fine old red sandstone
mansion house is set in 17½ acres of
beautifully manicured lawns and mature
trees. Public rooms are quite exceptional
and sumptuously furnished, and the
conservatory is a particularly attractive
feature. The master bedrooms are so
grand in scale that they might have come
straight off a Hollywood set which may
be one reason why ex-President Ronald
Reagan and his wife chose to stay there
on a visit to Scotland. Food in the
elegant dining room is cooked and
presented with the same imagination
and flair that is so evident throughout.
The Browns are charming and attentive
hosts and make everyone feel like a
personal guest.

Open all year
Rooms: 15 with private facilities
Dining Room/Restaurant Lunch 12 –
3 pm (c-d)
Victorian teas in Winter Garden
Conservatory 3 – 5 pm
Dinner 6 – 10 pm (e-f)
Reservations essential
No children
Bed & Breakfast £55 – £97.50
Special Dinner B & B Rates for 2+ nights
*• West coast mussel stew spiked with
Pernod, complemented with herb
dumplings. Collop of Aberdeen Angus
beef with fresh langoustine tails, served
with a gingered shellfish and coriander
sauce. Braised turbot fillet edged with a
light pesto, presented on a warm dill and
tomato dressing. Baked chocolate spiced
pudding with honey ice-cream and toddie
sabayon.*
Credit cards: 1, 2, 3, 5, 6 + SWITCH
Proprietors: Ian & Audrey Brown

DUCHALLY HOUSE HOTEL
Duchally, by Auchterarder
Perthshire PH3 1PN
Tel: 01764 663071
Fax: 01764 662464

Just off A823 Crieff-Dunfermline, 2 miles south of Auchterarder.
Duchally House is a Victorian country manor house set in 27 acres of landscaped grounds. It still retains some of the fine original features of the period including an impressive staircase and lovely old fireplaces, and a beautifully panelled billiard room. The house itself has been added to over the years and the owners have carried out tasteful and stylish refurbishment to provide a good standard of comfortable accommodation for their guests. Open log fires feature throughout the public rooms and there are beautiful views of the Ochil hills from the restaurants. Much thought and imagination has gone into the planning of the menus with a good range of choice at each course. The chef specialises in producing interesting sauces to complement the best quality produce available.
Open all year except Christmas Eve,
Christmas + Boxing Days
Rooms: 15 with private facilities
Bar Lunch 12 – 2.15 pm (a)
Dining Room/Restaurant Lunch 12 –
2 pm (b)
Bar Supper 6 – 9.30 pm (a)
Dinner 7 – 9.30 pm (d)
Facilities for disabled visitors
No smoking area in restaurant
Bed & Breakfast £35 – £50
Dinner B & B £50 – £60
Special Rates for 2+ nights
• Fillet of Scottish salmon steamed with lemon butter and garden herbs. Pan-fried fillet of halibut with apples and a light cider sauce. Fillet of Scotch beef in a pepper, brandy and cream sauce.
STB Highly Commended 4 Crowns
Credit cards: 1, 2, 3, 5, 6
Proprietor: Maureen Raeder

THE GLENEAGLES HOTEL
Auchterarder
Perthshire PH3 1NF
Tel: 01764 662231
Telex: 76105 • Fax: 01764 662134

Prestige Award Winner 1990

½ mile west of A9, 10 miles north of Dunblane, 1 mile south of Auchterarder.
A magnificent hotel of international reputation and a resort in itself with an exceptional range of leisure and sporting facilities. A spectacular Scottish 'palace' in rolling Perthshire countryside built in grand style in the early part of this century and immaculately restored. Food and accommodation are of the highest standard as would be expected from the first hotel in Scotland to have been awarded the AA's highest accolade of five red stars, and they are richly deserved. In the restaurants, the best of local produce is used to create dishes with a uniquely Scottish flavour, cooked and presented to standards of international excellence. Few will experience Gleneagles without full enjoyment of the occasion and a wish to return as soon as possible. French and German spoken.
Open all year
Rooms: 234 with private facilities
Bar Lunch 12 – 2.30 pm (a)
Dining Room/Restaurant Lunch 12.30 –
2.30 pm (d)
Dinner 7.30 – 10 pm (f)
Note: please telephone in advance for non-residential dining in Strathearn Restaurant, Dormy House and Equestrian Centre
No smoking area in restaurants
Bed & Breakfast £85 – £160
Dinner B & B £124.50 – £180
Room Rate £170 – £1000
Special Rates available on request
• Salad of Perthshire wood pigeon with garden herbs and apple vinegar. Casserole of monkfish with smoked bacon and Loch Alsh mussels. Roast loin of venison with a sweet onion marmalade. Rondel of Scotch beef topped with a meat marrow and spinach crust. Pistachio brûlée with poached pear and cinnamon ice-cream.
STB Deluxe 5 Crowns
Credit cards: 1, 2, 3, 5, 6

Auchtermuchty

Location 22

ARDCHOILLE FARM GUEST HOUSE
Dunshalt, Auchtermuchty
Fife KY14 7EY
Tel: 01337 828414
Fax: 01337 828414
On B936 just outside Dunshalt village, 1½ miles south of Auchtermuchty.
Donald and Isobel Steven welcome you to Ardchoille – a spacious, well appointed farmhouse, with superb views of the Lomond hills. The accommodation is in twin-bedded rooms with en suite or private facilities, colour TV and tea/coffee trays with home-made butter shortbread. Large comfortable lounge. Attractive dining room with elegant china and crystal where delicious freshly prepared meals are presented with flair and imagination. Just an hour's drive from Edinburgh and 20 minutes from St Andrews or Perth, Ardchoille makes an excellent base for touring, golfing – or just relaxing.
Open all year
Rooms: 3 with private facilities
Dinner 7 – 7.30 pm (c) 4 course set menu
Dinner for non-residents by prior arrangement only
Unlicensed – guests welcome to take own wine
No dogs
No smoking throughout
Bed & Breakfast £25 – £45
Dinner B & B £40 – £60
• Poached fresh salmon on crispy lettuce with a dill mayonnaise. Home-made cauliflower and courgette soup. Chicken breast stuffed with prune and bacon in a light savoury lemon sauce. Casserole of Aberdeen Angus beef with Dunshalt mushroom sauce. Fresh garden vegetables. Tuille basket with home-made vanilla ice-cream and fresh strawberries. Treacle and sultana sponge with ginger sauce.
STB Highly Commended 3 Crowns
Credit cards: 1, 3
Proprietors: Donald & Isobel Steven

Credit Card Code		Meal Price Range	
1.	Access/Mastercard/Eurocard	(a)	under £10
2.	American Express	(b)	£10 – £15
3.	Visa	(c)	£15 – £20
4.	Carte Bleu	(d)	£20 – £25
5.	Diners Club	(e)	£25 – £30
6.	Mastercharge	(f)	over £30

Auldgirth
by Dumfries
Location 23

LOW KIRKBRIDE FARMHOUSE
Auldgirth
Dumfries DG2 0SP
Tel: 0138 782 258

From Dumfries take A76 Kilmarnock for 2 miles, then B729 to Dunscore. Beyond Dunscore at crossroads go right. After 1½ miles take first left. Farm first on left.
This is a working farm with a prize-winning herd of Friesian cattle and lots of sheep, so there is much of interest for those who love the country and farm animals. It is located in splendidly remote, rolling cultivated countryside with fine views in all directions, and here you are genuinely away from it all. The traditional farmhouse building is surrounded by out-buildings and a colourful garden to the front. Guest rooms are attractively decorated with pretty duvet covers and pillow cases, with matching curtains. Electric blankets are provided and there is a tea/coffee making tray with a jug of fresh farm milk. Dinner is provided for residents if booked in advance and there are plentiful helpings of good wholesome food which you take in the family kitchen while Zan chats, cooks and serves. A real atmosphere of family living.
Open all year
Rooms: 2
Dinner 6 – 9 pm (a)
Residents only
Unlicensed
No dogs
No smoking in bedrooms
Bed & Breakfast from £15
Dinner B & B from £22
• Home-made soup. Carbonnade of beef. Roast leg of Low Kirkbride lamb. Rabbit casserole. Bramble and apple pie. Scotch trifle. Banoffi pie.
STB Commended Listed
No credit cards
Proprietors: Joe & Zan Kirk

Aultbea
Location 24

AULTBEA HOTEL & RESTAURANT
Seafront, Aultbea
Ross-shire IV22 2HX
Tel: 01445 731201
Fax: 01445 731214

Off A832, on the shores of Loch Ewe.
The Aultbea Hotel is situated in an exceptionally beautiful location at the waterside of Loch Ewe and has magnificent views over the Isle of Ewe to the Torridon Mountains. It is believed to have been built for Lord Zetland in the early 1800s. The hotel has been run by Peter and Avril Nieto for over eight years and its reputation for comfort and cuisine has continued to grow. There is a choice of eating styles – the Waterside Bistro which is open all day and where a varied menu from teas and coffees with home-baking to local fish and grills is available; and the more formal Zetland Restaurant, overlooking the loch, where three or four course daily changing table d'hôte menus are offered which feature local seafood, smoked salmon, game and a carvery, as well as an à la carte option.
Open all year except Christmas Day
Rooms: 8 with private facilities
Waterside Bistro 9 am – 9 pm (b)
Bar Meals 11 am – 9 pm (b)
Dinner 7 – 9 pm (d)
Bed & Breakfast £25 – £39
Dinner B & B £46 – £60
Special Rates available
• Home-made soups. Locally landed scallops poached in wine and spices, served in their shells with a rich lobster sauce. Prime Torridon venison with a rich Burgundy gravy. Grilled cutlets of Ross-shire lamb served with a rosemary sauce. Loch Broom lobster. Darne of salmon with a hollandaise sauce.
STB Commended 4 Crowns
Credit cards: 1, 3 + SWITCH
Proprietors: Peter & Avril Nieto

Aviemore
Location 25

Special Merit Award 1994

LYNWILG HOUSE
Lynwilg, by Aviemore
Inverness-shire PH22 1PZ
Tel: 01479 811685
Fax: 01479 811685

A9 Perth-Inverness, take Lynwilg road 1 mile south of Aviemore.
This impressive country house was built by the Duke of Richmond and is set on high ground commanding beautiful views across to the Cairngorms. Four acres of landscaped gardens include a kitchen garden contributing fresh fruit, vegetables and herbs for the house. Although only a mile from Aviemore, the beauty of the surroundings and the elegance of the house interior set it worlds apart. Fishing on a private loch, croquet on the lawn, log fires and comfort, confirm the best features of country house living. The food lives up to the same high standards, with imaginative menus, excellent presentation and efficient attentive service.
Open 27 Dec to 31 Oct
Rooms: 4 with private facilities
Dinner 7 – 8 pm (b)
Unlicensed – guests welcome to take own wine
Dogs by arrangement
No smoking in restaurant
Bed & Breakfast £20 – £30
Dinner B & B £33 – £45
• Carrot and lovage soup. Home-made chicken liver pâté with Brandy and herbs. Scallops Mornay. Venison casseroled in red wine. Home-made praline ice-cream. Lynwilg fruit desserts. Local cheeses.
STB Highly Commended 3 Crowns
Credit cards: 1, 3
Proprietor: Marjory Cleary

THE OLD BRIDGE INN
Old Dalfaber Road
Aviemore PH22 1PU
Tel: 01479 811137
Fax: 01479 810270

At south end of Aviemore, take B970 ski road (Cairngorms) for 300 yards then take turning on left for another 300 yards.
The Old Bridge Inn is a cosy Highland pub nestling beside the River Spey, just

off the ski road. It is a quaint little building in a quiet spot with tables and seats outside for summer evenings. The atmosphere is informal and the ingredients for the menus are carefully chosen to reflect the best of Scottish produce. There is also a children's menu and the Inn's own ice-cream which seems to please all ages. In the evening the menu is based on items prepared on the chargrill. A Highland evening is held every Tuesday in the summer, with a welcoming piper, entertainment and a four course menu.

Open all year
Bar Food 12 – 2 pm Mon to Sat: 12.30 – 2 pm Sun (a)
Bar Food 6 – 9 pm (a)
No smoking area in restaurant
• Home-made broths. Orcadian buidhe. Seafood bake. Poached brill with lemon sauce. Game pie topped with flaky pastry. Chargrill prime Scottish venison chop with a port and cranberry sauce. Barbecued Inverdruie trout with dill mayonnaise. Ecclefechan tart. Scottish cheeses.
No credit cards
Proprietor: Nigel Reid

THE ROWAN TREE RESTAURANT & GUEST HOUSE
Loch Alvie, by Aviemore
Inverness-shire PH22 1QB
Tel: 01479 810207
1½ miles south of Aviemore on old A9 (B9152) overlooking Loch Alvie.
One of Strathspey's oldest hotels (the Lynwilg) has been converted and restored to life as The Rowan Tree Restaurant and Guest House. Originally a coaching inn dating from the early 1800s, the property has been tastefully re-decorated, retaining and enhancing its many original features. Each of the bedrooms has a fine outlook and offers olde worlde charm with modern facilities. Under the ownership of George and Gillian Orr, who are attentive hosts, the restaurant has already established a reputation for high standards of food and service so booking for dinner is advisable. The Orrs pride themselves in producing good value home-cooked dishes using the best of fresh local produce. Guests can enjoy a pre-dinner drink while perusing the menu and wine list in front of a roaring log fire in the lounge. There is also a private dining room seating 20 to 30 available for special occasions.
Open 20 Jan to 31 Dec

Note: Jan to Mar, Nov + Dec open Fri Sat only
Rooms: 10 , 4 with private facilities
Dining Room/Restaurant Lunch 12 – 2 pm except Sun (a)
Dinner 7.30 – 9 pm except Sun (b)
Closed Sun
No smoking area in dining room
Bed & Breakfast £15 – £25
Special Rates available
• Parcels of smoked Scottish salmon filled with a salmon and chive mousse. Highland lamb and apple pie flavoured with rosemary. Salmon steak with a tangy herb and lemon butter. Local Badenoch venison cooked in a red wine and cranberry gravy. Rowan Tree Delight – home-made Scotch pancakes topped with soft fruits, hot syrup and fresh cream.
Credit cards: 1, 3
Proprietors: George & Gillian Orr

Ayr

Location 26
THE BOATHOUSE
4 South Harbour Street
Ayr KA7 1JA
Tel: 01292 280212
Fax: 01292 288718
At end of Fort Street on riverside, overlooking harbour.
The aptly named 'Boathouse' is an eyecatching old building by the harbour which was a 19th century lifeboat station and has seen various other uses down the years before being converted to the restaurant it is today. The room where the restaurant is now used to house the lifeboat, hence the high ceiling. Naturally a nautical atmosphere prevails. A racing scull is suspended from the rafters and there are oars hanging on the walls. The restaurant is set on two levels with oak-panelled walls, rafters and tiny windows. The restaurant has been awarded an AA Rosette for its food. The menus are imaginative and local fresh produce including shellfish is very much in evidence and can be enjoyed sitting by a window in the bar or restaurant, overlooking the harbour.
Open all year
Bar Lunch 12 – 2.30 pm (b)
Dining Room/Restaurant Lunch 12 – 2.30 pm (d)
Bar Supper 6.30 – 9.30 pm except Sat (b)
Dinner 6.30 – 9.30 pm (d)
Facilities for disabled visitors

Note: No pipes or cigars in restaurant
• Home-cured Scottish salmon with cucumber and shallot relish, roquette leaves and pear vinaigrette. Fresh mussels with orange butter sauce. Noisettes of lamb with a tapenade scented jus. Pan-fried monkfish on a saffron, spring onion and chilli beurre blanc. Scottish venison with a liquorice and red wine sauce. Ayr landed hake with a saffron and Noilly Prat sauce.
Credit cards: 1, 2, 3, 5
Proprietors: Robert Jones & Heather Clark

DUNURE ANCHORAGE
Harbour View, Dunure
nr Ayr KA7 4LN
Tel: 01292 500295
In Dunure village, off A719 (coast road) about 6 miles south of Ayr.
This corner of the Ayrshire coastline is positively steeped in history and nowhere does it come more alive than in the charming harbourside hostelry of Dunure Anchorage. There is a distinctly old world appeal about the place from the moment you find yourself in the welcoming reception area which leads to the bar and restaurant. Walls half-panelled in wood, stucco and stone, with pretty pictures, old brass ornaments and fishing paraphernalia, set the tone. The dining room is warm and cosy with beamed ceiling, thick carpet and comfortable chairs, and little windows overlooking the harbour. There is a good menu of interesting dishes which indicate a talented chef behind the scenes. The food is sensibly priced and good, served in a relaxed and friendly atmosphere by caring staff who seem keen to protect the restaurant's reputation.
Open all year
Note: only open Fri to Sun in Jan/Feb
Bar Meals 12 – 2.30 pm Mon to Fri; 12 – 9.30 pm Sat Sun (b)
Meals available all day Jul to Sep (incl)
Dinner 6 – 9.30 pm (c)
• Tarragon chicken cheesecake. Plaice, watercress and salmon terrine with home-made lemon vinaigrette. Noisettes of lamb with a grape and port sauce. Poached fillet of salmon on a bed of fresh spinach with a cream, vermouth and parsley sauce. Haunch of venison braised gently with redcurrants and wine.
Credit cards: 1, 3 + SWITCH, DELTA
Proprietors: The Smith Family

FAIRFIELD HOUSE HOTEL
12 Fairfield Road, Ayr
Ayrshire KA7 2AR
Tel: 01292 267461
Fax: 01292 261456

From Burns Statue Square, down Miller Road. Turn left (A719 Maidens) then first right.

Fairfield House was built originally as a mansion house for a Victorian Glasgow tea merchant. It stands in a quiet residential area of the town of Ayr, overlooking the Low Green which stretches across to the esplanade and seafront, with magnificent views of the Isle of Arran. From this quiet central situation it is only a few minutes walk to the town centre. The hotel's classic interior design was devised by Lady Henrietta Spencer Churchill to create elegant public rooms and spacious and well appointed individually styled bedrooms and suites. An added attraction is the modern leisure club with swimming pool, steam room, sauna, gymnasium, health and beauty salon, all available to resident guests. In the Fleur de Lys Gourmet Restaurant the menus offer a good selection of interesting dishes with some innovative combinations of ingredients.

Open all year
Rooms: 34 with private facilities
Bar Lunch 12 – 2 pm (b)
Dining Room/Restaurant Lunch 12 – 2 pm (c)
Bar Supper 6 – 9.30 pm (b)
Dinner 7 – 9.30 pm (d) 4 course menu
Facilities for disabled visitors
No smoking area in restaurant
Bed & Breakfast £45 – £110
Dinner B & B £60 – £125
Room Rate from £60
Special Rates for 2+ nights
• Salmon mousseline wrapped in leeks, with cherry tomato salad and dill dressing. Breast of chicken in a herb pastry crust stuffed with apricots, cream cheese and hazelnuts. Casserole of monkfish tails, with smoked bacon, pine kernels and tomatoes, glazed with cheese. Medallions of beef in a sharp red wine vinegar and strawberry essence with snipped tarragon and peppercorns.
Credit cards: 1, 2, 3, 5, 6 + SWITCH

FOUTERS BISTRO RESTAURANT
2A Academy Street, Ayr
Ayrshire KA7 1HS
Tel: 01292 261391

Town centre, opposite Town Hall.

Down a cobbled lane in the vaults of an old bank building is this charming little restaurant run by Laurie and Fran Black. Utilising the unusual architectural features of the bank vaults, they have created the cosy intimate atmosphere of the bistro. It is no small achievement to have been a leading restaurant in the town for over 20 years and the fact that Fouters has established such a high reputation is a tribute to the proprietors. The importance they place on quality has been recognised over the years with various restaurant awards for consistently good standards of food. With its stone-flagged floors and light stucco walls featuring stencils of the restaurant's motif, what better place to experience the appetisingly presented menus which focus on the wonderful produce Ayrshire has to offer and excellent local seafood. The friendly relaxed atmosphere is in no small way due to Laurie and Fran who are most congenial hosts. A popular eating place so it is best to book.

Open all year except 25 to 27 Dec, 1 to 3 Jan
Bistro Menu 12 – 2 pm except Sun Mon (a)
Restaurant Lunch 12 – 2 pm except Sun Mon (b)
Dinner 6.30 – 10.30 pm except Mon (e)
Closed Mon
• West coast mussels steamed with wine, lemon, garlic and cream. Scottish salmon with fresh asparagus, glazed with hollandaise sauce. Rendezvous of local seafood served with a light saffron vermouth cream sauce. Roast rack of Scottish lamb served with the pan juices, redcurrant jelly and crème de cassis. Chargrilled prime Scottish beef. Fouters bread and butter pudding.
Credit cards: 1, 2, 3, 5, 6 + SWITCH
Proprietors: Laurie & Fran Black

THE HUNNY POT
37 Beresford Terrace
Ayr KA7 2EU
Tel: 01292 263239

In the town centre of Ayr, close to Burns' Statue Square.

This small but popular and attractive coffee shop is run personally by Felicity Thomson. It has a cosy intimate atmosphere and the pine furniture and teddy bear theme give the place character. There is a range of eating available all day – from morning coffee and afternoon tea with home-baking, to more substantial snacks and meals. The Hunny Pot now has a table licence so you may enjoy a glass of wine with your meal.

Open all year except Christmas + Boxing Days, 1 + 2 Jan
Meals served all day from 10 am – 10 pm except Sun: 10.45 am – 5.30 pm Sun (a)
Traditional afternoon teas served 2 – 5.30 pm Sun
No smoking area in restaurant
• All home-made soups, scones, brown sugar meringues, cakes and dish of the day. Puddings include seasonal fruit crumbles, hazelnut meringue cake. Scottish cheeses with oatcakes.
No credit cards
Proprietor: Felicity Thomson

NORTHPARK HOUSE
Alloway Village, Ayr
Ayrshire KA7 4NL
Tel: 01292 442336
Fax: 01292 445572

Alloway Village, near Burns' cottage, 2 miles from Ayr town centre.

Northpark House was built in 1720 originally as a farmhouse for the Belleisle Estate and referred to as Northpark Lodge by Robert Burns, the national bard, whose birthplace is virtually next door. The property has been sympathetically restored and refurbished to create the small country house hotel it is today, standing in its own grounds between the 10th and 11th tees of one of Belleisle's two magnificent golf courses. The bedrooms are comfortable, well equipped and en suite, and have outlooks over the golf course or vegetable gardens. Four unique restaurants, each individually named, have been created from a series of small interconnecting rooms, the windows of which look out onto the grounds. The restaurant menus show a good range of interesting dishes created with skill by award winning Chef de Cuisine David Auchie and his kitchen brigade, utilising the best of local produce in both table d'hôte and à la carte menus. A conservatory forms the centrepiece around which these dining rooms are set and in its informal surroundings light snacks, breakfast and coffees are served. Within 20 minutes of the hotel are ten top quality championship golf courses and tee-off times can be arranged for guests. There are also many places of historical interest to visit in the area including Burns Cottage and Culzean Castle.

Open all year
Rooms : 5 with private facilities
Bar Lunch 12 – 2.30 pm (a)
Dining Room/Restaurant Lunch 12.30 – 2.30 pm (c)
Dinner 7 – 9.30 pm (c-d)
Facilities for disabled visitors
Two dining rooms non-smoking
Bed & Breakfast £40 – £80
Dinner B & B £59 – £99
• Pan-fried scallops with a delicate vermouth and tomato cream glazed under a crisp parsley crust. Loin of Scotch lamb served with a Stilton and pear purse. Medallions of halibut with sea kale and a julienne of pickled ginger. Pot roast Guinea fowl set on a rich lime essence with redcurrants. Baked suprême of wild salmon on an Arran mustard and tarragon cream.
STB Highly Commended 4 Crowns
Credit cards: 1, 2, 3, 6 + SWITCH
Proprietors: Graeme & Rosamond Rennie

THE STABLES COFFEE HOUSE
Queen's Court, Sandgate
Ayr KA7 1BD
Tel: 01292 283704
To the rear of the old courtyard at the corner of Sandgate and Newmarket Street.
In the centre of Ayr is a tiny Georgian courtyard which is a haven of little shops with a tea garden. The Stables were built of local stone probably in the late 1760s. The menu leans heavily towards ethnic Scots dishes, predominantly 'kail yard' rather than 'castle'. You may choose just tea and a scone or have a full meal. Children are welcome and there is a range of toys and books available, but burgers, beans and chips don't feature on the menu! The restaurant is non-smoking but a small

separate room (with air filters) is set aside for smokers.
Open all year except Christmas + Boxing Days, 1 + 2 Jan
Open 10 am – 4.45 pm Mon to Sat:
12.30 – 5 pm Sun – summer only (a)
No smoking in restaurant
• Home-baking. Haggis. Stovies. Ham and haddie pie. Tweed kettle. Clootie dumpling. Farm-made cheeses. Fruit wines from Moniack Castle.
No credit cards
Proprietor: Ed Baines

Ballachulish

Location 27

THE BALLACHULISH HOTEL
Ballachulish, nr Fort William
Argyll PA39 4JY
Tel: 0185 581 1606
Fax: 0185 581 1629
On A828 Oban, at the Ballachulish Bridge.
Just below the bridge spanning Loch Leven at the narrow strait where it joins Loch Linnhe, is the Ballachulish Hotel. From this vantage point it commands panoramic views over the loch to the peaks of Morvern and Ardgour. Now a family run hotel, this former drovers inn is well placed to visit Glencoe to the east and experience its dramatic scenery; to venture to the west via Appin to Oban – the gateway to the Hebrides; or to cross the bridge northwards to Fort William and beyond. The bedrooms are tastefully furnished, comfortable and well equipped. There are gracious baronial lounges for relaxing in. Guests can enjoy a leisurely aperitif in the cocktail bar before going in to dine in the Loch View Restaurant. While admiring that wonderful view, they can sample the interesting range of dishes created by the chefs. Resident guests enjoy complimentary membership of a nearby sister hotel's leisure centre, with swimming pool, turbo pool, sauna and steam room. French and German spoken.
Open all year
Rooms: 30 with private facilities
Bar Meals 12 – 9.30 pm (a-b)
Dining Room/Restaurant Lunch 12 – 2.30 pm (a) – booking advisable
Dinner 7 – 9.30 pm (d)
Bed & Breakfast £35.50 – £48.50
Dinner B & B £56 – £69
Room Rate from £39.95
Special Rates for 3+/7+ nights
• Islay scallops in filo pastry with dill and

tarragon, with an elderflower wine butter sauce. Highland game terrine set in smoked Ayrshire bacon, with a wild rowanberry and raspberry sauce. Suprême of wild Scottish salmon with Loch Leven prawns and tarragon mousse, on a ragout of chanterelle mushrooms. Pan-fried saddle of Letterfinlay venison with roast chestnuts, baked apples and a sweet basil sauce.
STB Highly Commended 4 Crowns
Credit cards: 1, 3
Proprietors: The Young Family

BALLACHULISH HOUSE
Ballachulish
Argyll PA39 4JX
Tel: 0185 581 1266
Fax: 0185 581 1498
From roundabout south of Ballachulish Bridge take A828 Oban. Signed on left, 200 yards beyond Ballachulish Hotel.
Ballachulish House is steeped in history. It has been the seat of the Stewarts of Ballachulish since the 16th century, though rebuilt after being burned down by Hanoverian troops in 1746. Indeed the final order for the massacre of Glencoe was signed here and Alan 'Breac' Stewart stayed at the house the night before the Appin murder. Today Ballachulish House offers peace, quiet and comfort, and John and Liz Grey treat the visitors to their home as personal guests. Rooms are spacious with many antiques and attractive furnishings, and some have spectacular views of Loch Linnhe and Morven Hills. In the oldest part of the house is the dining room with its low ceiling and windows facing onto the garden. Here amid antique furniture, fine glasswear and furnishing, guests can enjoy interesting dishes presented with care and style, incorporating local produce and quality fresh ingredients. An excellent centre for touring the west coast.
Open all year except Christmas
Rooms: 6 , 4 with private facilities
Dinner at 7.30 pm (d)
Restricted Hotel Licence
No smoking in dining room + bedrooms
Bed & Breakfast £25 – £38
Dinner B & B £49 – £60
• Pan-fried scallops with fresh garden herbs, cream and wine sauce. Roast venison with rowan jelly. Gooseberry and elderflower tart.
Scottish cheeses.
STB Highly Commended 3 Crowns
Credit cards: 1, 3 + DELTA
Proprietors: John & Liz Grey

Ballantrae

Location 28

BALKISSOCK LODGE
Ballantrae
Ayrshire KA26 0LP
Tel: 01465 831537
Fax: 01465 831537

Take first inland road off A77, south of River Stinchar at Ballantrae (signed to Laggan caravans) and follow for 2¼ miles. Turn right at T-junction and continue along single track 'no through road' to its end.

Leaving the A77 immediately south of Ballantrae takes you at once into another world of gentle rolling hills, total peace and quiet and wonderful panoramic views. It also takes you to Balkissock Lodge, which dates from around 1800. The Lodge has recently been refurbished and takes full advantage of its location to provide a thoroughly relaxing atmosphere. Janet and Adrian Beale are thoughtful hosts and Janet's skill in the kitchen is evident in her imaginative menus and the degree to which she makes use of the fine supply of local produce for which Ayrshire is famous. Occasional speciality and gourmet events are held for serious lovers of good food. Vegetarians and vegans can make their requirements known in advance and be well looked after. There is a wealth of sporting and recreational activities in the locality.

Open 1 Apr to 29 Oct
Rooms: 2 with private facilities
Dinner 7 – 9 pm (b-c)
Non-residents by prior arrangement
Unlicensed – guests welcome to take own wine
No dogs
No smoking in dining room
Bed & Breakfast £20 – £35
Dinner B & B £31 – £55
Special Rates for 3+/7+ nights
• Crisp pastry envelope of smoked chicken served with a creamy herb dressing. Roasted rack of lamb, flavoured with garlic and rosemary, served with a sauce of the juices, port wine and redcurrant jelly. Pheasant with Madeira wine, oranges and pecan nuts. Local salmon with champagne and asparagus. Carrot roulade with lemon and ginger sauce. Savoy parcels with cider and saffron.
Credit cards: 1, 3
Proprietors: Adrian & Janet Beale

COSSES COUNTRY HOUSE
Ballantrae
Ayrshire KA26 0LR
Tel: 01465 831363
Fax: 01465 831598

From A77 at southern end of Ballantrae, take inland road signed to Laggan. Cosses is c. 2 miles on right.

Cosses was originally a shooting lodge then a home farm for the Glenapp Estate, before it became privately owned. Its name originates from the word 'cosseted' and that is just how Robin and Susan Crosthwaite aim to make their guests feel in their home, a delightfully converted farmhouse within 12 acres of beautiful gardens and woodland set in a secluded valley. The accommodation is in two tastefully furnished cottage suites situated round the courtyard. Before dinner, guests are invited for an aperitif in the Crosthwaites' own sitting room. Susan is an accomplished Cordon Bleu cook and takes a lot of care in composing enticing menus, combining vegetables, herbs and fruits from the kitchen garden with quality local ingredients to create a very high standard of cuisine.

Open all year except 23 Dec to 6 Jan
Rooms: 2 with private facilities
Dinner 7 – 9 pm (d) 4 course menu
Dinner for non-residents by reservation only
Table Licence
Bed & Breakfast £30 – £45
Dinner B & B £48 – £65
Special Rates for 3+ nights
• Terrine of salmon, sole and prawns, served warm with a light cream sauce. Fresh ginger, parsnip and orange soup. Fillet of Ayrshire lamb with a rosemary and barbecue sauce. Crailloch pheasant cooked with whisky, cream, bay and thyme. Fillet of Scottish salmon cooked with lime and green peppercorns, served with a gooseberry and dill cream.
STB Deluxe 3 Crowns
No credit cards
Proprietors: Susan & Robin Crosthwaite

Ballater

Location 29

BALGONIE COUNTRY HOUSE
Braemar Place
Ballater AB35 5RQ
Tel: 013397 55482
Fax: 013397 55482

Prestige Award Winner 1993

Off Braemar Road (A93), a few hundred yards west of Church Green.

Built in 1899 in the heart of Royal Deeside, Balgonie is now a small country house hotel set in tranquil mature gardens overlooking the golf course towards the hills of Glenmuick. There is much to appeal to the visitor to this area, ranging from hill-walking, golf and fishing, touring castles and distilleries, or simply relaxing in peaceful surroundings. Balgonie makes an ideal home from which to explore the many facets of the area. The menu is well balanced and interesting, reflecting the wealth of local produce such as game, salmon, beef and lamb with seafood fresh from the coast, and herbs and soft fruits from Balgonie's own garden. French and German spoken.

Open 1 Mar to 5 Jan
Rooms: 9 with private facilities
Dining Room/Restaurant Lunch 12.30 – 1.45 pm (c) – reservation only
Dinner 7 – 9 pm (e) 4 course menu
Facilities for disabled visitors
No smoking in dining room
Bed & Breakfast £45 – £55
Dinner B & B £72.50 – £82.50

Special Spring/Autumn Rates available
• Salad of Orkney oysters served with a warm lemon and lime vinaigrette. Roulade of Guinea fowl filled with smoked ham, figs and dates, set on a rich Madeira jus. Fillet of Scottish salmon with a fricassée of monkfish and scallops in a dill flavoured velouté. Fillet of Scotch lamb garnished with lamb's kidneys and glazed baby onions set on a red Burgundy jus.
STB Deluxe 4 Crowns
Credit cards: 1, 2, 3
Proprietors: John & Priscilla Finnie

CRAIGENDARROCH HOTEL & COUNTRY CLUB
Braemar Road, Ballater
Royal Deeside AB35 5XA
Tel: 013397 55858 • Telex: 739952
Fax: 013397 55447
On A93 western end of Ballater, near Balmoral.
There was a time when this Victorian red sandstone building was the Highland retreat of the Keiller family of Dundee. Greatly expanded it is now a first class hotel and country club with spectacular indoor swimming pools, squash courts, sauna, trimnasium, solarium etc. Outdoors there is a dry ski slope and an all weather tennis court. If even the mere thought of all that exercise gives you an appetite you will be able to indulge it in any one of three restaurants. The Oaks, at the top of the range, has a fine reputation for excellent cuisine and impeccable service and the Master Chef demonstrates his skills with flair and imagination. Here you may expect a special occasion and a memorable meal. At a slightly different level, the Lochnagar with its splendid views of the mountain of that name concentrates on traditional Scottish fare, including the superb Aberdeen Angus beef for which the region is famed. Adjoining the pool area is the Clubhouse restaurant, offering light snacks to substantial meals.
Open all year except 5 + 6 Jan
Rooms: 49 with private facilities
Lunch (Clubhouse Restaurant) 12 – 2.30 pm (a-c)
Dinner (Clubhouse Restaurant) 5 – 10 pm (a-c)
Dinner (The Oaks) 7 – 10 pm (c-f)
Dinner (Lochnagar) 7 – 10 pm Fri Sat (c)
No smoking in The Oaks
Bed & Breakfast £52.50 – £105
• Oak-smoked salmon with lime and chervil dressing. Mussel and fennel broth with dill cream. Pot roast Guinea fowl in

an onion sauce. Braised pigeon in red wine with cured ham on a bed of red cabbage. Layers of home-made shortbread and raspberry cream on a red berry sauce. Tangy lemon tart with vanilla cream.
STB Commended 5 Crowns
Credit cards: 1, 2, 3, 5 + SWITCH, DELTA

DARROCH LEARG HOTEL
Braemar Road, Ballater
Aberdeenshire AB35 5UX
Tel: 013397 55443
Fax: 013397 55252
On A93 at western edge of Ballater on road to Braemar.
Originally a Victorian country house, the Darroch Learg is now a family owned hotel of 20 bedrooms. There are log fires in the drawing room and a separate smoke room where pre-dinner drinks can be enjoyed in a relaxing and welcoming atmosphere. The dining room is a conservatory with a bright and airy feeling and a wonderful outlook into the Grampian Hills. The head chef and his team use the best of Scottish beef, lamb, game and fish to prepare the interesting and daily changing menu.
Open 1 Feb to 3 Jan closed Christmas
Rooms: 20 with private facilities
Bar Lunch 12.30 – 2 pm except Sun (a)
Dining Room/Restaurant Lunch 12.30 – 2 pm Sun only (b)
Dinner 7 – 8.30 pm (d)
No smoking in dining room
Bed & Breakfast £37 – £47
Dinner B & B £58 – £68
Special Rates for 3+/7+ nights

• Casserole of fresh queen scallops, langoustines and smoked mussels steeped in a Noilly Prat and dill sauce. Suprême of wild Dee salmon on a bed of mixed beans in a watercress, lemon balm and carrot sauce. Roasted stuffed saddle of lamb scented with garlic and parsley, with baked shallots and baby turnips in a thyme flavoured lamb jus.
STB Highly Commended 4 Crowns
Credit cards: 1, 2, 3, 5
Proprietors: Nigel & Fiona Franks

THE DEESIDE HOTEL
Braemar Road, Ballater
Aberdeenshire AB35 5RQ
Tel: 013397 55420
On west side of Ballater, set back from A93 Braemar road.
The Deeside Hotel is an attractive pink granite building which sits back from the road in its own informal well maintained garden. This a small family owned and run hotel with eight comfortably furnished en suite bedrooms, two of which are on the ground floor. In the sitting room there is an impressive oil painted frieze of wild animals and the original Victorian mantelpiece and tiled fireplace has been retained. Through an open archway from the lounge bar is the dining room with its varnished wooden floor and oil paintings of mountain scenery on the walls. In the evening a choice of freshly prepared dishes is available both in the restaurant and the bar, where you can also sample Scottish real ales. The atmosphere is informal and friendly, and the quality of food good.
Open 1 Feb to 30 Nov
Rooms: 9 with private facilities
Bar Supper 6 – 9 pm (b)
Dinner 6 – 9 pm (b)
Facilities for disabled visitors
No smoking in restaurant
Bed & Breakfast £18 – £25
Dinner B & B £28 – £35
Special Rates available
• Fish soups and chowders. Baked mussels with garlic and parsley butter. Home-made game pie. Grilled gigot of lamb with an orange, rosemary and port wine sauce. Poached fillet of salmon and queen scallops in a vermouth and chervil sauce. Clootie dumpling served with cream. Chocolate marquise with raspberry and mango coulis. Scottish cheeses.
STB Commended 3 Crowns
Credit cards: 1, 3
Proprietors: Donald & Alison Brooker

THE GLEN LUI HOTEL
Invercauld Road, Ballater
Aberdeenshire AB35 5RP
Tel: 013397 55402
Fax: 013397 55545

Off A93 at western end of Ballater.
The picturesque little village of Ballater is, of course, the very heart of Royal Deeside, an area in which there is so much to see and do. The Glen Lui Hotel is therefore well placed for those who wish to explore and enjoy the area. It is a small friendly country house in a quiet corner of the village with delightful views over the golf course and Lochnagar. Bedrooms are very comfortable and well equipped and there are a number of executive suites. A great deal of imagination goes into the preparation of the bistro and restaurant menus. The food is first class with a suitably supportive and extensive wine list. Conference facilities available.
Open all year
Rooms: 19 with private facilities
Bistro Lunch 12 – 2 pm (b)
Dinner (Bistro) 6 – 9 pm (b)
Dinner (Garden Restaurant) 7 – 9 pm (c)
No smoking in restaurant + conference room
Bed & Breakfast £25 – £40
Special Rates for 3+ nights
• Green lip mussels in a half shell topped with a smoked seafood sauce grilled with garlic bread. Pan-roasted breast of pigeon on a red wine and almond jus. Grilled suprême of Orkney salmon topped with a lemon and herb butter. Medallions of Angus fillet steak on a green peppercorn sauce. Sticky toffee pudding with a rich butterscotch glaze.
STB Highly Commended 4 Crowns
Credit cards: 1, 2, 3
Proprietors: Serge & Lorraine Geraud

THE GREEN INN
9 Victoria Road
Ballater AB35 5QQ
Tel: 013397 55701

In centre of Ballater on village green.
The Green Inn is best described as a restaurant with rooms. It is a two-storey granite building, formerly a temperance hotel, overlooking the village green and parish church. Green and white awnings deck the windows on either side of the door and there are colourful window boxes and hanging baskets.
Chef/proprietor Jeffrey Purves has a creative flair with food and focuses on maximum use of fresh local produce. He is keen to observe a healthy approach to cooking – minimum use of cream, replacing sugar with honey wherever possible etc. Each evening the Chef's Specials change to reflect the best of what is available to him that day. Traditional Scottish specialities are also a regular feature on the menu. Chef Purves is happy to produce a set vegetarian menu but asks for this to be arranged with him in advance so he may give it the attention it deserves. Service in the restaurant is informal and friendly. The Green Inn has a well established reputation for good food and it is good to learn that through the week an interesting light lunch is now available.
Open all year except Christmas Day + Sun Oct to Mar
Rooms: 3 with private facilities
Dining Room/Restaurant Lunch 12.30 – 1.45 pm except Sat (a)
Dinner 7 – 9 pm (c)
No smoking in dining room
Bed & Breakfast £25 – £30
Dinner B & B £41.50 – £50
• Chowder of Orkney scallops and Ayrshire bacon simmered in white wine, herbs and double cream. Fillet of Aberdeen Angus beef with thyme and red wine sauce and a haggis mousse. Suprême of salmon on a bed of sorrel with tomato and basil butter sauce. Loin of pork on a mushroom risotto topped with St Andrews cheese, served on an anchovy and lemon cream. Burnt cream with a lemon brose.
STB Commended 3 Crowns
Credit cards: 1, 3, 6
Proprietors: Carol & Jeffrey Purves

HAYLOFT RESTAURANT
Bridge Square, Ballater
Aberdeenshire AB35 5QS
Tel: 013397 55999

Central Ballater, close to the bridge.
A 19th century stables building down by the river has been tactfully converted to form this attractive bistro style licensed restaurant. It retains many original features and others have been added to create surroundings on the stable theme. The restaurant has the high wood ceiling of the hayloft and is laid out on two levels with a raised gallery along one side. Tables on the lower level are separated by horse-stall style partitions. The decor is simple and interesting, with horse-tack, rakes and even bales of hay decorating the room. Pine tables and chairs add to this rustic atmosphere. There is a comprehensive and varied menu offering traditional cuisine and this is supplemented by a selection of daily specials. An interesting wine list complements the range of dishes. The Hayloft is also open for coffee and freshly made pastries and cakes.
Open all year except 2 wks early Dec
Note: Nov to Mar closes 1 day per wk
Restaurant Lunch 11 am – 2 pm (b)
Dinner 6.30 – 10 pm (b)
Facilities for disabled visitors
No smoking area in restaurant
• Orkney herring marinated in dill, sherry and juniper berries. Breast of Gressingham duck, cooked pink, served with home-made orange sauce. Grilled local salmon steak with parsley butter. Escalope of venison served with hollandaise sauce. Chargrilled prime Aberdeen Angus steaks. Sticky toffee pudding.
Credit cards: 1, 2, 3, 5, 6 + SWITCH, DELTA
Proprietors: Brodie & Winifred Hepburn

Ballindalloch

Location 30

THE DELNASHAUGH INN
Ballindalloch
Banffshire AB27 9AS
Tel: 01807 500255
Fax: 01807 500389

From A9 Aviemore, take A95 via Grantown-on-Spey, or 4941 from Elgin, to Ballindalloch.
The Delnashaugh Inn is an old drovers inn dating from the 16th century. Set down off the road, this delightful white-painted inn overlooks the wooded valley of the River Avon, in the Spey Valley countryside. David and Marion Ogden have taken great care in the renovation and refurbishment so as to retain the best of the original features of the inn while providing the modern comforts expected by the guests of today. Part of the Ballindalloch Estate, the Delnashaugh Inn has access to the River

Avon for salmon and seatrout fishing. Shooting and stalking can also be arranged. It is well placed for following the Whisky Trail and visiting the many interesting castles and historic homes. In the evening the restaurant offers a four course dinner menu giving guests the opportunity to sample the produce so readily available locally.

Open 6 Mar to end Nov
Rooms: 9 , 8 with private facilities
Bar Lunch 12 – 2 pm (a)
Dinner 7 – 8.30 pm (d)
Facilities for disabled visitors
Bed & Breakfast £35 – £50
Dinner B & B £50 – £65
Special Rates available
• *Smoked Ballindalloch venison served with warm onion marmalade. Roast breast of local wild duck with plum sauce. Baked wild Spey salmon served with hollandaise.*
STB Highly Commended 4 Crowns
Credit cards: 1, 3
Proprietors: David & Marion Ogden

Balquhidder

Location 31

MONACHYLE MHOR FARMHOUSE/HOTEL
Balquhidder, Lochearnhead
Perthshire FK19 8PQ
Tel: 01877 384 622
Fax: 01877 384 305

North of Callander A84 to Balquhidder. 4 miles beyond village at end of lochside.

In a land of mountains and lochs, Monachyle Mhor sits in its own 2,000 acres of farmland in the heart of The Braes o' Balquhidder. It is a small family run farmhouse/hotel of great character and offers a unique blend of modern comfort and country living. All bedrooms are en suite, and in the restaurant and cosy bar you will find good food and a wealth of hospitality. For those who like to go as they please, the hotel has three luxury cottages each of which sleeps six people.

Open all year
Rooms: 5 with private facilities
Bar Lunch 12 – 2.30 pm (a)
Dining Room/Restaurant Lunch 12 – 2.30 pm (c)
Bar Supper 6.30 – 10 pm (a)
Dinner 7.30 – 10 pm (c)
No dogs
Bed & Breakfast £23 – £25
Dinner B & B £38 – £48

• *Warmed smoked chicken, mushroom and mangetout in a spicy claret sauce. Smoked High Creighton lamb with red onions and black olives. Butter-baked fillet of salmon with west coast mussels and lemon sauce. Suprême of Guinea fowl with a wild mushroom sauce. Monkfish tails with scallops, spring onions and ginger. Entrecôte of venison with a prune and garlic sauce.*
STB Commended 3 Crowns
Credit cards: 1, 3
Proprietors: Rob & Jean Lewis

Banchory

Location 32

RAEMOIR HOUSE HOTEL
Banchory
Kincardineshire AB31 4ED
Tel: 01330 824884 • Telex: 73315
Fax: 01330 822171

Off A980, 2½ miles north of Banchory.
This is a beautiful old granite mansion house sitting in open parkland within a 3,500 acre estate. It became a hotel over 50 years ago when Kit Sabin came to Raemoir and has been in the same family ownership ever since. In fact there are three generations of the family actively involved – Kit, her daughter and son-in-law, Judy and Mike Ollis and their daughter Nikki, who is now manager. Part of the house dates from the 18th century and many of the bedrooms have fine period furniture and furnishings. But there has been a subtle incorporation of all the amenities of modern day living and a gradual programme of tasteful refurbishment is underway. For those who enjoy outdoor pursuits there is a tennis court, mini nine hole golf course and a croquet lawn, not to mention shooting, fishing and stalking in season. And for those who take their leisure at a more gentle pace there is a sauna, sunbed and trimnasium in the house. The whole atmosphere is one of gracious living, coupled with caring attentive service and good food.

Open all year except first 2 wks Jan
Rooms: 28 with private facilities
Bar Lunch 12.30 – 2 pm except Sun (a)

Dining Room/Restaurant Lunch 12.30 – 2 pm Sun only (b) – other days by prior arrangement
Dinner 7.30 – 9 pm (d)
Bed & Breakfast £47.50 – £79
Dinner B & B £77 – £103.50
Special Rates available
• *Roast loin of Scottish lamb with a minted apricot confit and a rosemary jus. Roast Guinea fowl served with bacon rolls, straw potatoes and bread sauce. Roast haunch of venison with a port and Madeira sauce. Langoustine and brill in a creamy brandy and shallot sauce. Poached darne of Dee salmon glazed with a hollandaise sauce.*
STB Highly Commended 4 Crowns
Credit cards: 1, 2, 3, 5
Proprietors: Kit Sabin, Judy & Mike Ollis

Beauly

Location 33

CHRIALDON HOTEL
Station Road, Beauly
Inverness-shire IV4 7EH
Tel: 01463 782336

On A862 main road through Beauly, 12 miles from Inverness.
Step through the entrance of this detached red sandstone Victorian villa into a timbered hallway of Highland charm. The Chrialdon is elegant, yet informal, small yet spacious, where comfort and enjoyment of good food are of the utmost importance. Anthony and Jennifer Bond create interesting menus for the small dining room overlooking the garden and offer exceptionally good value for money. The hotel provides an ideal base for touring the Highlands.

Open 1 Mar to end Oct
Rooms: 8, 6 with private facilities
Dinner 7 – 8.15 pm (b)
No smoking in dining room
Bed & Breakfast £24 – £32
Dinner B & B £38 – £46
Residents only
Special Rates for 2+ nights
• *Navet and ginger soup. Little goats cheese soufflés with chives. Sauté of monkfish with saffron sauce. Prime Angus steak and kidney pie with shortcrust pastry. Poached fillets of Scottish salmon with dill sauce. Venison steak with a sauce of juniper berries and redcurrant. Strawberry pavlova. Bread and butter pudding with apricot sauce.*
STB Commended 3 Crowns
Credit cards: 1, 3
Proprietors: Anthony & Jennifer Bond

PRIORY HOTEL

The Square, Beauly
Inverness-shire IV4 7BX
Tel: 01463 782309
Fax: 01463 782531

A862, 12 miles north-west of Inverness.
The Priory is a bustling local hotel with an excellent reputation for good food and friendly efficient service. It is situated in the main square in Beauly, close to the ancient Priory ruins. The hotel has all the facilities required for an enjoyable stay and is an ideal base for touring the beautiful north and west of Scotland. Families with children welcome.
Open all year
Rooms: 24 with private facilities
Selection of food available all day
Bar/Restaurant Lunch from 12 noon (a)
Dining Room/Restaurant Lunch 12 – 2 pm (a)
Bar Supper from 5.30 pm (a)
Dinner from 7.15 pm (b-d)
Bed & Breakfast £25 – £34.75
Dinner B & B £35 – £47.75
Special Weekend Rates available
• Fresh Loch Leven mussels poached with garlic butter. Poached darne of local salmon finished with a rich seafood and peppercorn sauce. Medallions of wild venison fillet steak, pan-fried with wild mushrooms and finished in a red wine sauce. Fillet of lemon sole with a delicate white wine, prawn and lobster sauce served in a puff pastry nest. Prime Aberdeen Angus steak sizzlers.
STB Highly Commended 4 Crowns
Credit cards: 1, 2, 3, 5, 6 + SWITCH, DELTA
Proprietors: Stuart & Eveline Hutton

Isle of Benbecula

Location 34

DARK ISLAND HOTEL

Liniclate, Isle of Benbecula
Western Isles PA88 5PJ
Tel: 01870 602414/602283
Fax: 01870 602347

Benbecula lies between North and South Uist (Western Isles). A865 to Liniclate. Hotel is c. 6 miles from the airport.
A large low ranch-style hotel with a large welcome as is the nature of the islanders. This unusually named hotel is acclaimed as one of the best hotels in the Hebrides. The finest of fresh local produce is presented in the Carriages Restaurant, where the menus offer a

wide choice of locally caught fish and shellfish all carefully selected by the chef. The restaurant caters for everything from intimate dinners to major functions. There is also a comfortable and spacious residents' lounge. The hotel is an ideal spot from which to explore the adjacent islands, or for fishing, golf, bird-watching and visiting interesting archaeological sites.
Open all year except Christmas Day, 1 + 2 Jan
Rooms: 42 with private facilities
Bar Meals 12 – 10 pm (a)
Dining Room/Restaurant Lunch 12 – 2 pm (b)
Dinner 6.30 – 9.30 pm (c)
Bed & Breakfast £30 – £60
Dinner B & B £45 – £88
Special rates available
• Local king scallops lightly cooked in butter. A wing of fresh local skate, butter baked and dressed with minced peat-smoked salmon and lumpfish caviar. Variety of seafood crêpes. Roast savoury stuffed shoulder of Highland mutton with hawthorn jelly and rosemary gravy. Prime fillet steak served with a rich Madeira and brandy sauce on a croûte of pâté.
STB Commended 4 Crowns
Credit cards: 1, 3

Biggar

Location 35

HARTREE COUNTRY HOUSE HOTEL

Biggar
Lanarkshire ML12 6JJ
Tel: 01899 21027
Fax: 01899 21259

Just off A702 on western outskirts of Biggar.
A fine old baronial building dating back to the 15th century, and now a delightful country house hotel in peaceful and pleasant Lanarkshire countryside. It has been extensively refurbished to provide modern standards of comfort in elegant public rooms and bedrooms. The menu includes many Scottish specialities and there is a wide range of choice from bar lunches to à la carte dinners. Almost equidistant (about 40 minutes) from both Edinburgh and Glasgow, Hartree House makes a very convenient and central base.
Open all year except Christmas Day
Rooms: 14 with private facilities
Bar Lunch 12 – 2 pm Sun only (b)
Dining Room/Restaurant Lunch 12 – 2 pm Sun only (c)

Bar Supper 6 – 9 pm (b)
Dinner 6 – 8.30 pm (c)
No dogs
Bed & Breakfast £20 – £35
Dinner B & B £32.50 – £52
Room Rate £40 – £70
• Roast poussin with cranberries and honey. Prime beef with local Broughton ale, served with a puff pastry lid. Salmon fillet with cream, saffron and wine sauce. Prime fillet steak stuffed with prawns, served with a mushroom and cream sauce.
STB Commended 3 Crowns
Credit cards: 1, 2, 3, 5
Proprietors: John & Anne Charlton, Robert & Susan Reed

SHIELDHILL HOTEL

Quothquan, by Biggar
Lanarkshire ML12 6NA
Tel: 01899 20035
Fax: 01899 21092

From A702 in Biggar, take B7016 Carnwath for 2 miles, then turn left to Quothquan – hotel is signposted.
This is a delightful old country house set in its own grounds overlooking the beautiful Lanarkshire rural landscape. Part of the house dates from the 12th century. The charmingly sensitive and elegant decor and furnishings enhance the many historic features which include a priest-hole – originally with an altar – accessed via a small staircase within the depth of the wall to the room above. The house exudes an air of comfort and traditional character with wood panelling, high ceilings and ornate cornices, and bay windows with window seats for guests to appreciate the lovely views across the lawns. Some of the bedrooms have four poster beds and jacuzzi, but all are sumptuously appointed. During 1994 there has been a change in ownership and Neil and Joan Mackintosh, the new owners, intend to maintain and increase the hotel's well-earned reputation for hospitality and good food. The arrival of Head Chef Paul Whitecross with his new team in the kitchen, has already firmly established Shieldhill as a destination

for discerning diners. Children over 11 years welcome.
Open all year
Rooms: 11 with private facilities
Dining Room/Restaurant Lunch 12 – 1.30 pm (b)
Afternoon Tea 2 – 4.30 pm (a)
Dinner 7 – 9 pm (e)
No dogs
No smoking in restaurant + bedrooms
Bed & Breakfast £49 – £64
Dinner B & B £67 – £84
Special Rates for 2+ nights
• *Smoked haddock with Welsh rarebit and plum tomatoes in pesto. Aberdeen Angus beef fillet, braised pearl barley broth and parsley dumplings. Lasagne of turbot, red pepper and young leeks, with a mussel and saffron velouté. Clafoutis of spiced apple, vanilla ice-cream and raspberry coulis.*
STB Highly Commended 4 Crowns
Credit cards: 1, 2, 3, 5 + SWITCH, DELTA
Proprietors: Neil & Joan Mackintosh

Blair Atholl

Location 36

THE LOFT RESTAURANT
Invertilt Road, Blair Atholl
Perthshire PH18 5TE
Tel: 01796 481377
6 miles north of Pitlochry in the heart of Blair Atholl.

As the name suggests, The Loft is a splendid conversion from a former hayloft and it still retains all the genuine characteristics of twisted oak beams, stone walls and oak floors. In this small unpretentious restaurant, diners will be pleasantly surprised by the high standard of cooking produced from the compact kitchen. Chef/proprietor Martin Hollis is an award winning chef – most recently winner of the 1994 Taste of Scotland Scotch Lamb Challenge standard category. His menus are compiled from available fresh local produce and are imaginative both in content and presentation. Martin and his wife Stella both put a lot of effort into ensuring that customers have a most enjoyable dining experience, be it just for a light snack or a leisurely dinner. The atmosphere of The Loft is relaxed and informal and it is a popular restaurant so it is advisable to book, particularly for dining in the evening.
Open 24 Mar to 29 October
Light all day menu available 10 am –

5.30 pm except Sun (a)
Light Lunch 12 – 5.30 pm (a)
Restaurant Lunch 12.30 – 4 pm Sun only (b)
Dinner 6.30 – 9.30 pm (b-c)
Table Licence
Children welcome – lunchtime only
• *Fresh Oban mussels with herbs, shallots, wine and cream. Roulade of Scotch lamb with a fennel, mushroom and basil filling. Pan-fried halibut in a prawn and thyme glaze. Saddle of venison on a soft peppercorn and whisky essence. Heather honey and Glayva mousse centred with raspberries on shortbread biscuits.*
No credit cards
Proprietor: Martin Hollis

WOODLANDS
St Andrews Crescent, Blair Atholl
Perthshire PH18 5SX
Tel: 01796 481 403
A9, 7 miles north of Pitlochry.
Woodlands is a delightful old fashioned house which was built in 1903. It is situated in its own sheltered garden down a quiet lane off the main road through Blair Atholl. Under the caring and careful ownership of Dolina McLennan, it offers good old genuine hospitality in relaxed and comfortable surroundings. Guests are invited to gather for a glass of sherry at seven before moving through to the dining room for a leisurely dinner, prepared by Dolina. She is a very good cook and a convivial host whose friendly generous nature sets the tone for Woodlands.
Open all year except Christmas
Rooms: 4
Dinner from 7.30 pm (c)
Dinner for non-residents by arrangement
Unlicensed – guests welcome to take own wine
Bed & Breakfast £18 – £20
Dinner B & B £32 – £35
• *Jugged kippers and kedgeree for breakfast. Home-made bread and preserves. Game soups. Rannoch venison in wine and juniper berries. Seafood from the islands. Local*

pheasant. Lewis salmon. Nut roasts and vegetarian dishes. Scottish cheeseboard.
No credit cards
Proprietor: Dolina MacLennan

Boat of Garten

Location 37

HEATHBANK – THE VICTORIAN HOUSE
Boat of Garten
Inverness-shire PH24 3BD
Tel: 01479 831 234
Situated in village of Boat of Garten.
Heathbank House was built around 1900 and is set in gardens primarily of heathers – hence the name – and herbs. In keeping with the house's Victorian origins, the bedrooms are filled with Victoriana – fans, lace, tapestries, pictures and mirrors. Each room is characterful and beautifully appointed, with its own individual style and colour theme. There are four poster beds in two of the rooms and a sunken bathroom in another. Guests can relax in front of the log fire in the large comfortable lounge and peruse the excellent selection of books there. The dining room which is charmingly set with flowers and candles offers food that is varied, interesting, of unusually high standard and excellent value. Not surprising when you learn that Graham Burge is a qualified chef with many years' cooking experience both in this country and abroad. Before Heathbank he owned and ran a successful restaurant in the Highlands. There is a strong commitment here to Scottish dishes and produce, and an obvious anxiety to satisfy guests' every need.
Open 26 Dec to 31 Oct
Rooms: 7 with private facilities
Dinner at 7 pm (b) 4 course menu
Restricted Licence
No smoking throughout
Bed & Breakfast £20 – £35
Dinner B & B £35 – £50
• *Broccoli and toasted hazelnut soup. Escalope of Spey salmon wrapped in smoked ham, with a sauce of white wine, cream and Scottish whole grain mustard. Scottish lamb steak with mint hollandaise. Home-made ice-creams e.g. chocolate mousse ice-cream flavoured with Drambuie.*
STB Highly Commended 3 Crowns
No credit cards
Proprietors: Graham & Lindsay Burge

Bothwell

Location 38

THE GRAPE VINE RESTAURANT & CAFE BAR

27 Main Street, Bothwell
Lanarkshire G71 8RD
Tel: 01698 852014

On main street in Bothwell, ½ mile off M74 (East Kilbride exit).

The Grape Vine is situated in the centre of the picturesque conservation village of Bothwell. Whether for informal dining – a light meal or snack in the bar – or a more leisurely experience in the restaurant, both are available all day. Menus with the emphasis on fresh local produce have been carefully and creatively prepared under the guidance of the owner, Colin Morrison.

Open all year except Christmas + Boxing Days, 1 + 2 Jan
Food Service 10 am – 10 pm (a-c)
• Smoked salmon in filo pastry with a sesame seed dressing. Roast rack of lamb on a cherry and mint sauce. Breast of roasted duck with an orange and ginger marmalade. Steak and Guinness pie. Oven-baked salmon with a light lemon and hollandaise sauce. Fillet steak on a croûton topped with pâté and served with a rich wine sauce.
Credit cards: 1, 2, 3, 5 + SWITCH
Proprietor: Colin Morrison

Braemar

Location 39

BRAEMAR LODGE

Glenshee Road, Braemar
Aberdeenshire AB35 5YQ
Tel: 013397 41627
Fax: 013397 41627

On main A93 Perth-Aberdeen road, on the outskirts of Braemar.

Braemar Lodge is a restored granite-built Victorian shooting lodge set amidst spectacular Highland scenery on the edge of Braemar. This a small friendly hotel where wood panelling and roaring log fires contribute to the cosy atmosphere. Alex and Caroline are most welcoming hosts. The individually

decorated bedrooms are spacious and very comfortable. Braemar Lodge has been awarded two AA Rosettes in recognition of Caroline's dedicated approach to cooking. Dinner served in the tastefully appointed candlelit restaurant is of a very high standard and shows imaginative use of fresh local ingredients.

Open 26 Dec to 31 Oct
Rooms: 5 with private facilities
Dining Room/Restaurant Lunch – by arrangement only (c)
Dinner 7 – 9 pm (c)
No smoking except in bar
Bed & Breakfast £34 – £50
Dinner B & B £54 – £70
Special Rates for 2+ nights
• Cullen skink. Asparagus and mushroom feuilleté. Breast of duck with apple and green peppercorns flamed in Brandy and cream. Grilled salmon steak with a sweet pepper sauce. Venison fillet with mushrooms, white wine and cream. Grilled sirloin steak served with Scottish mustards. Cranachan – whisky, honey and oatmeal cream with raspberries.
STB Highly Commended 3 Crowns
Credit cards: 1, 3
Proprietors: Alex Smith & Caroline Hadley-Smith

Bridge of Allan

Location 40

THE ROYAL HOTEL

55 Henderson Street, Bridge of Allan
Stirlingshire FK9 4HG
Tel: 01786 832284
Fax: 01786 834377

On main street of Bridge of Allan (Junction 11, M9), c. 2 miles north of Stirling.

This impressive Victorian hotel built in 1842 sits right in the centre of Bridge of Allan, home of the University of Stirling. The building has been carefully restored and refurbished throughout creating an atmosphere of elegance and comfort which blends with the original character of the hotel. Bedrooms are beautifully appointed and have all the facilities expected of a hotel today. The furnishings and decor of The Rivendell Restaurant are in keeping with the Victorian flavour throughout. Before dining in the restaurant, guests can relax with an aperitif in front of an open fire in the oak-panelled lounge, perusing the menu. The selection of items on the menu changes with the seasons and the

standard of food presented has earned the hotel an AA Rosette.

Open all year
Rooms: 32 with private facilities
Bar Lunch 12 – 2.30 pm (a)
Dining Room/Restaurant Lunch 12 – 2.30 pm Mon to Sat: 12 – 6 pm Sun (a)
Bar Supper 6 – 9.30 pm Mon to Sat: 6 – 8.30 pm Sun (a)
Dinner 7 – 9.30 pm Mon to Sat: 7 – 8.30 pm Sun (c)
Room Rate £39.50 – £54.50
Special Rates available
• Loch Fyne mussels in white wine, cream and parsley. Warm Highland venison with rowanberry jelly and seasonal leaves. Poached Scottish Tay salmon with a champagne and chive sauce. Medallions of beef in a Madeira sauce. Steak Diane cooked at the table. Grilled whole lemon sole with lemon and herb butter.
STB Commended 4 Crowns
Credit cards: 1, 2, 3, 5, 6 + SWITCH, DELTA

Brig O' Turk

Location 41

THE BYRE INN

Brig O' Turk, The Trossachs
Perthshire FK17 8HT
Tel: 01877 376292

North of Callander on A84, turn onto A821 at Kilmahog: Brig O' Turk 5 miles.

A mellow old farm building in a wooded area, just off the main road, which has been converted into a most attractive timbered bar full of rusticity and charm. A more modern design of dining room leads off from it and the whole effect is restful and pleasing. Good quality country cooking and presentation of wholesome dishes from a fairly extensive menu. A daily vegetarian dish is also available. This is a delightful and popular stopping-off place for people touring The Trossachs.

Open all year except 9 Jan to 6 Feb

Note: closed Wed Nov to Mar
Bar Lunch 12 – 2.30 pm: 12 –
3 pm Sun (a)
Dining Room/Restaurant Lunch 12 –
2.30 pm: 12 – 3 pm Sun (a)
Dinner 6 – 9 pm (c)
Facilities for disabled visitors
No smoking in restaurant
• Smoked salmon with scrambled eggs.
Grilled Tay salmon topped with fresh dill
butter. Suprême of chicken filled with
skirlie in a leek sauce. Lamb cutlets pan-
fried with garlic and rosemary. Quail
stuffed with herbs, chestnuts and apricot
on a rich red wine sauce. Sirloin steak
pan-fried with wild mushrooms and
Madeira. Guinea fowl served with an
orange sauce.
Credit cards: 1, 3
Proprietor: John Park

Brodie

Location 42

BRODIE COUNTRYFARE
Brodie, by Forres
Morayshire IV36 0TD
Tel: 013094 555

On A96 between Forres and Nairn.
Brodie Countryfare has been growing
recently – in fact it has more than
doubled in size since both the
restaurant and shop have been
extended. This is a very popular self-
service restaurant which has a
reputation for good food. Indoors the
furnishings are country style and the
dining area is enhanced by a
conservatory, while out of doors there
are pine picnic benches. Brodie
Countryfare forms part of a shopping
complex and visitors will find crafts,
produce, exclusive fashions and
designer knitwear all under the same
roof.
Open all year except Christmas +
Boxing Days, 1 + 2 Jan
Food service 9.30 am – 5 pm Apr to Jun,
Sep Oct: 9.30 am – 6 pm Jul Aug:
9.30 am – 4.30 pm Nov to Mar (a)
Facilities for disabled visitors
Restaurant is non-smoking with small
smoking area
• Home-made soups. Dish of day
prepared from fresh ingredients daily e.g.
steak and kidney pie, peppered pork,
beef olives. Salad bar a speciality.
Seasonal soft fruit. Selection of home-
baking and desserts.
No credit cards
Proprietor: Kathleen Duncan

Brora

Location 43

ROYAL MARINE HOTEL
Golf Road, Brora
Sutherland KW9 6QS
Tel: 01408 621252
Fax: 01408 621181

Leave A9 Inverness-Wick at bridge in
Brora, heading towards beach and golf
course.
A most attractive country mansion built
by Sir Robert Lorimer in 1913 and
converted into a hotel in 1939. Leaded
windows, magnificent woodwork, log
fires, a gracious ambience of yesteryear,
allied to courteous service justify its
claim to be the North's favourite golfing
and fishing hotel. Adjacent to Brora's 18
hole James Braid links golf course and
overlooking the mouth of the famous
salmon river, the site has much to
commend it. The food is exactly what the
hungry sportsman or traveller would
want. Good quality, generous portions of
fresh traditional fare, nicely presented
and served with charm.
Open all year
Rooms: 11 with private facilities
Bar Lunch 12 – 2 pm Mon to Sat: 12 –
2.30 Sun (b)
Dining Room/Restaurant Lunch 12.30 –
2.30 pm Sun (b) – weekdays by
reservation
Bar Supper 6.30 – 9 pm (b)
Dinner 7 – 9 pm (c)
Bed & Breakfast £43 – £50
Dinner B & B £59 – £70
Room Rate £100
Special Weekly Rates available
• Terrine of smoked salmon, trout and
halibut with a creamy dill and watercress
sauce. Loin of lamb roasted with garlic
and herbs, sered with a casserole of
baby onions, mushrooms and tomatoes.
Fillets of haddock roasted with sesame
seeds and garlic, served with braised
lettuces. Medallion of beef fillet with
caramelised shallots and Madeira sauce.
STB Commended 4 Crowns
Credit cards: 1, 2, 3, 5 + SWITCH

Cairndow

Location 44

LOCH FYNE OYSTER BAR
Cairndow
Argyll PA26 8BH
Tel: 014996 217/264

A83 Glasgow-Oban-Campbeltown, at
head of Loch Fyne near Cairndow.
Set by the roadside, this makes an
excellent stopping place on the long
sweep round the north of Loch Fyne. Old
farm buildings by the loch side were
converted and cleverly transformed to
provide simple surroundings in which to
enjoy the freshest of fish and shellfish.
Based on the great success of this the
original Loch Fyne Oyster Bar, the
concept has been extended to England
(Nottingham and near Peterborough).
Over the past year or so this restaurant
has been extended and refurbished. The
rustic rough-hewn wooden tables may
have given way to smooth pine, but the
original theme of simplicity and good
food prevails. There is no set pattern of
starters and main courses so you can
select any dish or selection of dishes
from the menu in whatever order you
choose. Non-fish dishes are available too
as is a carefully selected wine list. As
well as indulging in the delights the
restaurant has to offer, you can also
purchase fresh fish and shellfish from
the shop or get details of the home
delivery service.
Open all year except Christmas Day to
1 Jan
Menu available throughout the day 9 am
– 9 pm (c)
Note: closes 6 pm Nov to Feb
• Fresh rock oysters from Loch Fyne.
Queen scallops roasted with bacon.
Bradhan rost (salmon smoked in a hot
kiln) served hot with a whisky sauce.
Shellfish platter – fresh oysters,
langoustines, queen scallops, brown
crab and clams. Spicy seafood chowder.
Credit cards: 1, 3 + SWITCH, DELTA
Proprietors: Andrew Lane & John Noble

Callander

Location 45

BRIDGEND HOUSE HOTEL
Bridgend, Callander
Perthshire FK17 8AH
Tel: 01877 330130
Fax: 01877 331512

On A81 – 250 yards from Callander main street, just over the bridge.

There is a hint of Tudor architecture in the style of this timbered 17th century building, so conveniently located just off the centre of the town. It is a rambling old building but bright, clean and welcoming with a pleasing and restful garden from which there are lovely views of Ben Ledi. Bedrooms are en suite with TVs and tea-makers. Bar lunches are popular and in the evening there is a choice of a bar supper or a more extensive menu in the restaurant which often includes traditional Scottish dishes and game in season. Children and pets welcome.

Open all year except Christmas + Boxing Days, 1 + 2 Jan: reservations only
Rooms: 7, 5 with private facilities
Bar Lunch 12 – 2 pm (a)
Dining Room/Restaurant Lunch 12 – 2 pm Sun only Oct to Apr:
7 days May to Sep (a)
Bar Supper 6 – 8 pm (a)
Dinner 6 – 9 pm Fri Sat only Oct to Apr:
7 days May to Sep (b-c)
Note: pipe and cigars only after 9 pm in restaurant
Bed & Breakfast £25 – £42.50
Dinner B & B £37.50 – £55
Special Rates for 3+ nights
• Locally smoked trout with horseradish and gooseberry sauces. Creamed haggis on toast. Prime Scottish steaks on sizzle platters. Suprême of chicken coated in oatmeal, pan-fried and served with a whisky and fresh cream sauce. Fresh Scottish salmon. Scotch lamb cutlets with redcurrant jelly.
STB Commended 3 Crowns
Credit cards: 1, 2, 3, 5
Proprietors: Sandy & Maria Park

HIGHLAND HOUSE HOTEL
South Church Street, Callander
Perthshire FK17 8BN
Tel: 01877 330269

Just off A84 (main street through town centre).

This neat Georgian house with roses round the door has a most inviting appearance and reflects something of the warm and welcoming haven inside. It is not surprising that Highland House won the title 'Best Place to Stay' in the area's tourism awards. The bedrooms are comfortably appointed with colour TV, full central heating and en suite facilities. In the small tastefully furnished dining room which faces onto the street, guests can enjoy Dee Shirley's excellent home-cooking. There is plenty of evidence of fresh produce in the well composed and balanced menus and Dee is a very enthusiastic cook. The Shirleys have gained a fine reputation for their hospitality and constantly strive to maintain the high standards they have set. Callander is the gateway to The Trossachs, an area associated with the famous Rob Roy. Special breaks can be arranged for guests to include visits to local attractions and historic buildings in the area.

Open 1 Mar to 5 Nov
Rooms: 9, 8 with private facilities
Bar Supper 6.30 – 8 pm (a-b)
Dinner 7 – 8 pm (b-c)
No smoking in dining room + bedrooms
Dogs accepted at proprietors' discretion
Bed & Breakfast £18 – £29
Dinner B & B £29 – £45
Special Rates available
• Home-made soups and pâtés. Scottish lamb chops with port and redcurrant sauce. Local salmon steak with seafood sauce. Vegetarian dish of the day. Selection of desserts. Scottish cheeses. Children's menu available.
STB Commended 3 Crowns
Credit cards: 1, 2, 3
Proprietors: David & Dee Shirley

ROMAN CAMP HOTEL
Callander
Perthshire FK17 8BG
Tel: 01877 330003
Fax: 01877 331533

Signposted off main route through Callander (A84).

Look out for the hotel sign at the east end of the long main street through Callander and follow the drive down to the banks of the River Teith where this fine old house has been standing for almost 400 years. It is set in 20 acres of beautiful gardens and has gracious public rooms and an atmosphere of unhurried dignity and relaxation. The dining room service is quietly efficient and the food is of the high standard one would expect in such a charming old country house. As a base from which to explore the Trossachs it is ideally situated.

Open all year
Rooms: 14 with private facilities
Dining Room/Restaurant Lunch 12 – 2 pm (c)
Dinner 7 – 9 pm (f) 4 course menu
Facilities for disabled visitors
No smoking in restaurant
Bed & Breakfast £40 – £72.50
Dinner B & B £72 – £104.50
Special Rates for 2+ nights
• Red pepper mousse encased in leeks with a warm potato and rocket salad on a chive butter sauce. Fillet of halibut wrapped with a scallop mousse and spinach steamed on wild mushrooms. Rack of spring lamb with a herb crust, on a garlic and button onion confit with a Stilton tart. Caramelised lemon tart with a blackcurrant coulis.
STB Highly Commended 4 Crowns
Credit cards: 1, 2, 3, 5, 6 + SWITCH
Proprietors: Eric & Marion Brown

Campbeltown

Location 46

SEAFIELD HOTEL
Kilkerran Road, Campbeltown
Argyll PA28 6JL
Tel: 01586 554385
Fax: 01586 552741

On the shores of Campbeltown Loch – 4 minutes walk from town centre.

The external appearance of this Victorian villa is deceptive. Originally built by the founders of the Springbank Distillery, it has a pleasing site overlooking the shore and is reputed to be the first home in Campbeltown fitted with a bath! There is an attractive dining room with well spaced tables and a menu offering a good range and balance of choice. A garden court annexe in the walled garden at the rear of the hotel offers quiet peaceful accommodation.

Open all year
Rooms: 9 with private facilities
Bar Lunch 12.30 – 2 pm (a)
Dining Room/Restaurant Lunch 12.30 – 2 pm Mon to Sat (a): Buffet Lunch Sun

(b) 4 course menu
Bar Supper 5.30 – 8.30 pm (b)
Dinner 7 – 8.30 pm (c)
Bed & Breakfast £29 – £35
Special Rates for 3+ nights
*• Home-made soups. Haunch of venison
roasted with bacon, served with
redcurrant and port wine sauce. Leg of
lamb cooked with root ginger, with a
brandy and mushroom sauce. Scallops,
scampi tails and white fish poached
lightly with spring onion, vermouth,
cream and cheese. Medallions of fillet
steak pan-fried with whole grain mustard,
whisky, mushrooms and tomato.*
STB Commended 3 Crowns
Credit cards: 1, 3
Proprietors: Alastair & Elizabeth Gilchrist

WHITE HART HOTEL
Main Street, Campbeltown
Argyll PA28 6AN
Tel: 01586 552440/553356
Fax: 01586 554972
On main street in centre of town.
The White Hart is a prominent building in
this busy fishing port and market town.
This well established white-painted old
world hotel sits on a corner site right in
the centre of the town and is a well
known haven to yachtsmen and golfers.
During the Summer of 1994 a new
conservatory bistro and coffee shop was
added to the hotel, providing all day
facilities for light meals and informal
dining. This is in addition to the main
dining room where there is a natural
emphasis on the excellent local seafood
and lamb in the menus.
Open all year except 1 to 4 Jan
Rooms: 17 with private facilities
Bar Lunch 12 – 2 pm except Sun (a)
*Dining Room/Restaurant Lunch 12 –
2 pm except Sun (a)*
Bar Supper 5.30 – 9 pm except Sun (a)
Dinner 7 – 9 pm except Sun (b)
Bed & Breakfast £34.50 – £36.50
Dinner B & B £48 – £50
Special Weekend Rates available
*• Baked ramekin of prawns, mushrooms
and cheese. Poached Kintyre salmon
with a citrus sauce. Braised Jura venison
casserole in red wine. Noisettes of Mull
of Kintyre lamb, surrounded with a
mushroom duxelle wrapped in a lattice
pastry, served with redcurrant and brandy
sauce. Tournedos of fillet beef on a rosti
potato pancake served with prawns on
an Islay mustard sauce.*
Credit cards: 1, 3
Proprietors: P Stogdale & B Kennedy

Cardross

Location 47

KIRKTON HOUSE
Darleith Road, Cardross
Dunbartonshire G82 5EZ
Tel: 01389 841 951
Fax: 01389 841 868
*At west end of Cardross village turn
north off A814 up Darleith Road. Kirkton
House drive ½ mile on right.*
Kirkton House sits in an elevated and
tranquil rural position above the village of
Cardross with panoramic views of the
River Clyde. This unique and charming
little country hotel was created by the
tasteful conversion of old 18th/19th
century farm buildings, set around an
attractive courtyard. Stewart and Gillian
Macdonald's hallmark is their friendly
unobtrusive personal service, ensuring
guests are well looked after in this cosy
and comfortable house. The
accommodation is homey, informal and
unpretentious, with all the facilities
expected of a hotel. On chilly nights a
roaring open fire blazes in the residents
lounge where guests and their friends
may enjoy pre-dinner drinks. The
comfortable and informal atmosphere of
the dining room is enhanced by the glow
of oil lamps at each table and exposed
stone walls. There is an extensive choice
offered in the dinner menus which
change daily. Guests may choose from
the four course table d'hôte or à la carte
menu. Kirkton House has established an
enviable reputation for its hospitality and
food, and its "house party" atmosphere.
It is well placed for touring the Loch
Lomond and Trossachs area and has
good access to the main routes –
Glasgow, Inveraray, Oban, Ayr, Stirling or
Edinburgh being an easy day's outing by
car. Also convenient for Glasgow Airport
which is only a 25 minute drive away.
Open 10 Jan to 19 Dec
Rooms: 6 with private facilities
Snacks served throughout day
*Dinner 7.30 – 8.30 pm (c) 4 course
menu*
Residents only
Restricted Licence
*Facilities for disabled visitors (downstairs
rooms only)*
No smoking in dining room
Bed & breakfast £26 – £36
Dinner B & B £42.50 – £52.50
Special Rates for 2+/5+ nights
*• Cockles and mussels in brandy cream
sauce. Grilled venison steak. Breast of
chicken in a mushroom and pepper*

*sauce topped with crisp breadcrumbs.
Pork in a light ginger sauce. Banana
flambé with ice cream smothered in
caramel sauce. Raspberry meringue
roulade.*
STB Highly Commended 3 Crowns
Credit cards: 1, 2, 3
Proprietors: Stewart & Gillian Macdonald

Carradale

Location 48

CARRADALE HOTEL
Carradale
Argyll PA28 6RY
Tel: 0158 33 223
Fax: 0158 33 223
*From Tarbert (Loch Fyne) 26 miles via
A83, B8001 and B842. From
Campbeltown about 17 miles on B842.*
Quite the most prominent feature of the
village, the Carradale Hotel occupies a
splendid location above the harbour in its
own grounds and gardens, overlooking
Kilbrannan Sound and the Isle of Arran.
Comfortable accommodation and a
reputation for high quality Scottish
cooking make it an ideal centre for
fishing, golfing or exploring the Kintyre
peninsula. Mountain bikes, squash
courts, sauna and the adjacent nine hole
golf course are all part of the facilities.
Open all year except 20 to 27 Dec
*Rooms: 14 with private facilities,
3 children's rooms (adjacent to parents'
rooms) + 1 family suite*
Bar Lunch 12 – 2 pm (a)
Bar Supper 6 – 7.30 pm (a)
Dinner 7.30 – 9 pm (c)
No smoking in restaurant
Bed & Breakfast £25 – £30
Dinner B & B £35 – £45
Special Rates available
*• Smoked mackerel mousse with crisp
salad. Medallions of Carradale Sika
venison served with a julienne of
mangetout, port and cranberry sauce.
Oven-baked wild Lussa river salmon
stuffed with wild rice and cold water
prawns, glazed with hollandaise. Home-
made orange and Cointreau ice-cream.*
STB Commended 3 Crowns
Credit cards: 1, 3
STB Commended 3 Crowns
Proprietors: Marcus & Morag Adams

Carrbridge

Location 49

DALRACHNEY LODGE HOTEL
Carrbridge
Inverness-shire PH23 3AT
Tel: 01479 841252
Fax: 01479 841382

On A938 to Dulnain Bridge, c. 400 yards from Carrbridge.

A former Victorian shooting lodge set in 16 acres of peaceful grounds on the banks of the Dulnain River on the outskirts of the village. Internally there is much that is old and much that is new but they have been blended with skill and the hotel now offers 11 tastefully furnished and generously proportioned bedrooms. A further five comfortable rooms are in the adjacent Keeper's House. The Lodge Restaurant has a pleasant outlook on to the garden. There is a fairly wide choice on the four course table d'hôte menu which is inexpensively priced, and a much more ambitious à la carte menu is also available. Provision is made for anyone with food allergies or special needs. The log fire in the cosy Stalkers Bar makes it popular for a pre-prandial drink or an after dinner malt whisky from a large selection.

Open all year
Rooms: 16 with private facilities
Bar Lunch 12 – 2 pm (a)
Dining Room/Restaurant Lunch 12 – 2 pm (b)
Bar Supper 5.30 – 9.30 pm (a)
Dinner 7 – 8.30 pm (c)
No smoking area in restaurant
Bed & Breakfast £25 – £36
Dinner B & B £45 – £56
Special Rates available
• Grilled rainbow trout with pan-fried mushrooms and prawns. Scampi cooked with Pernod, finished with cream and served with rice. Venison casserole with red wine, button mushrooms, lardons of bacon and croûtons. Duck breast marinated with honey, lemon and rosemary. Salmon fillet in a creamy cheese and dill sauce encased in puff pastry. Highland game pie.
STB Highly Commended 4 Crowns
Credit cards: 1, 2, 3 + SWITCH
Proprietor: Helen Swanney

ECCLEFECHAN BISTRO
Main Street, Carrbridge
Inverness-shire PH23 3AJ
Tel: 01479 841374

Main road Carrbridge, on Carrbridge by-pass off A9 north of Aviemore.

A pleasant wayside stopping place on the way through Carrbridge, this scrupulously clean and attractive family run bistro concentrates on the best of straightforward Scottish food with a slight touch of French influence. At coffee and teatime you can enjoy delicious scones and doughnuts – and coffee that tastes like coffee. For lunch or dinner there is a frequently changing menu ranging from Hebridean soups and scallops to steaks and venison, and an interesting variety of speciality desserts like Ecclefechan tart.

Open all year except Nov, Christmas Day
Open 10 am – 3 pm except Tue (a)
Dinner 6.30 – 9.30 pm except Tue (b)
Closed Tue
Facilities for disabled visitors
• Hebridean skink – a creamy fish soup with pieces of salmon, smoked fish, prawns etc. Local smoked salmon. Scottish prawns with dill. Yorkshire pudding with roast beef in gravy. Venison in claret. Haggis and clapshot. Ecclefechan tart.
Credit cards: 1, 3
Proprietors: Duncan & Anne Hilditch

FEITH MHOR COUNTRY HOUSE
Station Road, Carrbridge
Inverness-shire PH23 3AP
Tel: 01479 841621

One mile west of village of Carrbridge on road signed to Dalnahaitnach.

Feith Mhor is a charming 19th century country house set in an acre of delightful gardens and surrounded by peaceful unspoilt countryside. The comfortable well appointed en suite bedrooms enjoy beautiful views. There is an attractive dining room and comfortable lounge. Here you will experience the best of home-cooked fare, simply presented, based on local and garden produce in season. Vegetarian dishes are available by arrangement. This is a wonderful area for those who enjoy walking, bird-watching or touring.

Open 27 Dec to 10 Nov
Rooms: 6 with private facilities
Dinner at 7 pm (b) set menu
It is requested that guests confirm dinner by 6 pm
No smoking in dining room + lounge
No children under 12 years
Bed & Breakfast – £21
Dinner B & B £29 – £32
• Fruity spiced gammon, roast Scotch lamb and beef, poached fresh salmon. Vegetarian lentil bake, leek and dumpling casserole. Desserts include meringue sunrise, pavlova with raspberries, fresh fruit crumbles.
STB Commended 3 Crowns
No credit cards
Proprietor: Penny Rawson

Castle Douglas

Location 50

LONGACRE MANOR
Ernespie Road, Castle Douglas
Kirkcudbrightshire DG7 1LE
Tel: 01556 3576

Off A75 Dumfries-Stranraer (eastern exit) to Castle Douglas, c. ¾ mile.

A small but charming country house on the outskirts of the town set in a beautiful woodland garden and having fine views to Screel and the Galloway Hills. All four bedrooms have been delightfully furnished – one features a king-size four poster and another twin four poster beds – and each has en suite facilities. There is thoughtful attention to every aspect of a guest's comfort, and TV, radio, tea/coffee-making equipment, direct dial telephone, hairdryer and trouser press are standard. Meals are planned on a daily basis consistent with the availability of fresh produce, are well presented and good value. Castle Douglas, of course, is close to the famous Threave Gardens and there are lots of other interesting things to see locally plus a full range of sporting and recreational activities.

Open all year

Credit Card Code		Meal Price Range	
1.	Access/Mastercard/Eurocard	(a)	under £10
2.	American Express	(b)	£10 – £15
3.	Visa	(c)	£15 – £20
4.	Carte Bleu	(d)	£20 – £25
5.	Diners Club	(e)	£25 – £30
6.	Mastercharge	(f)	over £30

Rooms: 4 with private facilities
Dinner at 7.30 pm (b)
Bed & Breakfast £25 – £30
Dinner B & B £40 – £45
Dinner for non-residents by prior arrangement
Restricted Licence
No children
No smoking in dining room
• Cream of watercress soup. Orkney herring in dill marinade. Leg of lamb stuffed with spinach and herbs. Lemon sole with prawn and cream sauce. Galloway sirloin steak. Venison in red wine sauce. Sticky toffee pudding with butterscotch sauce. Strawberry and hazelnut meringue.
STB Highly Commended 3 Crowns
Credit cards: 1, 3 + DELTA
Proprietors: Charles & Elma Ball

Chapel of Garioch

Location 51

PITTODRIE HOUSE HOTEL
Chapel of Garioch, nr Pitcaple
Aberdeenshire AB51 5HS
Tel: 01467 681444 • Telex: 739935
Fax: 01467 681648

Off A96 just north of Pitcaple, 21 miles north of Aberdeen, 17 miles north of airport.

This imposing turreted Scottish baronial style mansion is approached by a long drive through parkland. It stands gracefully in its own beautiful grounds at the foot of Bennachie. Pittodrie House was originally the home of the owner, Theo Smith, and much of the grand old decor and furnishings remain, in particular in the public rooms with their antiques and family portraits. The original building underwent skilful and sympathetic extension four years ago to provide additional bedrooms and a function room. The bedrooms are decorated and furnished to a good standard, with some original features retained in the older part of the house such as a splendid old Victorian bathroom. There is also a beautifully kept three acre walled garden. Oil paintings adorn the peacock blue walls of the formal dining room. The Orangery is an extension of the dining room with a glass roof and lots of greenery. Daily changing four course dinner menus feature an interesting range of dishes.
Open all year
Rooms: 27 with private facilities
Bar Lunch 12 – 2 pm except Sun (a)
Dining Room/Restaurant Lunch 12.30 –

2 pm (c)
Dinner 7.30 – 9 pm (e) 4 course menu
Bed & Breakfast £55 – £89
Dinner B & B £65 – £80
Room Rate £89 – £110
Special Rates for 2+ nights
• Smoked salmon with avocado mousse. Haggis with a whisky cream sauce. Steamed fillet of plaice with white wine cream. Haunch of venison with a Paris brown mushroom sauce. Roast leg of lamb with rosemary. Poached salmon with saffron cream. Grilled sirloin steak with a blue cheese sauce. Brandy snap basket with a Bennachie brose.
STB Commended 4 Crowns
Credit cards: 1, 2, 3, 5, 6 + SWITCH

Cleish

nr Kinross

Location 52

NIVINGSTON HOUSE
Cleish
Kinross-shire KY13 7LS
Tel: 01577 850216
Fax: 01577 850238

In country, 2 miles from Junction 5 on M90.

The phrase "an oasis of tranquillity" is sometimes overdone, but not here. The commanding site has superb views over the rolling countryside and with its 12 acres of pleasant garden this Victorian mansion really is a peaceful haven, yet only a couple of miles from the M90. It has been comfortably furnished and the relaxed and friendly country house atmosphere is apparent as soon as you enter. Allied to this is a reputation for fine food, interestingly prepared and presented, with regularly changing menus showing a sound degree of creativity. Sitting outside with a cool drink on a summer's evening can be very pleasant, but so too are the log fires and flickering candles on the table in winter.
Open all year except Boxing Day + first 2 wks Jan

Rooms: 17 with private facilities
Bar Lunch 12 – 2 pm (b)
Dining Room/Restaurant Lunch 12 – 2 pm (c)
Dinner 7 – 9 pm (e)
Bed & Breakfast £40 – £80
Dinner B & B £65 – £105
Special Rates available for long stays
• Orkney vegetable soup. Salad of sweet herring with raspberry vinegar. Grilled local salmon with a mussel and oyster sauce. Breast of pheasant in a honey and apple sauce. Grilled lamb cutlets with a Marsala sauce. Apple and sultana pie with toffee fudge ice-cream. Raspberry brûlée.
STB Highly Commended 4 Crowns
Credit cards: 1, 2, 3 + SWITCH, DELTA
Proprietors: Allan & Pat Deeson

Colvend

Location 53

CLONYARD HOUSE HOTEL
Colvend, Dalbeattie
Dumfriesshire DG5 4QW
Tel: 01556 630372
Fax: 01556 630422

4½ miles south of Dalbeattie on A710 Solway coast road. 18 miles west of Dumfries.

Victorian country house hotel in six acres of wooded grounds. Typical 19th century dining room overlooking lawns. Also pleasant large cocktail bar for informal meals. Ground floor bedroom wing with full facilities. One room fitted for disabled guests. Safe grounds for children. French and some German spoken. Dogs welcome (small charge).
Open all year
Rooms: 15 with private facilities
Bar Lunch 12 – 2 pm (a)
Bar Supper 6 – 9.30 pm (a)
Dinner 7 – 9 pm (c)
Facilities for disabled visitors
Bed & Breakfast £27.50 – £38
Dinner B & B £42 – £53
Special Rates available
• Mussels baked in a fresh herb butter. Home-made soup with fresh baked rolls. Solway salmon with watercress sauce. Loin of lamb served on a small spinach pancake, with a tarragon sauce. Seafood – scallops, prawns, scampi and mussels – in Chardonnay. Baked halibut with a light mousseline sauce.
STB Commended 4 Crowns
Credit cards: 1, 2, 3 + SWITCH
Proprietors: Nick, David & Joan Thompson

Comrie

Location 54

THE DEIL'S CAULDRON LOUNGE BAR & RESTAURANT

27 Dundas Street, Comrie
Perthshire PH6 2LN
Tel: 01764 670352

On A85 west end of Comrie.
The Deil's Cauldron is a most attractive bar restaurant which takes its name from a well known local beauty spot. It has been created from a 200 year old Listed building. Internally the place has lots of character and a good atmosphere, with original stone walls and furniture and fittings of a very high standard, interesting paintings, prints and old photographs. The menu is carefully constructed and reasonably priced, with everything freshly produced on a daily basis. The style is Auld Alliance cooking featuring local beef, lamb, fish, home-grown vegetables and game in season. A raised dining area above the bar leads onto to a pretty garden with well stocked ponds and heathers which is a delightful and pleasant place to stroll in fine weather. A popular place so reservations are advisable.
Open all year except Christmas Day,
31 Dec to 2 Jan
Note: Nov to Mar advisable to check opening times
Bar Lunch 12 – 2.30 pm except Tue (a)
Dining Room/Restaurant Lunch 12 – 2.30 pm except Tue (b)
Bar Supper 6 – 9 pm except Tue (b)
Dinner 6 – 9 pm except Tue (c)
Closed Tue
Separate dining room for non-smokers
• Grilled goats cheese with salad and walnut dressing. Smoked Tay salmon. Noisettes of venison with honey and gin sauce. Fillet of lamb served on spinach with a wine and redcurrant sauce flavoured with rosemary. Poached fillet of salmon with tarragon cream sauce. The Angler's Lunch – grilled fillet of trout with almonds, fresh vegetables and a baked jacket potato.
Credit cards: 1, 2, 3
Proprietors: Robert & Judith Shepherd

THE GRANARY

Drummond Street, Comrie
Perthshire PH6 2DW
Tel: 01764 670838

On main street of Comrie (A85 west of Crieff) – opposite garage.
There is a comfortable Edwardian air about this charming little coffee shop in the centre of the bustling village of Comrie. The large windows with sunny flowered curtains overlook the main street and the hills beyond, and the antique mahogany counter is laden with a mouth watering array of home-baking for which visitors would tread miles. Local water-colours decorate the walls and a richly hued collection of home-made jams and chutneys crowd the shelves. Proprietors Liz and Mark Grieve have made The Granary a special place with a warm and welcoming atmosphere tempting visitors with a delicious choice of home-made food and baking. Liz bakes wholemeal soda bread which is served with a choice of home-made soup and also forms the basis of a hearty ploughman's lunch. There is a wide selection of teas including fruit and herbal, and a range of ground coffee is served in cafetieres. The full menu is available all day. Visitors need not go away empty-handed the baking, bread and preserves can be purchased to enjoy later or as gifts for friends.
Open Mar to Oct
Food available 10 am – 5 pm except Mon (a)
Closed Mon
Unlicensed
Facilities for disabled visitors
No smoking throughout
• Home-made soups. Baked potatoes with fillings. Ploughman's lunch with home-made soda bread. Toasties. Lemon and blueberry meringue. Banoffee pie. Sticky toffee pudding. Raspberry roulade. Mincemeat crumble cake. Lemon gateaux. Traybakes and scones.
No credit cards
Proprietors: Mark & Elizabeth Grieve

TULLYBANNOCHER FARM FOOD BAR

Comrie
Perthshire PH6 2JY
Tel: 01764 670827

Just outside Comrie on A85 Lochearnhead road.
This is a very popular stopping place for people enjoying the drive along Loch Earn. A solid timber construction, it stands on a prominent knoll among trees

and lawns just outside the pretty village of Comrie and with plenty of parking alongside. The self-service restaurant offers a wide choice of freshly prepared meats, fish and quiche with simple but varied salads. There is a refreshing aura of healthy eating and home-baking about the place. Freshly brewed coffee and tea and a selection of wines, beers and soft drinks are available. In fine weather people enjoy eating outside on the rustic tables on the lawns, but there is lots of dining space inside for those who prefer it.
Open 28 Mar to mid Oct
Meals available 10 am – 7 pm (a)
Table Licence
Dogs allowed outside only
• Home-baked ham. Local smoked trout. Scottish salmon. Home-made quiches. Spit roasted chicken. Meat pies. Coronation chicken. Hot dishes of the day. Fresh strawberry flan. A large selection of home-baking.
No credit cards
Proprietor: Peter Davenport

Conon Bridge

Location 55

KINKELL HOUSE

Easter Kinkell, Conon Bridge
Ross-shire IV7 8HY
Tel: 01349 861270

One mile from A9 on B9169, 10 miles north of Inverness.
Kinkell House is situated on the 'Black Isle' with panoramic views of Ben Wyvis, the Cromarty Firth and Wester Ross hills. It is a small country house hotel within its own peaceful grounds, surrounded by trees and pasture land. Once a farm mansion house, it now has all the atmosphere of a private house while providing the comforts expected of a good hotel. All three en suite bedrooms are individually decorated and furnished to a high standard, and colour televisions are provided on request. The style of furnishings in the public rooms is traditional as befits the house. A log fire burns in the drawing room which is a lovely place in which to relax. In the evening the restaurant captures the setting sun and there are beautiful views over the garden and the Cromarty Firth. Marsha Fraser presents interesting daily changing menus offering the best local ingredients. In recognition of the high standard of food the restaurant has been awarded an AA Rosette. To complement

the food, there is a selection of fine wines. The restaurant is also open to non-resident diners but it is requested that reservations are made for lunch or dinner.

Open 1 Mar to 24 Dec
Rooms: 3 with private facilities
Dining Room/Restaurant Lunch 12 – 2 pm (a) – reservation essential
Dinner 7 – 9 pm (c) – reservation essential
No smoking area in dining room
No smoking in bedrooms
Bed & Breakfast £25 – £42
Dinner B & B £43 – £60
Special Rates available
• Warm salad of pigeon breast and wild mushrooms on tossed leaves. Savoury crusted salmon fillet and scallops with a lime and coriander tartare sauce. Peppered sirloin steak with mushroom and onion marmalade. Collops of venison fillet with port and rowanberry sauce. Iced chocolate and Drambuie parfait with red berry coulis.
STB Highly Commended 3 Crowns
Credit cards: 1, 3
Proprietor: Marsha Fraser

Contin
by Strathpeffer
Location 56
CONTIN HOUSE
Contin, by Strathpeffer
Ross-shire IV14 9EB
Tel: 01997 421920
Fax: 01997 421851
On A853 at eastern end of Contin village – follow sign to Contin Church.
Contin House dates from 1794 and was formerly a most substantial manse. It sits in its own gardens surrounded by the grandeur of the Highlands. David and Daphne Du Boulay are convivial hosts and make guests feel so comfortable that they could be staying with friends. The friendly welcome and high standard of hospitality won the Du Boulays the Scotcom award for most welcoming hotel. Guests relax in front of log fires amid the traditional furniture and family items. Silver and crystal sparkle in the candlelit dining room where the best of local produce, including fresh vegetables from the garden, can be sampled from the imaginative dinner menus.
Open 1 Mar to 31 Oct
Rooms: 5 with private facilities
Dinner at 8 pm or by arrangement (e)

5 course menu
Dinner for non-residents by arrangement
Restricted Licence
Children over 8 years welcome
Dogs by arrangement
No smoking in dining room + bedrooms
Bed & Breakfast £42 – £50.50
Dinner B & B £67 – £75
Room Rate £84 – £101
Special Rates available
• Terrine of gravadlax and crabmeat. Marinaded roast fillet of venison served with Stilton cheese sauce. Filo parcels of salmon, spinach and ricotta cheese.
STB Deluxe 3 Crowns
Credit cards: 1, 3
Proprietors: David & Daphne Du Boulay

COUL HOUSE HOTEL
Contin, by Strathpeffer
Ross-shire IV14 9EY
Tel: 01997 421487
Fax: 01997 421945
On A835 to Ullapool, 17 miles north-west of Inverness.
This country house hotel commands fine views over the area and the Mackenzies of Coul, whose secluded country mansion it was, obviously had this in mind when they chose the site. There are log fires and spacious public rooms, and all bedrooms are en suite with colour tele-text TV, radio, direct dial telephone, hospitality tray, hairdryer and trouser press. Bar lunches get a high rating and there is an extensive à la carte menu majoring in seafood and steaks to complement the daily changing dinner menu in Mackenzie's Taste of Scotland Restaurant. The hotel has some salmon and trout fishing rights and there is a choice of nine golf courses within easy reach.
Open all year
Rooms: 21 with private facilities
Bar Lunch 12 – 2 pm Mon to Sat: 12.30 – 2.30 pm Sun (a)
Dining Room/Restaurant Lunch 12 – 2 pm (b) by arrangement only
Bar Supper 5.30 – 9 pm (a)
Dinner 7 – 9 pm (d)
Bed & Breakfast £34 – £56
Dinner B & B £49 – £78.50
• Pan-fried mussels flamed in whisky

and finished with cream. Tomato and courgette soup. Roasted duckling with cider sauce. Prime Scottish beef slowly cooked with thyme and Scotch ale. Baked whole lemon sole with parsley butter. Ecclefechan butter tart. Caramelised oranges in Drambuie.
STB Highly Commended 4 Crowns
Credit cards: 2, 5
Proprietors: Martyn & Ann Hill

Corsemalzie
Location 57
CORSEMALZIE HOUSE HOTEL
Corsemalzie, Port William
Newton Stewart
Wigtownshire DG8 9RL
Tel: 01988 860254
Fax: 01988 860213
Halfway along B7005 Glenluce-Wigtown, off A714 Newton Stewart-Port William or A747 Glenluce-Port William.
There are 40 acres of woodland and gardens surrounding this 19th century Scottish mansion house and it is not uncommon to see a few gamebirds strutting about the lawns together with the domestic peacocks. Whilst primarily a sporting country house hotel with its own extensive game, fishing and shooting rights, it has a much wider appeal as a base from which to explore the many interesting corners of this largely unknown part of the country. The menu is broadly based and much of the excellent local game finds its way to the hotel kitchen.
Open 5 Mar to 10 Jan except Christmas + Boxing Days
Rooms: 15, 14 with private facilities
Bar Lunch 12.30 – 2 pm (a)
Dining Room/Restaurant Lunch 12.30 – 2 pm (b)
Bar Supper 7.15 – 9 pm (a)
Dinner 7.30 – 9 pm (c)
Dogs accepted (small charge)
Bed & Breakfast £31 – £51
Dinner B & B £41 – £68.50
Special Rates available
• Venison sausages with mustard sauce. Fresh mussels in cream and Pernod sauce. Smoked Bladnoch salmon. Local pheasant with orange and walnut sauce. Roast loin of pork with apricot and brandy sauce. Queen scallops with lime and ginger butter. Grilled salmon with prawns and asparagus.
STB Commended 4 Crowns
Credit cards: 1, 3
Proprietor: Peter McDougall

Craigellachie

CRAIGELLACHIE HOTEL
Craigellachie
Banffshire AB38 9SR
Tel: 01340 881204
Fax: 01340 881253

On A941, 12 miles south of Elgin.
An imposing hotel in its own grounds just off the main square of the village and with the famous Spey walk at the foot of the garden. It is decorated and furnished to a very high standard and in excellent taste. The same care and attention that is so evident in the furnishing of the hotel is also reflected in the quality of the food. The high reputation it enjoys is well earned. Craigellachie of course is very much fishing and shooting country but it is also on the whisky trail and there are several distinguished distilleries nearby. French, Swedish and Danish spoken.
Open all year
Rooms: 30 with private facilities
Bar Lunch 12.30 – 2 pm (a)
Dining Room/Restaurant Lunch 12.30 – 2 pm (b)
Dinner 7.30 – 9.30 pm (e) 4 course menu
No smoking in dining room
Bed & Breakfast £48.50 – £81
Dinner B & B £75 – £107.50
Special Weekend Rates available
• *Cured Spey salmon with a wholegrain mustard sauce. Goats cheese baked in filo pastry served on vegetable ribbons and a sweet onion marmalade. Smoked venison with a pine kernel dressing. Roast fillet of beef with wild mushrooms and cured pheasant breast. Medley of seafood with a tomato and basil cream. Seasonal fruits and berries glazed with a honey sabayon.*
STB Highly Commended 4 Crowns
Credit cards: 1, 2, 3, 5 + SWITCH

Crail

CAIPLIE GUEST HOUSE
53 High Street, Crail
Fife KY10 3RA
Tel: 01333 450564

High Street, Crail.
A three storey villa that was at one time the village bakery but is now a well maintained and comfortable guest house, right in the centre of this historic and quaint little fishing village. Guests

are invited to select their evening meal by 4 pm to enable it to be prepared to order and there is usually a choice of fish, poultry or meat for the main courses. Good value, good home cooking.
Open 1 Mar to 30 Oct
Rooms: 7
Dinner at 7 pm (b)
It is requested that guests select their menu by 4 pm
Residents only
No smoking area in dining room
Bed & Breakfast £15 – £16.50
Dinner B & B £27 – £28.50
• *Home-made soups. Potted smoked haddock. Chicken with tarragon and mushroom sauce. Pork with peach sauce. Lamb with rosemary and garlic. Cloutie dumpling. Athol brose. Strathbogie mist.*
STB Commended 1 Crown
No credit cards
Proprietor: Jayne Hudson

HAZELTON GUEST HOUSE
29 Marketgate, Crail
Fife KY10 3TH
Tel: 01333 450250

In town centre opposite tourist office and Tolbooth.
The Hazelton is one of an impressive terrace of Victorian merchants houses in the centre of Crail. This is a charming guest house offering extremely comfortable accommodation, all rooms having central heating, colour television, tea-making facilities etc and wash-hand basin. Rita Brown's award winning culinary skills are evident in the high standard of food preparation and presentation. The menus change daily often featuring the local fish and seafood for which the East Neuk is famed and even some home-smoked specialities. Rita will also produce interesting options

for vegetarians with prior notice. The Browns' attention to detail combined with the relaxed and friendly atmosphere and the outstanding standard of food ensure that a great number of guests choose to return to Hazelton time and again.
Open 1 Feb to 13 Nov
Rooms: 7
Dinner at 7 pm (b) except Mon Tue – unless by prior arrangement
It is requested that guests select their menu by 4 pm
Residents only
No dogs
Bed & Breakfast £15 – £18
Dinner B & B £29 – £32
• *Home-smoked cod's roe pâté. Hot Crail crab mousse. Fresh fillet of haddock and salmon wrapped in filo pastry with watercress, served with white wine sauce. Roast topside of Scottish beef, gravy and batter pudding. Poached fillet of salmon with leeks and pink peppercorns. Venison and wild mushroom pie. Leg of Scotch lamb filled with spinach and ginger, with red wine sauce.*
STB Commended Listed
No credit cards
Proprietors: Alan & Rita Brown

Crianlarich

ALLT-CHAORAIN COUNTRY HOUSE
Crianlarich
Perthshire FK20 8RU
Tel: 01838 300283
Fax: 01838 300238

Off A82, 1 mile north-west of Crianlarich.
Perched on a hill in its own grounds, Allt-Chaorain is so sited that it looks out over the picturesque countryside of Benmore and Strathfillan from the south facing sun lounge. Roger McDonald bids his guests 'welcome to my home' and is a most hospitable host. The house is most welcoming and comfortable with cosy compact rooms. Throughout the year generally there is an open log fire burning in the lounge and a 'trust bar' for the convenience of guests. There is a quiet air of quality about the place. Roger himself prepares a simple well balanced menu each evening for his guests. The wood-panelled dining room is furnished with three beautifully polished wooden tables each seating six. Guests share tables and the atmosphere is informal and friendly.

Open 20 Mar to 28 Oct
Rooms: 8 with private facilities
Dinner 7 – 8 pm (c)
Residents only
No smoking in dining room, bedrooms +
main lounge
A sun lounge is set aside for those who
wish to smoke
Bed & Breakfast £30 – £46
Dinner B & B £45 – £55
Special Rates for 2+ to 7+ nights
• Home-made soups – spicy parsnip,
carrot and orange. Local salmon and
trout. Lamb steaks with a haggis crust.
Traditional steak and kidney pie. Home-
made desserts – orange meringue pie,
bread and butter pudding, cranachan,
Ecclefechan tart, cloutie dumpling.
STB Commended 3 Crowns
Credit cards: 1, 3
Proprietor: Roger McDonald

Crieff

Location 61

CRIEFF VISITORS CENTRE
Muthill Road, Crieff
Perthshire PH7 4A7
Tel: 01764 654014
Fax: 01764 652903
On A822 leading out of Crieff to the
south.
The self-service restaurant is part of a
visitor complex of showroom, shops,
audio-visual presentation and garden
centre beside two rural factories
producing thistle pattern Buchan pottery
and high quality Perthshire Paper-
weights. Open seven days a week, it is
within an hour's drive of Glasgow,
Edinburgh or St Andrews, and close by
Gleneagles. The restaurant itself is
spacious and smooth running and the
intelligent use of wood, brick and glass
gives it a light open atmosphere. The
large self-service area is clearly laid out
with good displays of food and an
impressive home-baking section. The
standard menu is augmented with daily
dishes to incorporate a wide range of

good interesting food. There are
children's menus with reduced portions
available, and in good weather there is al
fresco eating in a large patio area.
Open all year except Christmas +
Boxing Days, 1 + 2 Jan
Food service 9 am – 6 pm (a)
(Note: hours restricted in winter)
Facilities for disabled visitors
Credit cards: 1, 2, 3 + SWITCH

MURRAYPARK HOTEL
Connaught Terrace, Crieff
Perthshire PH7 3DJ
Tel: 01764 653731
Fax: 01764 655311
Turn off A85 at Connaught Terrace, uphill
to residential part of town.
Pink-stoned large Victorian house set in
its own gardens in the residential part of
the town. The comfortable restaurant
has an uncrowded atmosphere and
overlooks the pleasant garden. Menus
are based on established Scottish foods
with many interesting variations. French
is spoken. Children and dogs welcome.
Open all year except Christmas Day
Rooms: 21 with private facilities
Bar Lunch 12 – 2 pm (a)
Bar Supper 7 – 9.30 pm (b)
Dinner 7.30 – 9.30 pm (d) 4 course
menu
No smoking in restaurant
Bed & Breakfast £34 – £50
Dinner B & B £50 – £70
• Sliced mushrooms poached in cream
and port wine, finished with Stilton
cheese. Smoked seafood platter. Partan
bree – a creamy crab soup. Fillets of
trout poached in white wine, served with
a raspberry sauce. Charcoal grilled
venison cutlets with rowan jelly and fresh
apple. Tender loins of lamb with
rosemary and walnuts. Baked halibut
wrapped in pastry.
STB Commended 4 Crowns
Credit cards: 1, 2, 3, 5, 6 + SWITCH
Proprietors: Ann & Noel Scott

SMUGGLERS RESTAURANT
Glenturret Distillery
The Hosh, Crieff
Perthshire PH7 4HA
Tel: 01764 656565
Fax: 01764 654366

Prestige Award Winner 1989

Signed from A85 in Crieff and from A822
(Sma' Glen) at Gilmerton (off A85 to east
of Crieff).
Glenturret is Scotland's oldest
Highland malt distillery and its award
winning visitors centre is an immensely
popular tourist attraction. Within a
converted 18th century whisky
warehouse there are audio-visual
presentations, the Spirit of the Glen
Exhibition and a whisky tasting bar to
sample 12 to 21 year old Glenturret
and The Glenturret Original Malt
Liqueur. On the first floor of the
building are two restaurants. Smugglers
is a self-service operation of an
unusually high standard, cleverly
constructed and adaptable for
functions of different sizes. Then there
is the Pagoda Room which extends
from Smugglers and is a smaller more
formal setting offering waitress service.
In warm weather visitors can sit at
tables with sun-shades out on the
balcony which runs the length of the
restaurant. As one would expect, the
menus feature local venison, salmon
and trout in a wholesome cooking style,
and there is always a vegetarian dish
and a good choice of sweets or
cheeses. Morning coffees and
afternoon teas with home-baking are
also available. The whole complex
attracts much favourable comment
from visitors and children are most
welcome.
Open all year except Christmas +
Boxing Days, 1 + 2 Jan
Note: closed weekends Jan + Feb
Bar Lunch (Smugglers) 12 – 2.30 pm (a)
Dining Room/Restaurant Lunch (Pagoda
Room) 12 – 2.30 pm (b)
Dinner – by private arrangement only
Complete facilities are no smoking but a
smoking area is provided in Smugglers
Restaurant
Disabled access
• Glenturret smoked salmon. Home-
made soups. Venison in illicit whisky
sauce. Highland beef in red wine sauce.
Tay salmon. Haggis neeps and tatties.
Steak pie. Smugglers chicken. Glenturret
ice-cream. Cranachan.
Credit cards: 1, 2, 3

Crinan

CRINAN HOTEL
Crinan, Lochgilphead
Argyll PA31 8SR
Tel: 0154 683 261
Fax: 0154 683 292

Prestige Award Winner 1991

A82 Glasgow-Inveraray, then A83 to Lochgilphead. Follow A816 (Oban) for c. 5 miles, then B841 to Crinan.

Magnificent scenery is part of the Scottish heritage, but for genuinely stunning views and breathtaking sunsets, dine in the renowned Lock 16 roof top restaurant. The Crinan Hotel has the best of both worlds. The yachting enthusiasts who use the Crinan Canal invariably want to eat here as do the many visitors who have heard of its reputation. Seafood, but particularly shellfish, is a speciality. It is landed daily at the Canal entrance and is so fresh that it may be 5 pm before the chef knows what will be available for dinner that night. The ground floor Westward Restaurant is less seafood based than the specialised Lock 16, but enjoys an equally fine reputation. The bedrooms have been individually designed by Frances Ryan, an artist of repute, some have their own private balconies and each has a sea view.

Open all year except 1 wk Christmas
Rooms: 22 with private facilities
Bar Lunch 12.30 – 2 pm (a)
Dinner (Westward Restaurant) 7 – 9 pm (e)
Dinner (Lock 16 mid Apr to Sep only) at 8 pm except Sun Mon (f) – booking essential
Bed & Breakfast £57.50 – £67.50
Special Winter Rates available
• *Mussels marinière. Locally smoked wild Scottish salmon. Loch Crinan prawns Corryvreckan. Scottish beef dishes.*
STB Highly Commended 4 Crowns
Credit cards: 1, 2, 3
Proprietors: Nick & Frances Ryan

SEALGAIR
c/o Wave Yacht Charters
1 Hazel Drive
Dundee DD2 1QQ
Tel: 01382 668501
Fax: 01382 668501

Yacht based at Bellanoch, by Crinan, Argyll

For those who love sailing and enjoy good food, this is the ideal way to combine both pursuits. Beauty and craftsmanship combine in 'Sealgair', the first cruising yacht to be featured in the Taste of Scotland Guide. This magnificent 46 foot wooden ketch is equipped to the highest standards for comfort, performance and safety, and is maintained in top condition. From her base on the Crinan Canal, Sealgair (which is pronounced 'shallachar' and is Gaelic for 'hunter') will happily meander round secluded bays, or offer a taste adventure on a trip to St Kilda. The experienced skipper ensures that the guests can relax without worry while the cook makes best use of quality fresh ingredients to produce delicious and imaginative meals from the galley. French spoken.

Open 1 May to mid Sep
Cabins: 4
Unlicensed – guests welcome to take own wine
No dogs
No smoking in dining area + cabins
Daily rate £60 per person (min 5 people) includes all meals + accommodation
• *Tasty soups e.g. Cullen skink, broccoli and almond, beetroot and yoghurt. Hot poached salmon stuffed with mussels and dill with a light watercress mayonnaise. Venison with cranberry and tarragon. Lamb with Dijon and demerara with an orange and honey glaze.*
No credit cards
Proprietor: Wave Yacht Management Ltd

Cromarty

ROYAL HOTEL
Marine Terrace, Cromarty
Ross-shire IV11 8YN
Tel: 01381 600217
Fax: 01381 600217

On A832, 20 miles north-east of Inverness.

Welcoming log fires are a prominent feature of this white-painted hotel situated overlooking the beach and harbour in the ancient and historic village of Cromarty. The furnishing and decor are of a high standard throughout and all the rooms have views of the sea and Ross-shire mountains. The bright sunny dining room looks out over the Cromarty Firth and there is a comfortable bar with an interesting bar lunch and supper menu. The hotel has a good reputation for traditional Scottish hospitality, excellent food and sound value for money.

Open all year except 1 + 2 Jan
Rooms: 10 with private facilities
Bar Lunch 12 – 2 pm (a)
Dining Room/Restaurant Lunch 12 – 2 pm (b)
Bar Supper 5.30 – 9 pm (b)
Dinner 6 – 8 pm except Sun (c)
No smoking in dining room
Bed & Breakfast £25 – £30
Special Weekly Rates
• *Smoked salmon and avocado mousse. Home-made chicken and broccoli ravioli. Cream of wild mushroom soup. Whole local prawns in garlic and white wine. Lamb cutlets with mustard and honey glaze. Grilled whole trout with lemon butter. Escalopes of venison in ginger and cream.*
STB Commended 3 Crowns
Credit cards: 1, 2, 3, 6
Proprietors: Yvonne & Stewart Morrison

Cullen

BAYVIEW HOTEL
Seafield Street, Cullen
Banffshire AB56 2SU
Tel: 01542 841031

A98 between Banff and Fochabers – overlooking Cullen Harbour.

Cullen is a pleasant little harbour town on the Moray Firth and the Bayview is a splendid place to stay when you are there. A really charming little hotel, it has been cleverly converted to provide interesting public rooms and well equipped bedrooms. On a fine day there is a view to Caithness from the top floor breakfast room. The hotel makes good use of its harbour location by specialising in some of the excellent fish soups and fish dishes for which this part of the north-east is noted.

Open all year except Christmas
Rooms: 6 with private facilities
Bar Lunch 12 – 2 pm (a)
Dining Room/Restaurant Lunch 12.30 – 2 pm Sun only (b)
Bar Supper 6.30 – 9 pm (b)
Dinner 6.30 – 9 pm (c)
No dogs
Bed & Breakfast £27.50 – £35
• Cullen skink – local speciality – smoked fish soup. Fisherman's pie – local haddock, halibut, salmon and prawns in a parsley cream sauce topped with potato and cheese. Poached darne of salmon with a champagne cream sauce. Grilled jumbo trout stuffed with almonds and prawns. Fillet of beef cooked with onions, mushrooms, mustard, sherry and cream. Salmis of Guinea fowl with a red wine sauce.
STB Commended 4 Crowns
Credit cards: 1, 3
Proprietor: David Evans

THE SEAFIELD ARMS HOTEL
Seafield Street, Cullen
Moray AB56 2SG
Tel: 01542 840791
Fax: 01542 840736

Situated on A98 (main road through Cullen) up from town square.
A fine old coaching inn, built in 1822 by the Earl of Seafield, and described in the statistical account of Scotland 1845 as having "no superior between Aberdeen and Inverness". In keeping with that inherited reputation, the staff of the Seafield Arms work hard to maintain the tradition of courtesy and caring attention. A very extensive menu caters for a wide range of diners of all age groups and does so successfully judging by the level of activity. The proprietors are much in evidence, supervising the smooth running of the dining room, ably supported by a team of smart, well-trained local staff.

Open all year
Rooms: 25, 23 with private facilities
Bar Lunch 12 – 2 pm (a)
Dining Room/Restaurant Lunch 12 – 2 pm (b)
Bar Supper 6 – 9 pm (a)
Dinner 6 – 9 pm (b)

No dogs
Facilities for disabled visitors
Bed & Breakfast £24 – £33
Room Rate £33 – £65
• Seafield Arms Cullen skink – a local traditional smoked haddock soup. Salmon and rock turbot fillets gently poached and served in a lobster, brandy and cream sauce. Honey roast duckling with an orange and apricot sauce. Poached haddock finished in a mushroom, prawn and fresh cream sauce. Chargrilled steaks.
STB Commended 4 Crowns
Credit cards: 1, 2, 3, 5, 6 + SWITCH, DELTA
Proprietors: Herbert & Alison Cox

Cupar
Location 65
OSTLERS CLOSE
Bonnygate, Cupar
Fife KY15 4BU
Tel: 01334 655574

Prestige Award Winner 1989

Via A91/A92 to centre of Cupar.
This charming little restaurant is situated just off the main road through Cupar in the small lane or 'close' from which it takes its name. Ostlers Close has earned a fine reputation for the excellent standard of food produced by chef/proprietor Jimmy Graham. He is particularly outstanding in his treatment of fish and shellfish, but the same deft and imaginative touch can be seen in the game and meat dishes he creates. In the cosy almost cottage-like atmosphere of the restaurant, Amanda Graham looks after their guests with much friendliness and charm.

Open all year except first 2 wks Jun, Christmas + Boxing Days, 1 Jan
Dining Room/Restaurant Lunch 12.15 – 2 pm except Sun Mon (b)
Dinner 7 – 9.30 pm except Sun Mon (d)
Closed Sun Mon
• Local seafood broth. Pan-fried terrine of goats cheese and potato served with mixed salad leaves. Roast saddle of

lamb served with a herb scented sauce. Fillet of turbot with langoustines and asparagus on a fresh herb butter sauce. Roast fillet of beef served with a green peppercorn sauce. Selection of seafood with a shellfish stock.
Credit cards: 1, 2, 3 + SWITCH, DELTA
Proprietors: Jimmy & Amanda Graham

Dalbeattie
Location 66
AUCHENSKEOCH LODGE
by Dalbeattie
Kirkcudbrightshire DG5 4PG
Tel: 0138 778 0277
Fax: 0138 778 0277

5 miles south-east of Dalbeattie on B793.
This is a former Victorian shooting lodge set amid delightful gardens in a peaceful and secluded setting. The atmosphere is that of a delightful and gracious country home, with period furnishings throughout. Woodlands, formal gardens and rhododendron walks provide privacy and tranquillity. Facilities include fishing on the lodge's own loch, a billiard room, croquet lawn, and a turf and gravel maze. Christopher and Mary Broom-Smith are friendly and charming hosts. Great emphasis is placed on the quality and freshness of the food offered. Therefore the menu is kept small, though a choice of two dishes is given at each course, and it changes daily to make full use of the excellent meat and fish available locally. Wherever possible the vegetables, salads, herbs and soft fruit are fresh from the garden.

Open 1 Apr to 31 Oct
Rooms: 5 with private facilities
Dinner 7.30 – 8 pm (b)
Booking essential for non-residents
Facilities for disabled visitors
Bed & Breakfast £24 – £33
Dinner B & B £34 – £45
Special Spring/Autumn Rates for 3+ nights
• Small menu, changing daily. Emphasis on fresh local produce. Spinach roulade stuffed with ham and walnuts. Grilled lamb cutlets with herb butter. Casserole of venison with red wine. Salmon steak baked with white wine. Poached pear with apricot sauce. Lemon syllabub.
STB Commended 3 Crowns
Credit cards: 1, 3
Proprietors: Christopher & Mary Broom-Smith

by *Dalry*

Location 67

BRAIDWOODS RESTAURANT
Drumastle Mill Cottage, by Dalry
Ayrshire KA24 4LN
Tel: 01294 833544

A737 Kilwinning-Dalry. On southern outskirts of Dalry, take road to Saltcoats for 1 mile and follow signs.

Travelling down a short drive through open fields in rural Ayrshire, you come upon this attractive 200 year old miller's cottage which is now Braidwoods Restaurant. The long low converted cottages have been transformed into a stylish and contemporary restaurant offering the very best in quality dining out. Keith and Nicola Braidwood are an expert husband and wife team, both of whom have high culinary qualifications and a history of luxury hotel cooking behind them. Attention to detail, a demand for only the highest calibre of ingredients and a startling intensity of flavour characterise the food here. The atmosphere is comfortable and relaxed, just right for enjoying the superb dining experience. Children welcome at lunchtime.

Open all year except first 2 wks Jan
Dining Room/Restaurant Lunch 12 –
2 pm except Mon (b)
Dinner 7 – 9 pm except Sun Mon (d)
4 course menu
Closed Mon
No smoking in restaurant
• Warm mousseline of lemon sole centred with smoked salmon on ribbons of cucumber, glazed with a horseradish and chive hollandaise. Pan-fried loin of woodland roe deer on savoury Du Puy lentils with port and thyme sauce. Honey glazed breast of Gressingham duck with a confit of its own leg and a caramelised cranberry and ginger essence. Trio of caramel puddings. Banana brûlée. Praline mousse.
Credit cards: 1, 3 + SWITCH
Proprietors: Keith & Nicola Braidwood

Daviot

nr Inverness

Location 68

DAVIOT MAINS FARM
Daviot
Inverness IV1 2ER
Tel: 01463 772215
Fax: 01463 772215

On B851 (B9006) to Culloden/Croy, 5 miles south of Inverness.

Daviot Mains is a comfortable early 19th century Listed farmhouse in a quiet situation just five miles from Inverness, under the personal supervision of Margaret and Alex Hutcheson. Relax in the warm atmosphere of this friendly home where delicious meals are thoughtfully prepared and where log fires burn in both sitting room and dining room. Guests are offered a light supper of tea and home-baking around 9.30 pm. Recommended by Elizabeth Gundrey's 'Staying off the Beaten Track'.

Open all year except Christmas Eve + Christmas Day
Rooms: 3, 2 with private facilities
Dinner at 6.30 pm except Sun Sat 6 May to 23 Sep; except Sun rest of year (b)
Unlicensed – guests welcome to take own wine
Dogs accepted by arrangement
No smoking in dining room + bedrooms
Bed & Breakfast £16 – £22
Dinner B & B £25 – £32
Special Rates for 3+ nights Oct to Apr (excl Easter + Christmas holiday period)
• According to season – home-made soups, fresh local salmon and trout, Scottish meats, vegetables and cheeses. Local fruits and home-made puddings.
STB Highly Commended 2 Crowns
Credit cards: 1, 3
Proprietors: Margaret & Alex Hutcheson

Dirleton

Location 69

THE OPEN ARMS
Dirleton
East Lothian EH39 5EG
Tel: 01620 850241
Fax: 01620 850570

Off A198 to Dirleton village, between Gullane and North Berwick.

The charming East Lothian village of Dirleton is a mere half hour's drive from Edinburgh and attracts visitors for a variety of reasons. Some go to see the 13th century castle which overlooks the picturesque village green, but many go to eat at The Open Arms. This lovely old market inn flanks the village green and has pleasant gardens and comfortable accommodation. It has earned a good reputation over the years for its high quality standards. A cosy little cocktail bar and a comfortable lounge adjoin the dining room which takes full advantage of its setting to provide restful views across to the castle. The menus reflect the abundance of local agricultural produce, fish and shellfish for which East Lothian is noted. French, German and Gaelic spoken.

Open all year except New Year's Day
Rooms: 7 with private facilities
Bar Lunch 12.30 – 2.30 pm (a)
Dining Room/Restaurant Lunch 12.30 – 2.30 pm (c)
Dinner 7 – 9.30 pm (d)
Bed & Breakfast £35 – £65
Dinner B & B £55 – £85
• Smoked salmon parcels filled with avocado mousse served with a pink peppercorn sauce. Mussel and onion stew. Roast suprême of duck with a port and orange sauce. Pan-fried medallions of lamb served with a timbale of courgettes and mint on a sherry sauce. Trio of fish with a light shellfish sauce.
STB Highly Commended 4 Crowns
Credit cards: 1, 3

Dornoch

Location 70

DORNOCH CASTLE HOTEL
Castle Street
Dornoch IV25 3SD
Tel: 01862 810216
Fax: 01862 810981

In the centre of the cathedral town of Dornoch, 2 miles off A9.

Dornoch is a peaceful little town but, as the 13th century cathedral testifies, it is not without historic significance. At about the same time the cathedral was being built so was the Bishop's Palace and parts of it are still incorporated in Dornoch Castle Hotel in the centre of the town. The majority of the comfortable bedrooms overlook the sheltered garden and there is a coffee lounge opening on to the terrace. The Bishop's Room restaurant was once the palace kitchen and now offers diners a good selection of fine food based on local specialities and the abundance of excellent game, fish, shellfish so easily available.

Open 6 Apr to 29 Oct
Rooms: 17 with private facilities
Bar Lunch 12.15 – 2 pm Mon to Sat:
12.30 – 2 pm Sun (a)
Dining Room/Restaurant Lunch 12.15 –
2 pm Mon to Sat: 12.30 – 2 pm Sun (a)
Bar Supper 6 – 9 pm (b)
Dinner 7.30 – 8.45 pm (c) 4 course
menu
No smoking in restaurant
Bed & Breakfast £31 – £39.50
Dinner B & B £49 – £57.50
Special Rates for 2+ to 5+ nights
• Cassoulet of seafood in leek and
Pernod cream sauce served in a pastry
box. Roast loin of pork with cider and
prunes. Grilled prime Angus sirloin steak.
Lamb cutlets with redcurrant and
rosemary. Atholl brose. Warm coconut
and pear tart with cream.
STB Commended 4 Crowns
Credit cards: 1, 2, 3, 6 + SWITCH
Proprietor: Michael Ketchin

THE MALLIN HOUSE HOTEL
Church Street, Dornoch
Sutherland IV25 3LP
Tel: 01862 810335
Fax: 01862 810810

Down to centre of town, turn right.
The Mallin House is a family run hotel
with a very good reputation for its food.
There is a good range of choice on both
bar and restaurant menus which have
been carefully compiled to take best
advantage of locally available
specialities. The standard of food
available in the bar lounge is exceptional
which makes this a very popular place
for informal meals. The bar lounge leads
on to the restaurant with its magnificent
views of the Dornoch Firth and Struie
Hills. Golf is the theme of the impressive
à la carte menu which features local fish,
shellfish and game, and excellent
steaks. A programme of refurbishment is
already underway, upgrading the interior
of the hotel.
Open all year
Rooms: 11 with private facilities
Bar Lunch 12.30 – 2.15 pm (a-b)
Bar Supper 6.30 – 9 pm (a-b)
Dinner 6.30 – 9 pm (c)
Kennel for dogs
Facilities for disabled visitors: wheelchair
ramp
Bed & Breakfast £22 – £28
Dinner B & B £40 – £46
• King scallops with diced red onions,
fresh herbs and flamed with Pernod.
Rack of spring lamb roasted with
rosemary, with port wine sauce and a

tartlet case filled with rowanberry jelly.
Whole local lobster in hot garlic and herb
butter. Fresh salmon escalope filled with
crab and lemon forcemeat served with a
sauce of prawns, mushroom and dry
white wine.
Credit cards: 1, 2, 3, 6 + SWITCH, DELTA
Proprietors: Malcolm & Linda Holden

THE ROYAL GOLF HOTEL
1st Tee, Dornoch
Sutherland IV25 3LG
Tel: 01862 810283
Fax: 01862 810923

From A9, 2 miles into Dornoch town
square.
This aptly named hotel is virtually on the
golf course. Indeed you can almost lie in
bed and watch the players on the first
tee, or look beyond that to the sandy
beaches of the Dornoch Firth.
Comfortable bedrooms and suites have
all the usual facilities and the restaurant
offers high class cuisine with an
appropriate inclusion of local regional
produce. Bar lunches and suppers are
served in the sun lounge in which there
is usually entertainment on Saturday
evenings. Golf may well be the pre-
eminent activity of many of the guests –
tee times can easily be arranged – but
there is also a fine range of other
recreational pursuits in the vicinity.
Open Mar to early Nov
Rooms: 30 with private facilities
Bar Lunch 12 – 2 pm (a)
Bar Supper 6.30 – 9 pm (a)
Dinner 7 – 9 pm (c)
Bed & Breakfast £37 – £60
Dinner B & B £40 – £62
Special Rates for 7+ nights
• Fresh vegetables and wild mushrooms
stir-fried and simmered in cream and
saffron, served with a timbale of rice.
Smoked salmon parcel filled with
prawns.
STB Commended 4 Crowns
Credit cards: 1, 2, 3, 5, 6

Drymen
by Loch Lomond
Location 71

BUCHANAN ARMS HOTEL
Main Street, Drymen
by Loch Lomond
Stirlingshire G63 0BQ
Tel: 01360 60588
Fax: 01360 60943

A811 Balloch (Loch Lomond)/Stirling.
Drymen is c. 7½ miles east of Balloch.
This has long been a favourite hotel for
those who enjoy the lovely scenery of the
Trossachs and Loch Lomond, and when
you have finished seeing the countryside
there is so much to return to. This
attractive old 18th century building has a
fully equipped leisure club with swimming
pool, sauna, solarium, gymnasium and
squash courts. It also has a bowling
green and can arrange tennis, golf or
fishing for those so inclined. Public
rooms are spacious and comfortably
furnished. Tapestries is the name of the
hotel's main restaurant and it offers both
à la carte and table d'hôte menus,
complemented by an extensive
international wine list. There is also a
sandwich and snack menu available in
the comfortable lounge and
conservatory. Breakfasts are quite
something, with a great range of choice.
The staff have been well trained and it
shows in polite, attentive and informed
service.
Open all year
Rooms: 51 with private facilities
Dining Room/Restaurant Lunch
(Tapestries) 12.30 – 2.30 pm (a)
Dinner (Tapestries) 7 – 9.30 pm (c)
Facilities for disabled visitors
Bed & Breakfast £55 – £75
Dinner B & B £54 – £57 (min 2 nights
stay)
Special Rates available
• Steamed west coast mussels
flavoured with garlic and herbs, served
with a white wine liquor. Broccoli and
ginger soup. Baked fillet of river trout on
a vermouth cream and grape sauce.
Roast leg of Border lamb with braised
shallots, bacon lardons and a claret
wine jus. Medallions of veal set on a
bed of spinach leaves cordoned in a
black cherry sauce.
STB Commended 4 Crowns
Credit cards: 1, 2, 3, 5, 6 + SWITCH

Dufftown

Location 72

A TASTE OF SPEYSIDE
10 Balvenie Street, Dufftown
Banffshire AB5 4AB
Tel: 01340 20860

Prestige Award Winner 1988

50 yards from Tourist Information Centre on Elgin road (A941).
This is real malt whisky territory and A Taste of Speyside bases its business on that. Originally set up primarily as a whisky tasting centre and restaurant, it has earned a fine reputation as an inexpensive good quality restaurant promoting the best of Speyside food and Speyside malts of which it has an unrivalled selection. This is home-cooking at its best, and the Taste of Speyside Platter is something special and wonderful value for money. There are no pretentious frills just honest to goodness food. Group bookings out of season can be arranged.
Open 1 Mar to 31 Oct
Bar Meals 11 am – 5.30 pm (a)
Restaurant Lunch 11 am – 5.30 pm (a)
Dinner 6 – 9 pm (b)
• Cullen skink. A Taste of Speyside Platter. Large local scampi cooked in a birch wine sauce. Prime Scottish beef steak with a grain mustard cream and malt whisky sauce. Medallions of roe deer in a Madeira sauce. Heather honey and malt whisky cheesecake topped with walnuts, with fresh cream and raspberry coulis. Hot fruit dumpling with Drambuie cream.
Credit cards: 1, 2, 3
Proprietors: J Thompson & R McLean

Dulnain Bridge

Location 73

AUCHENDEAN LODGE HOTEL
Dulnain Bridge, Grantown-on-Spey
Morayshire PH26 3LU
Tel: 01479 851347

On A95, 1 mile south of Dulnain Bridge.
A comfortable country house hotel on a knoll commanding some of the finest views across the River Spey and Abernethy Forest towards the Cairngorm Mountains. At one time an Edwardian hunting lodge, it has been furnished with good taste and retains much of its Edwardian elegance. The welcome is genuine, the log fires are cheerful, and the award winning home-cooked dinners usually feature game, hand-picked wild fungi, plants and berries from the local countryside, complemented with home-grown speciality potatoes and vegetables. An extensive wine cellar and a wide choice of malt whiskies will add to your enjoyment. Numerous walks in the woods behind the hotel. Pets welcome. French spoken.
Open all year except early Jan to early Feb
Rooms: 7, 5 with private facilities
Dinner 7.30 – 9 pm (d) 4 course menu
No smoking in dining room + one of the lounges
Bed & Breakfast £23.50 – £40.50
Dinner B & B £35 – £63
Special Rates for 3+ nights
• Home-cured beef and gravadlax. Carrot and lovage soup. Arbroath smokie baked in ale and cream. Halibut with chanterelles. Venison steak in rowan jelly sauce. Mountain hare and ceps. Apple-stuffed pheasant breast with Calvados sauce. Black and white chocolate truffle cake. Banana baked pudding with a rum and caramel sauce.
STB Highly Commended 3 Crowns
Credit cards: 1, 2, 3, 5
Proprietors: Eric Hart & Ian Kirk

MUCKRACH LODGE HOTEL
Dulnain Bridge, Grantown-on-Spey
Morayshire PH26 3LY
Tel: 01479 851257
Fax: 01479 851325

On A938, ½ mile west of Dulnain Bridge.
This traditionally built former shooting lodge stands in its own ten secluded acres, adjacent to the Dulnain River. Muckrach Lodge is a good example of Victorian design and comfort. It is tastefully furnished and has a warm welcoming atmosphere. Guests may relax with a drink by the log fire in the elegantly furnished cocktail bar before dining in the Garden Conservatory Restaurant, where the emphasis is on the best of local produce and friendly efficient service. Both table d'hôte and à la carte dinners are offered complemented by an extensive wine list. All rooms have colour TV, telephone, tea/coffee-making facilities and are fully centrally heated. There is also a special suite for accompanied disabled persons.
Open all year except Nov
Rooms: 12 with private facilities
Bar Lunch 12 – 2 pm (a)
Dining Room/Restaurant Lunch 12 – 2 pm (b)
Dinner 7.30 – 9 pm (d) 5 course menu
Facilities for disabled visitors
Bed & Breakfast £41 – £54
Special Rates available
• Aberdeen Angus steaks. Lightly grilled wild Spey salmon with herb butter sauce. Galette of Highland venison and pheasant coated with a juniper berry and red wine sauce. Crab, asparagus and grapefruit fillets served with a seasonal salad and new boiled potatoes. Poached baby oranges in a Chablis and mint syrup. Lunch: Muckrach 'substantial' sandwiches and chef's hot dishes.
STB Highly Commended 4 Crowns
Credit cards: 1, 2, 3, 5, 6 + SWITCH, DELTA
Proprietors: Roy & Pat Watson

Dumfries

CAIRNDALE HOTEL

English Street, Dumfries
Dumfriesshire DG1 2DF
Tel: 01387 54111
Fax: 01387 50555

Situated on the old A75 route running through the centre of Dumfries.

This well established family run hotel has a prime location in the centre of the town. It has grown in size and reputation over recent years and now offers all the facilities and services to be expected of one of the region's leading three star hotels. All rooms have private bathrooms, TV, radio, direct dial telephone, hairdryer and hospitality tray as standard, while the executive rooms and suites have queen size double beds. mini-bars, trouser presses and jacuzzi spa baths. To top all that there is a leisure centre – the Barracuda Club – with heated indoor swimming pool, sauna, steam room, gymnasium and toning table salon. Overlooking the pool is the Forum continental cafe bar with its tempting array of pastries, cakes and scones. A carvery menu is available in Sawney Bean's restaurant which is named after the last cannibal in south west Scotland! In the main dining room there is a wide selection of dishes on à la carte and table d'hôte menus featuring local produce and delicacies.

Open all year
Rooms: 76 with private facilities
Bar Lunch 12 – 2 pm (a)
Restaurant Lunch (Sawney Bean's) 12 – 2 pm (a)
Bar Supper 7 – 9 pm (a)
Dinner (Carvery) 7 – 10 pm (b)
Dinner 7 – 9.30 pm (c)
Bed & Breakfast £40 – £80
Dinner B & B £55 – £70
Special Rates available
• Solway smoked mackerel fillet with a crunchy apple salad. Roast rib of Galloway beef with a caper and mushroom wine sauce. Pot roast haunch of venison served with a port wine jus and fresh raspberries. Poached suprême of salmon set on a Noilly Prat cream sauce with fresh langoustines.
STB Commended 5 Crowns
Credit cards: 1, 2, 3, 5
Proprietors: The Wallace Family

STATION HOTEL

Lovers Walk, Dumfries
Dumfriesshire DG1 1LT
Tel: 01387 54316
Fax: 01387 50388

Just outside town centre opposite railway station.

This imposing old red sandstone building has undergone refurbishment in recent years but many of the hallmarks of a typical 19th century station hotel still remain such as ornate cornices and ceilings in some of its public rooms. The spacious and elegant dining room has been tastefully decorated to retain the charm of its original style. For more informal eating there is a bistro with stone floor tiles, patio style tables and beamed ceilings. In addition the lounge bar is a comfortable meeting place at any time of day for a drink or a snack. The à la carte menu in the dining room has some very enterprising dishes, while the cafe bar bistro menu restricts itself to popular demand snacks and pasta.

Open all year except 25 + 26 Dec, 2 + 3 Jan
Rooms: 32 with private facilities
Bar Lunch 12 – 2 pm (a)
Bar Supper 5 – 10 pm (a)
Dinner 7 – 9.30 pm (b)
Taste of Scotland applies to main restaurant only
No smoking area in restaurant
Bed & Breakfast £30 – £65
Dinner B & B £40 – £45
Special Weekend Rates available
• Tartlet of prawns in a creamy ginger sauce. Locally made haggis served on warm oatcakes. Sirloin steak in a sauce with mushrooms flavoured with Drambuie. Sea bass and salmon plait on a fennel and asparagus sauce. Selection of Scottish cheeses.
STB Commended 4 Crowns
Credit cards: 1, 2, 3, 5 + SWITCH, DELTA

Dunbar

THE COURTYARD HOTEL & RESTAURANT

Woodbush Brae, Dunbar
East Lothian EH42 1HB
Tel: 01368 864169

From A1 take A1087 to Dunbar. At south end of High Street, take road towards seashore.

The water washes against the walls of what were once traditional fishermen's cottages which have been sympathetically converted into a pleasant restaurant with rooms. From the large windows in the restaurant on the first floor diners can appreciate an uninterrupted view of the North Sea, giving them the sense of dining on board ship. Self-taught chef/patron, Peter Bramley, and his small brigade have established a good reputation for the high standard of cooking and have gradually built up a regular clientele over the five years since opening. Their menus combine the best of locally procured fresh produce from land, sea and river, with classically prepared sauces. This blend of Scottish/French food is present both at lunchtime and in the evening, complemented by a good sized wine list. The Courtyard is convenient for the railway station at Dunbar, which is only 20 minutes by train from Edinburgh (and 28 miles by road). The hotel is right in the heart of golf country and ideally placed for touring the Border country with its wild and beautiful coastline.

Open all year except Christmas Day night
Rooms: 7, 2 with private facilities
Dining Room/Restaurant Lunch 12 – 2 pm (a)
Dinner 7 – 9.30 pm (b)
No smoking in restaurant
Bed & Breakfast £26.50 – £45.50
Dinner B & B £41.50 – £60.50
Special Rates available
• Minted cucumber cheesecake served with salad. Pan-fried fillet of pork with a wild mushroom sauce. Rib eye steak with a Madeira sauce. Noisettes of local lamb. Medley of salmon trout, lemon sole, langoustine and scallops served in a light saffron sauce. Traditional bread and butter pudding with cream. Poached peach served on home-made ice-cream with a fresh strawberry coulis.
STB Commended 2 Crowns
Credit cards: 1, 2, 3, 5
Proprietor: Peter W Bramley

Dunblane

Location 76

CROMLIX HOUSE
Kinbuck, by Dunblane
Perthshire FK15 9JT
Tel: 01786 822125
Fax: 01786 825450

Off A9, B8033 to Kinbuck, through village, cross narrow bridge, drive is second on left. From Crieff A822 to Braco, then B8033 Kinbuck.

One of Scotland's finest country houses, Cromlix stands within its own 5,000 acre estate and is easily accessible from Perth, Edinburgh, Glasgow. Built in 1874, the house is steeped in history and full of antiques. It retains the informal welcome and atmosphere of a well loved home, making it a comfortable house in which to relax. The six rooms and eight spacious suites are all delightfully individual. There is a feeling of space and comfort throughout, with three public rooms, three dining rooms, and a conservatory. Cromlix even has its own private chapel which is suitable for weddings. David and Ailsa Assenti came to Cromlix about two years ago with their Head Chef Stephen Robertson. His young kitchen team produce delicious and imaginative meals for the daily changing menus featuring the best of fresh produce for the discriminating palate. Cromlix is a uniquely pleasurable experience.

Open all year except mid Jan to mid Feb
Rooms: 14 with private facilities
Light Lunch & Snacks 12.30 – 1.30 pm (a-b)
Dining Room Lunch 12.30 – 1.15 pm: Sun Sat only Oct to Mar (d)
Dinner 7 – 8.30 pm (f) 5 course menu
No smoking in dining rooms
Bed & Breakfast £50 – £100 Oct to Mar: £70 – £120 Apr to Sep
Dinner B & B £85 – £135 Oct to Mar: £105 – £155 Apr to Oct
Special Rates for 2+ nights Oct to Mar
• Poached Tay salmon crowned with mushroom duxelle and hollandaise over a herb cream sauce. Cutlets of Perthshire lamb with a garlic and savoy cabbage crust flavoured with a shallot and rosemary reduction. Hot lemon tart with a raspberry water-ice presented on a lime sauce anglaise.
STB Deluxe 4 Crowns
Credit cards: 1, 2, 3, 5, 6
Proprietors: David & Ailsa Assenti

STAKIS DUNBLANE HYDRO
Perth Road, Dunblane
Perthshire FK15 0HG
Tel: 01786 822551 • Telex: 776284
Fax: 01786 825403

At northern exit (B8033) from Dunblane.

Built in 1878 as a hydropathic, this splendid Victorian hotel has been extended, modernised and refurbished to a high standard. High on a hill on the fringe of the town, it commands wonderful views across the countryside and has some 44 acres of private mature policies. It is a popular conference centre but also attracts much family trade. There are extensive leisure facilities, both indoors and outdoors, and regular entertainment.

Open all year
Rooms: 219 with private facilities
Dining Room/Restaurant Lunch 12.30 – 2 pm (a-b)
Dinner 6.30 – 9.30 pm (c)
No smoking area in restaurant
Bed & Breakfast £31.50 – £39.50
Dinner B & B £41.50 – £49.50
• Terrine of pheasant served with a bramble coulis. Roast best end of lamb with a garlic and herb crust served with a red wine jus. Whole baked trout with flaked almonds and lemon butter. Roast sirloin of beef with a pickled walnut sauce. Suprême of grilled salmon with a lemon and dill hollandaise.
STB Commended 4 Crowns
Credit cards: 1, 2, 3, 5

Dundee

Location 77

THE OLD MANSION HOUSE HOTEL
Auchterhouse
by Dundee DD3 0QN
Tel: 0182 626 366

Take A923 out of Dundee to Muirhead, then B954 for 2 miles – hotel entrance on left.

A most attractive 16th century baronial house which has been tastefully converted into a delightful small luxury hotel. Set in 10 acres of beautiful gardens and woodland, the house is steeped in Scottish history having, at different times, been in the hands of the Ogilvies, the Strathmores and the Earls of Buchan. A heavy wooden door leads into the vaulted entrance hall with its flagstone floor. From here rises the stairway to the main reception area. On the first floor are the library bar with lots of interesting old books and the

restaurant which was originally the drawing room of the house. Good quality crystal and china enhance the atmosphere of this room with its very ornate ceiling and huge old Jacobean fireplace. Menus are reasonably priced and indicative of locally procured produce with interesting sauces.

Open 6 Jan to 25 Dec
Rooms: 6 with private facilities
Bar Lunch 12 – 1.50 pm (a)
Dining Room/Restaurant Lunch 12.30 – 1.50 pm (b)
Bar Supper 7 – 9.20 pm (b)
Dinner 7 – 9.20 pm (d)
No smoking in restaurant
Bed & Breakfast £50 – £80
• Arbroath smokie terrine lined with smoked salmon served with a lemon cream. Roast loin of lamb on a Madeira sauce with mixed capsicums. Medallions of venison with a wild mushroom and artichoke cream sauce. Pan-fried entrecôte steak with a pink peppercorn and onion sauce. Poached escalope of salmon with an orange and pink grapefruit sauce.
STB Highly Commended 4 Crowns
Credit cards: 1, 2, 3, 5, 6 + SWITCH
Proprietors: Nigel & Eva Bell

THE SANDFORD COUNTRY HOUSE HOTEL
Newton Hill
Wormit, nr Dundee
Fife DD6 8RG
Tel: 01382 541802
Fax: 01382 542136

Near to B946 junction with A914 route which links Forth Road Bridge, Edinburgh, with Tay Bridge, Dundee.

The Sandford is a Listed country house of fine architectural beauty which was built at the turn of the century for the Valentine family of Dundee. It is set in attractive gardens within seven acres of private grounds. In these most tranquil surroundings the atmosphere of the country house prevails. A programme of refurbishment carried out during 1994 has enhanced the fine interior of the building. All the public areas have been upgraded as have the bedrooms. In the tastefully appointed dining room, fresh flowers, fine table linen and quality place settings set the scene for a most enjoyable dining experience. There are a lot of innovative touches in the range of dishes presented making full use of good local ingredients and seasonally available specialities. A comprehensive wine list has been carefully selected to complement the menu. Naturally the skills of the kitchen team are displayed to full advantage in the dining room, but they are just as evident in the interesting selection of dishes available in the bar. The hotel manages neighbouring Newton Hill Country Sports and can arrange clay pigeon shooting, four by four off the road driving and fly-fishing for trout. German, Italian and some Japanese spoken.

Open all year except 4 to 6 Jan
Rooms: 16 with private facilities
Bar Lunch 12 – 2.30 pm (a)
Dining Room/Restaurant Lunch 12 – 2.30 pm (a)
Bar Supper 6 – 9.30 pm (a)
Dinner 7 – 9.30 pm (c)
No smoking in restaurant
Facilities for disabled visitors
Bed & Breakfast £40 – £60
Dinner B & B from £57.50
• Crail crab soup with prawn dumplings fresh herbs and a little cream. Fillet of salmon roasted in a nut brown balsamic butter with fresh pasta, spring onion, coriander and chilli. Medallion of beef fillet with shredded horseradish in a claret sauce. Fillet of rock turbot in a potato crust with basil and whole grain Arran mustard.
STB Highly Commended 4 Crowns
Credit cards: 1, 2, 3 + SWITCH

THE SHAFTESBURY HOTEL & RACHEL'S RESTAURANT
1 Hyndford Street, Dundee
Angus DD1 1HQ
Tel: 01382 669216
Fax: 01382 641598

West end of Dundee, off A90 (formerly A85) Perth-Dundee. Follow signs Sinderins and University.
This red sandstone former 'Jute Baron's' mansion was built in 1870. The building was sympathetically renovated and converted by the present owners in 1990 to create a fine town house hotel still retaining many of the original features. A Victorian sampler dated 1890 stitched by Rachel Robertson Buist was found during the renovations, and this is where the hotel's restaurant gets its name. Rachel's is an attractive room with a

thoughtful blend of the old and the new, and a good reputation for its food. Restaurant menus offer a good selection of flavoursome dishes, 'something tasty' being the motto.

Open all year
Rooms: 12 with private facilities
Bar Supper 5 – 9 pm except Sun (a)
Dinner 7 – 9 pm except Sun (b)
Residents only Sun
No smoking in restaurant
Bed & Breakfast £34 – £49.50
Dinner B & B £48.50 – £64
Special Rates available
• Arbroath smokie soup. Smoked salmon pâté. Home-made haddock and sole fish cakes served with a spicy tomato sauce. Baked escalope of chicken filled with haggis, served with home-made crab apple jelly and a butter and cream sauce with strips of vegetables. Collops of beef fillet with sauté of onions, a little chicken liver pâté, wrapped in puff pastry, served with a mushroom sauce.
STB Highly Commended 3 Crowns
Credit cards: 1, 2, 3, 5, 6
Proprietor: Dennis H Smith

SOUTH KINGENNIE HOUSE RESTAURANT
Kellas, by Broughty Ferry
Dundee DD5 1BJ
Tel: 0182 625 562

From A92 Dundee-Arbroath, take B978 to Kellas then road to Drumsturdy to signpost for South Kingennie, 2 miles.
A converted Scottish farmhouse now operating as a lounge bar and licensed restaurant. It is owned and run by Peter and Jill Robinson whose high standards are demonstrated in the elegance of the restaurant with its fine linen and fresh flowers. Menus are well balanced and imaginative and utilise to the full the pick of fresh market and local produce, to give value for money meals in a friendly relaxed atmosphere. Peter's skills in the kitchen are well matched by his wife's caring supervision of the front of the house.

Open all year except last wk Jan + first wk Feb
Dining Room/Restaurant Lunch 12 – 2 pm except Mon (b)
Dinner 7 – 9 pm except Sun Mon (c)
Closed Sun evening + Mon
Facilities for disabled visitors
• Baked fillets of sole finished with smoked salmon and lemon sauce. Sirloin steak seasoned with garlic, served with Madeira sauce and shallots.

Medallions of venison haunch finished with burgundy sauce and bacon. Loin of new season lamb glazed with mint hollandaise. Fillets of Scottish salmon with vermouth sauce, tomato and cucumber.
Credit cards: 1, 3, 6 + SWITCH
Proprietors: Peter & Jill Robinson

STRATHDON HOTEL
277 Perth Road, Dundee
Tayside DD2 1JS
Tel: 01382 65648

On main Perth road, in Dundee's west end – close to Ninewells Hospital, Dundee Airport and the University.
The Strathdon Hotel is in an attractive Edwardian terrace and many of its rooms enjoy delightful views over the River Tay. It is personally run by chef/proprietor Ian Hornsby and his wife, Carole, who take pride in ensuring their guests are made to feel welcome and at home during their stay. There is a cosy and comfortable little lounge for guests to relax in. The Strathdon's popular restaurant has gained a reputation for exceptional cuisine using fresh local produce, complemented by a fine selection of wines.

Open all year except Christmas Day + 1 Jan
Rooms: 10 with private facilities
Dinner 7 – 8.30 pm except Sun (c)
Restricted Hotel Licence
No dogs
No smoking in restaurant
Bed & Breakfast £24 – £35
Dinner B & B £41 – £52
• Game parfait presented in a casket of puff pastry on a warm sherry and sesame seed vinaigrette. Gigot chop of new season lamb pan-fried in rosemary butter, presented on a minted tarragon sauce and topped with croûtons, grapes and mushrooms. Terrine of smoked salmon, lemon sole and spinach with dill flavoured mayonnaise.
STB Commended 3 Crowns
Credit cards: 1, 3
Proprietors: Ian & Carole Hornsby

Dundonnell

Location 78

DUNDONNELL HOTEL

Dundonnell, by Garve
Ross-shire IV23 2QR
Tel: 01854 633204
Fax: 01854 633366

On A832 south of Ullapool.
The Florence family have been running this acclaimed hotel for over 30 years and during that time it has grown both in size and in reputation. It is set by the shores of Little Loch Broom, right on the roadside midway between Ullapool and Gairloch, on a splendidly remote and spectacular route. The hotel is very comfortably equipped with high standards of furnishings and decor throughout. It is an ideal place from which to explore and enjoy the local hills and glens as well as better known attractions such as Inverewe Gardens. The menus offer an excellent selection of dishes, are well balanced with a lot of original touches, and represent good value. This is a hotel that attracts lots of repeat business from satisfied guests.
Open 1 Mar to 22 Nov + Christmas/ New Year
Rooms: 24 with private facilities
Bar Lunch 12 – 2.15 pm (b)
Bar Supper 6 – 8.15 pm (b)
Dinner 7 – 8.30 pm (d)
Bed & Breakfast £32.50 – £46
Dinner B & B £55 – £66
Special Rates for 3+ nights
• Crab and scallop patties rolled in sesame seeds on an Arran mustard sauce. Poached escalope of Ardessie salmon topped by a vermouth sorrel sauce and garnished with a julienne of cucumber and trout caviar. Tenderloin of lamb marinated with fresh thyme and garlic, sauted and presented with a provençal tartlet. Sirloin steak with a wholegrain mustard sauce.
STB Highly Commended 4 Crowns
Credit cards: 1, 3, 6 + SWITCH, DELTA
Proprietors: Selbie & Flora Florence

Dunfermline

Location 79

DAVAAR HOUSE HOTEL & RESTAURANT

126 Grieve Street, Dunfermline
Fife KY12 8DW
Tel: 01383 721886/735365

From M90 Junction 3 to Dunfermline, follow A907 Kincardine into Carnegie Drive. Right into Chalmers Street, then second left to Grieve Street.
This fine old house is over 100 years old and still retains the splendid oak staircase and elaborate ornate ceiling cornices that were such a feature of the Victorian period. It is now a comfortably furnished and tastefully decorated small hotel, with eight en suite bedrooms and a pleasingly relaxed and informal atmosphere. Doreen Jarvis' skill in the kitchen is demonstrated in the excellent variety and style of her cooking and is augmented by having a husband who is a local greengrocer and florist and ensures that she is supplied with really fresh produce from the market and local growers.
Open all year except Christmas Day, 26 + 31 Dec, 1 Jan
Rooms: 8 with private facilities
Dining Room/Restaurant Lunch (b) – by appointment
Supper 6 – 8.30 pm except Sun (b): High Tea 4 – 6.30 pm Sun (a)

Dinner 7 – 8.30 pm except Sun (c)
Restricted Licence
No dogs
Facilities for disabled visitors
No smoking in restaurant
Bed & Breakfast £25 – £36
Dinner B & B £40 – £50
Room Rate £48 – £55
Special Weekend Rates available
• Home-made cream of mushroom soup. Grilled sirloin steak served with pepper sauce and mushrooms. Roast rack of spring lamb served with fresh rosemary, mint sauce and carrot florets. Grilled local trout stuffed with prawns and rice, garnished with lemon. Spring rhubarb and ginger pie.
STB Commended 3 Crowns
Credit cards: 1, 3
Proprietors: Jim & Doreen Jarvis

Dunkeld

Location 80

ROYAL DUNKELD HOTEL

Atholl Street, Dunkeld
Perthshire PH8 0AR
Tel: 01350 727322
Fax: 01350 728989

From A9 follow signs for Dunkeld. Over Telford's Bridge, hotel in prominent position on Atholl Street.
The famous Telford Bridge spanning the river at Dunkeld was completed in 1809 and so was the Royal Dunkeld Hotel. This former coaching inn, extended many times over nearly two centuries, is now a comfortable hotel with recently refurbished bedrooms which are attractive and well equipped. An enthusiastic and innovative chef produces some excellent food and is constantly striving to keep his menus interesting and inviting. In addition to the restaurant there is the informal Gargoyles bistro lounge. The little cathedral town of Dunkeld is a haven for golf enthusiasts with numerous courses within easy reach, and is also a splendidly central point for many of the other attractions of Perthshire.
Open all year
Rooms: 35 with private facilities
Bar Lunch 12 – 2.30 pm (a)
Dining Room/Restaurant Lunch 12 – 2.30 pm (b)
Bar Supper 5 – 9.30 pm (a)
Dinner 7 – 9.30 pm (c)
No pipes or cigars in restaurant
Facilities for disabled visitors
Bed & Breakfast £30 – £45

Credit Card Code		Meal Price Range	
1.	Access/Mastercard/Eurocard	(a)	under £10
2.	American Express	(b)	£10 – £15
3.	Visa	(c)	£15 – £20
4.	Carte Bleu	(d)	£20 – £25
5.	Diners Club	(e)	£25 – £30
6.	Mastercharge	(f)	over £30

Special Rates available

• Home-made carrot, leek and mustard soup garnished with a cheese and almond crouton. Poached white fish stuffed with fresh langoustine tails with a fish and fresh herb cream reduction. Rack of Scottish lamb with a mint pesto sauce and a potato and courgette gâteau. Home-made chocolate and orange sponge pudding with a hot vanilla and coffee sauce.

STB Commended 3 Crowns
Credit cards: 1, 2, 3, 5 + SWITCH
Proprietors: Graham & Ann Rees

STAKIS DUNKELD HOUSE HOTEL
Dunkeld
Perthshire PH8 0HX
Tel: 01350 727771 • Telex: 76657
Fax: 01350 728924

A9 to Dunkeld, hotel lies c. 1 mile east of village.

Pass through the old gatehouse and follow the elegant drive winding through the trees, and you come to Dunkeld House. Built originally for the seventh Duke of Atholl, this old Edwardian house has been carefully extended and is now a combination of luxury hotel and country house but with a touch of originality and individuality. The hotel sits in beautifully kept lawns and garden within its own 280 acre estate on the banks of the River Tay, one of Scotland's finest salmon rivers, and has a private two mile salmon beat. This is also a haven for bird-watchers and walkers. The excellent leisure centre has a heated indoor pool among its many facilities, and there are all-weather tennis courts, a croquet lawn and clay pigeon shooting. The dining room offers a good choice of interesting dishes on its menus which will meet the requirement of the most discerning diner. It should be noted that during the quiet season the dining room is not always available at lunchtime, but the quality of the bar lunch menu makes it a good alternative.

Open all year
Rooms: 92 with private facilities
Bar Lunch 12 – 2 pm (a)
Dining Room/Restaurant Lunch 12 – 2 pm (b)
Dinner 7 – 9.30 pm (d)
Bed & Breakfast £56 – £82.50
Dinner B & B £73 – £95.50
Room Rate £92 – £139
Special Rates available

• Timbale of smoked trout mousse with strips of smoked salmon with a lemon and dill dressing. Fillet of lemon sole

filled with a seafood mousse, served with a chive butter sauce. Pork fillet with woodland mushrooms and brandy sauce. Casserole of Highland game with a burgundy and shallot sauce.

STB Highly Commended 5 Crowns
Credit cards: 1, 2, 3, 5

Dunoon

Location 81

ARDFILLAYNE HOTEL
Beverley's Restaurant
Bullwood Road, Dunoon
Argyll PA23 7QJ
Tel: 01369 2267
Fax: 01369 2501

At west end of Dunoon (A815).

Ardfillayne sits in its own beautiful gardens, perched on a hill on the outskirts of the town, and is a country house with a difference. The hotel is furnished in the style and grandeur of a bygone age with a fine collection of antique furniture and clocks, conveying an air of enduring quality. Beverley's Restaurant continues the theme with lace tablecloths, candlelight reflecting on polished silver and glassware, and fresh flowers. There is quite an extensive menu presenting a clever combination of classical French dishes and a selection of the best traditional Scottish recipes for the local game, seafood and beef so readily available. The high standard of food is well supported by a fine wine list.

Open all year
Rooms: 8 with private facilities
Dinner 7 – 9 pm (d)
Restaurant closed Sun evening in winter
No smoking in restaurant
Bed & Breakfast £35 – £45
Dinner B & B £58 – £68

• Fresh oysters. Smoked salmon. Broccoli and almond soup. Roast marinated wild boar. Sliced fillet of Aberdeen Angus beef. Grilled wild salmon and parsley butter.

STB Deluxe 4 Crowns
Credit cards: 1, 2, 3, 5
Proprietors: Bill & Beverley McCaffrey

CHATTERS
58 John Street, Dunoon
Argyll PA23 8BJ
Tel: 01369 6402

On John Street, Dunoon, opposite the cinema.

Chatters continues to go from strength to strength and is now firmly established as a premier restaurant in Dunoon. A traditional cottage has been imaginatively converted to create this charming little restaurant with its relaxed and friendly atmosphere. The great success of Chatters stems both from the consistently excellent standard of the food and from the welcoming care and attention given to guests. The team of young chefs in the kitchen are a credit to their profession. There is great emphasis in the menus on fresh ingredients and herbs, and some interesting combinations of food. In the front of house, Rosemary MacInnes displays all the qualities of quiet charm and efficiency that set her restaurant apart. Chatters is deservedly popular for lunches and people drop in for a light snack or coffee etc during the day. There is even a little patio with tables for sitting outdoors on good days. A leisurely evening meal is a memorable experience, in the category of 'serious eating'. Booking is advisable.

Open 17 Feb to 31 Dec except Christmas Day
Bar Lunch 12 – 2.30 pm except Sun (b)
Dining Room/Restaurant Lunch 12 – 2.30 pm except Sun (c)
Bar Supper 6 – 10 pm except Sun (b)
Dinner 6 – 9.30 pm except Sun (c)
Closed Sun
Table Licence
Smoking discouraged

• Warm tartlet of wild mushrooms on a Stilton and asparagus sauce. Baked breast of Guinea fowl and mango on a bed of honey and ginger glazed carrot ribbons on a natural jus. Fillet of Loch Fyne salmon, topped with a mousseline of scallops, wrapped in puff pastry. Collops of Scottish beef with pickled walnuts and wild mushroom dumpling with a juniper and port wine reduction.

Credit cards: 1, 3
Proprietor: Rosemary Anne MacInnes

ENMORE HOTEL

Marine Parade, Kirn
Dunoon
Argyll PA23 8HH
Tel: 01369 2230
Fax: 01369 2148

On seafront near Hunters Quay ferry, on road to Dunoon.

Originally built as a Summer house for a rich cotton merchant, Enmore occupies a splendid location with commanding views across the Firth of Clyde. It has all the charm of a Georgian country house and has been beautifully furnished by Angela and David Wilson. The Victorian dining room is light and airy, with original ceilings and features. It is attractively laid out with fine linen, china, crystal and silver. There may not be a wide choice on the menu but that has its advantages in that what is offered changes daily to reflect the best of produce available. There is every evidence that the food here is prepared with great skill and presented with professional flair, and this has earned the Enmore an AA Rosette. The hotel's own garden contributes to the fresh herbs and vegetables, and the fine produce for which Argyll and Loch Fyne are noted feature regularly on the menu.

Open all year except Christmas wk
Rooms: 10 with private facilities
Bar Lunch 12 – 3 pm (a)
Dining Room/Restaurant Lunch 12 – 3 pm (b)
Bar Supper 6 – 9.30 pm (b)
Dinner 7.30 – 9.30 pm (d)
Bed & Breakfast £30 – £70
Dinner B & B £55 – £85
Special Rates for 2+ to 7+ nights
• Warm salad of wild mushrooms with balsamic dressing. Argyll smoked venison. Salmon en papillote. Roast gigot of lamb with garden mint sauce. Monkfish cooked in white wine and served with a green sauce.
STB Highly Commended 4 Crowns
Credit cards: 1, 3
Proprietors: David & Angela Wilson

Edinburgh

Location 82

ATRIUM

10 Cambridge Street
Edinburgh EH1 2ED
Tel: 0131 228 8882

Within Saltire Court, at entrance to Traverse Theatre, adjacent to Usher Hall. From the day it opened the Atrium has attracted a great deal of favourable comment from the critics and now in its second year it has established itself as one of the city's foremost eating places. Indeed the restaurant achieved high national recognition when in July 1994 Andrew Radford was presented with the Caterer & Hotelkeeper's Catey Award for British Newcomer of the Year. Located on the ground floor of Saltire Court, The Atrium is decidedly different both in style and concept. Chef/patron Andrew Radford's approach to cooking is distinctive, lifting food out of the ordinary to create the exceptional. His ever-increasing circle of devoted patrons expect, and get, a special eating experience. In addition to the small à la carte menu which changes twice daily, a snack menu option is available at lunchtime and there are plans to introduce this for pre- and post-theatre eating in the evening.

Open all year except 1 wk Christmas
Dining Room/Restaurant Lunch 12 – 2.30 pm except Sun Sat (b)
Dinner 6 – 10.30 pm except Sun (d)
Closed Sun
• Crab cake with lemon butter. Scallops, noodles, asparagus and tomato concasse. Grilled sea bream with salsa and leek, with a parmesan gratin. Pan-fried Guinea fowl with root vegetables and tarragon. Baked salmon with spinach, roquette and mustard vinaigrette. Filo pastry of goats cheese with tomato and frisée salad. Tart of raspberries with raspberry sorbet.
Credit cards: 1, 2, 3 + SWITCH, DELTA
Proprietors: Andrew & Lisa Radford

THE BALMORAL HOTEL
EDINBURGH

1 Princes Street, Edinburgh EH2 2EQ
Tel: 0131 556 2414 • Telex: 727282
Fax: 0131 557 3747

Princes Street at corner of North Bridge. The Balmoral is a grand and impressive building which stands at the eastern end of the capital's famous Princes Street. Almost equally famous is the hotel's clock tower, one of the prominent landmarks of the city. Much of the bedroom accommodation has uninterrupted views across the gardens to Edinburgh Castle and along the mile long length of Princes Street, as indeed do many of the fine public rooms and function suites. The hotel has its own leisure club which is available to resident guests. No 1 Princes Street Restaurant is strikingly different in decor and furnishing. Sumptuous and elegant it has the dignified and calm atmosphere of a luxury club and makes a wonderful retreat from the bustle of the city. Executive Chef Billy Campbell was appointed during the last year and has already made his mark. Menus have lots of original touches and combinations, offering a fine selection of dishes beautifully prepared and presented. The restaurant staff provide first class service, are well trained and unobtrusive in their manner. A more informal style of eating is available in The Bridges which is a continental-style brasserie on the ground floor with all day service of light meals and snacks. NB's Bar has now been extended and makes a good venue for a bar lunch. The Palm Court off the main foyer is a pleasant setting for morning coffee and afternoon tea, and in the evening guests may relax over a drink while the pianist plays.

Open all year
Rooms: 189 with private facilities
Bar Lunch (NB's Bar) 12 – 2.30 pm (a)
Brasserie (Bridges) food served all day (b-d)
Dining Room/Restaurant Lunch (No 1 Princes St) 12 – 2.15 pm except Sun Sat (c-d)
Dinner (No 1 Princes St) 7 – 10.30 pm (f)
Guide dogs only
Facilities for disabled visitors
No smoking area in restaurants
Bed & Breakfast from £64
Dinner B & B from £89
Room Rate from £120
Special Rates available for Weekends/2+ nights
• NB's Bar: roast rib of Angus beef

served in a bap. Bridges: duo of smoked halibut and salmon on a scallion and lime crème fraîche. No 1 Princes St: grilled Oban scallops served with a broad bean salad and lardons of crispy bacon. Noisettes of Scottish lamb with a Lanark Blue cheese sauce. Suprême of River Tay salmon with a sharp fresh rhubarb sauce.
STB Deluxe 5 Crowns
Credit cards: 1, 2, 3, 5, 6 + SWITCH, DELTA

CALEDONIAN HOTEL
Princes Street
Edinburgh EH1 2AB
Tel: 0131 225 2433 • Telex: 72179
Fax: 0131 225 6632
Prestige Award Winner 1988 + 1992

West end of Princes Street.
The 'Caley' as it is affectionately known to the citizens of Edinburgh is a monument to grandeur and to the style and quality standards of those who designed and built it at the beginning of the century. This magnificent red sandstone hotel is indeed deserving of its five star status. Elegant public rooms and the grand staircase set the standard for the rest of the hotel. On the first floor is the graciously proportioned Pompadour Restaurant which has views out towards the Castle and is in every way the top choice in eating. The combination of superbly trained staff, imaginative menus and beautifully presented food in this dignified atmosphere certainly make a memorable dining experience. Menus in Carriages Restaurant are in a different price range, the emphasis being on informal dining, but there is no lessening in quality. A traditional Scottish menu is featured together with an informal à la carte which includes a fine range of pasta and other firm favourite dishes. There is also an all day service of coffee, light snacks and afternoon tea available in the comfortable foyer lounge.
Open all year
Rooms: 241 with private facilities
Bar Lunch (Platform 1) 12 – 2 pm except Sun Sat (a)
Lunch (Carriages) 12 – 2.30 pm Mon to Fri: 12.30 – 2.30 Sun (b)
Lunch (Pompadour) 12.30 – 2 pm except Sun Sat (d)
Afternoon Tea (Lounge) 3 – 5.30 pm
Dinner (Carriages) 7 – 10 pm (d)
Dinner (Pompadour) 7.30 – 10.30 pm (f)
No smoking area in restaurants
Bed & Breakfast £150 – £185

Dinner B & B £190 – £225
Room Rate £245 – £285
• Carriages: collops of Aberdeen Angus fillet with pickled walnuts and Madeira sauce. Stew of local seafood with fennel, tomato and saffron. Pompadour: pan-fried Dublin Bay prawns and collops of monkfish served in a filo pastry basket with stir-fried vegetables and grated horseradish and tomato sauce.
STB Highly Commended 5 Crowns
Credit cards: 1, 2, 3, 5, 6

CARLTON HIGHLAND HOTEL
North Bridge
Edinburgh EH1 1SD
Tel: 0131 556 7277
Telex: 727001
Fax: 0131 556 2691

City centre – North Bridge links the east end of Princes Street with the Royal Mile.
The Carlton Highland Hotel is a handsome Victorian building standing proud against the Edinburgh skyline, overlooking Princes Street and the historical Royal Mile. It is well situated for visiting both the old town on the castle side of the city and the 'New Town' which extends north from Princes Street. The building has been cleverly converted to provide almost 200 well furnished bedrooms and suites with every modern comfort, as well as a leisure club, gift shop, hair and beauty salon, patisserie and nightclub. There are two restaurants within the hotel under the experienced hand of Charles Price, a renowned senior Scottish chef. Top of the range is Quills Restaurant designed to give the impression of dining in the tranquil atmosphere of a library in a country house. The innovative menus display the full skill of the kitchen brigade, producing a high standard of food and interesting combinations of seasonal specialities. Or guests may choose the more informal surroundings of the Carlton Court, which offers a carvery style menu.
Open all year
Rooms: 197 with private facilities
Bar Lunch 12 – 2.30 pm except Sun (a)
Dining Room/Restaurant Lunch 12 – 5 pm (b)
Dinner 5 – 10.30 pm (b)
Facilities for disabled visitors
Bed & Breakfast £77 – £99
Dinner B & B £93 – £115
Special Rates for 2+ nights
• Warm lamb fillet and west coast

scallops on a bed of crisp lettuce leaves flavoured with a hint of garlic. Fillet of Scottish salmon served on a tarragon and vermouth cream sauce with saffron noodles. Fillet of beef pan-fried with foie gras and brioche on a Madeira flavoured jus. Lemon tart served warm with a vanilla and citrus sauce.
STB Highly Commended 5 Crowns
Credit cards: 1, 2, 3, 5, 6 + SWITCH

CHANNINGS
South Learmonth Gardens
Edinburgh EH4 1EZ
Tel: 0131 315 2226
Fax: 0131 332 9631

South Learmonth Gardens is parallel to Queensferry Road, a few minutes walk from the west end of Edinburgh city centre.
Channings is something rare today, a privately owned hotel, originally five Edwardian town-houses, where a cosy club-like atmosphere can be found. Considerable restoration of traditional features has been undertaken and the bedrooms have been individually designed. Peaceful lounges provide a retreat from the busy city. In Channings Brasserie, the menus change with the seasons and the selections range from a light lunch to a full evening dinner, all prepared from fresh local produce, emphasising an honest and natural cuisine with both a traditional Scottish and French flavour. The bustling bar offers an interesting range of malt whiskies.
Open all year except 24 to 27 Dec: open Christmas Day for lunch
Rooms: 48 with private facilities
Bar Lunch 12 – 2 pm except Sun (a)
Dining Room/Restaurant Lunch 12.30 – 2 pm except Sat (a)
Dinner 6.30 – 9.30 pm Sun to Thu: 6.30 – 10 pm Fri Sat (b-d)
Bed & Breakfast £82 – £128
Special Weekend Rates available
• A chowder of fine Scottish seafood. Fillet of Aberdeen Angus beef pan-fried with a pickled walnut and Madeira sauce. Pot roasted pheasant on a cabbage parcel with glazed apple and rowan jelly. Braised gigot of mutton with fresh root vegetables and butter beans. Grilled darne of salmon with a savoury dill butter. Caramelised orange and honey brose.
STB Highly Commended 4 Crowns
Credit cards: 1, 2, 3, 5, 6 + SWITCH
Proprietor: Peter Taylor

CRAMOND GALLERY BISTRO

4 Riverside Cramond, Cramond Village
Edinburgh EH4 6NY
Tel: 0131 312 6555

Follow Cramond Glebe Road down to harbour front.

With its narrow wynds, steep steps and huddle of cottages, Cramond still looks the lovely little fishing village it had been for centuries and it is difficult to believe that one is still within the city of Edinburgh. There are even the foundations of a Roman fort clearly visible alongside Cramond Kirk. This is a popular spot with locals and visitors alike and so the quayside is a good location for Alan and Evelyn Bogue to have established their charming little bistro which looks across the mouth of the River Almond to the Firth of Forth. Low timbered ceilings evoke the atmosphere of this traditional old 16th century building, built on the foundations of a second century Roman boatshed. Somewhat naturally the menu specialises in the east coast's excellent fish and shellfish but there is also a good choice of meat and game dishes according to the season. A recent addition is the availability of four luxury self-catering cottage apartments all with waterfront seascape views.

Open all year except Christmas Day
Dining Room/Restaurant Lunch 12 – 2.30 pm (a-b)
Afternoon Tea
Dinner 6.30 – 9.30 pm (d)
Note: closed Mon Tue from Oct to Jun
Unlicensed – guests welcome to take own wine
No smoking in restaurant
• Baked turbot with a dill and cream coulis. Lemon sole with an orange stuffing. Lobster. Freshwater crayfish tails with saffron rice. Medallions of roast lamb with port wine and cranberry cream. Mushroom and leek flan. Parsnip and apple casserole.
No credit cards
Proprietors: Alan & Evelyn Bogue

CRANNOG SCOTTISH SEAFOOD RESTAURANT

14 South St Andrew Street
Edinburgh EH2 2AZ
Tel: 0131 557 5589
Fax: 0131 558 3067

City centre between St Andrew Square and Princes Street, opposite Waverley Market.

Edinburgh at last has its own Crannog Restaurant. This is the third in Scotland, following on the success of the award winning original in Fort Willliam and the Glasgow restaurant. Each has its own character by the nature of the buildings in which they are located, but all are based on the same general principle – to offer the finest and freshest seafood in simple friendly surroundings. The Crannog in Edinburgh occupies a ground floor and basement between Princes Street and St Andrew Square. The ground floor is set out with rustic pine furniture for the self-service seafood and salad bar, but will also be open for coffees, afternoon teas etc. The restaurant itself is situated in the basement. A specially commissioned series of oil paintings by Alistair Smyth adorn the walls. There is a local Fort William focus in the characters featured and they seem to depict the Crannog philosophy, linking the fishermen and the produce of the sea with the chef and the restaurant. In the tranquil atmosphere you would hardly guess you were right in the city centre. The food lives up to expectation and is consistently good.

Open all year except Christmas Day + 1 Jan
Self service (ground floor) 10 am – 7 pm (a)
Dining Room/Restaurant Lunch 12 – 2.30 pm (b)
Dinner 6 – 10.30 pm (c)
• Langoustines with garlic butter. Salmon collops with fresh sorrel. Skate with dark vinegar butter and capers. Crannog special seafood platter. Chocolate marquise. Scottish farmhouse cheeses.
Credit cards: 1, 2, 3 + SWITCH, DELTA

DALMAHOY HOTEL COUNTRY CLUB RESORT

Kirknewton
nr Edinburgh EH27 8EB
Tel: 0131 333 1845
Fax: 0131 335 3203

On A71 Edinburgh-Kilmarnock, 7 miles from Edinburgh city centre.

Dalmahoy with its two challenging golf courses is well known to the golfing fraternity but this is now a much more sophisticated and extensive country club with superb hotel and leisure facilities. Delightfully situated in rolling acres of grassland, trees and little lochs, with views of Edinburgh Castle, it is little more than 15 minutes from the city centre or the airport. The hotel has pleasant and comfortable public rooms as well as conference rooms. The Pentland Restaurant is set on two levels allowing all those dining to appreciate the views. This is an elegant room with stately regency columns and yet a comfortable and relaxing atmosphere in which to enjoy a quality dining experience. The standard of food presentation is high and carefully compiled menus indicate the expertise and skill in the kitchen. Executive Chef Gary Bates was the overall winner of the 1994 Taste of Scotland Scotch Lamb Challenge.

Open all year
Rooms: 115 with private facilities
Bar Meals (Terrace Restaurant) 8 am – 10 pm (b)
Dining Room/Restaurant Lunch 12 – 2 pm except Sat (b)
Dinner 7 – 10 pm Mon to Fri: 7.30 – 10.30 pm Sun Sat (d)
No dogs
Facilities for disabled visitors
Bed & Breakfast £70 – £120
Dinner B & B £83 – £133
Room Rate £115 – £200
Special Rates available
• Galantine of corn fed chicken with vegetables and pistachio nuts. Best end of Scotch lamb with a gâteau of sweet basil stovies. Steamed panache of seafood with a saffron and butter sauce. Roulade of leek and carrot wrapped in spinach and filo pastry, served with a tomato and basil coulis.
STB Commended 5 Crowns
Credit cards: 1, 2, 3, 5

Credit Card Code		Meal Price Range	
1.	Access/Mastercard/Eurocard	(a)	under £10
2.	American Express	(b)	£10 – £15
3.	Visa	(c)	£15 – £20
4.	Carte Bleu	(d)	£20 – £25
5.	Diners Club	(e)	£25 – £30
6.	Mastercharge	(f)	over £30

DUBH PRAIS RESTAURANT
123B High Street
Edinburgh EH1 1SG
Tel: 0131 557 5732
Fax: 0131 557 5732

Edinburgh Royal Mile.
Look out for the sign showing the black pot (dubh prais) or you might miss the entrance to this quaint little restaurant which is a few steps down off the Royal Mile. Chef/proprietor James McWilliams creates interesting dishes using a light and skilled touch and the daily changing menus offer an excellent choice of fresh local produce prepared and presented with care. This cosy intimate cellar restaurant has earned a fine reputation for the high standard of food and the convivial atmosphere. It is indeed popular with both locals and visitors alike so booking is advisable particularly during the Summer season.
Open all year except 2 wks Christmas + 2 wks Easter
Dining Room/Restaurant Lunch 12 – 2 pm Tue to Fri (a)
Dinner 6.30 – 10.30 pm Tue to Sat (c-d)
Closed Sun Mon
• *Light seafood soup flavoured with chilli sauce, garnished with mussels, squid, salmon and smoked haddock. West coast scallops poached in white wine served in a tomato flavoured double cream sauce garnished with smoked salmon. Pan-fried loin of venison served on a honey and rosemary sauce. Medallions of fillet steak in a pickled walnut sauce.*
Credit cards: 1, 2, 3
Proprietors: James & Heather
McWilliams

GEORGE INTER-CONTINENTAL EDINBURGH
George Street
Edinburgh EH3 2PB
Tel: 0131 225 1251
Fax: 0131 226 5644

City centre of Edinburgh.
One of Edinburgh's premier hotels the George Inter-Continental is a long established prestigious hotel with a high reputation. Its central location in the New Town gives it a convenient proximity to the main attractions of the capital. Le Chambertin Restaurant serves the finest of good food in a comfortable and relaxed atmosphere and is a favourite of the business community while the Carvers Table in its lofty pillared grandeur concentrates primarily on traditional roasts. The Clans Bar has a predominantly Scottish theme and exhibits artifacts and curios of the whisky trade. Many of the 195 comfortable bedrooms have superb views over the city.
Open all year
Rooms: 195 with private facilities
Bar Meals 11 am – 10 pm (a)
Restaurant Lunch (Carvers Table) 12 – 2.30 pm (b)
Dining Room/Restaurant Lunch (Chambertin) 12.30 – 2 pm except Sun Sat (d)
Dinner (Carvers Table) 6.30 – 10 pm (b)
Dinner (Chambertin) 7 – 10 pm except Sun (c)
Note: Chambertin closed Sun
No smoking area in restaurant
Bed & Breakfast £45 – £90
Dinner B & B £60 – £105
Room Rate £130 – £180
• *Scottish salmon marinated with lime, peppers and coriander. Carpaccio of Highland venison with a whisky and onion chutney. Grilled peppered tuna steak with Pinot Noir, rainbow rice and plum tomato. Marinated sirloin steak of Aberdeen Angus beef with a ginger-garlic jus and potato gratin.*
STB Commended 5 Crowns
Credit cards: 1, 2, 3, 5, 6

HENDERSON'S SALAD TABLE
94 Hanover Street
Edinburgh EH2 1DR
Tel: 0131 225 2131

2 minutes from Princes Street under Henderson's wholefood shop.
Over 30 years ago, long before vegetarian diets aroused the interest and attention they get today, Henderson's pioneered healthy eating in the city of Edinburgh. In the Salad Bar the emphasis is on wholefoods and vegetarian dishes. There is a continuous buffet of salads, quiches, savouries and sweets, offering innovative and interesting combinations of ingredients. Although vegetarians and vegans naturally gravitate to this restaurant, so do hosts of others who enjoy the lively informal atmosphere. Live music is often a feature in the evenings. In addition Henderson's Bistro Bar – the entrance to which is just round the corner in Thistle Street – also offers vegetarian meals and light bites. There is a selection of wines, some Scottish, and some imported direct from growers who use organic methods.
Open all year except Christmas + Boxing Days, 1 + 2 Jan
Meals served all day from 11.30 am:
open from 8 am
Breakfast 8 – 11.30 am except Sun (a)
Bistro Bar 11 am – 8 pm Mon to Sat: 12 – 8 pm Sun (a)
Lunch 11.30 am – 3 pm except Sun (a)
Dinner 4.30 – 10.15 pm except Sun (a)
Closed Sun except during Edinburgh Festival
Main restaurant areas non-smoking
• *Wide selection of herb teas, wines from growers using organic methods, hand-made bakery items made with stoneground flour, free range eggs.*
Credit cards: 1, 2, 3 + SWITCH
Proprietors: The Henderson Family

THE HOWARD
32/36 Great King Street
Edinburgh EH3 6QH
Tel: 0131 557 3500
Fax: 0131 557 6515

Great King Street is off Dundas Street, the continuation of Hanover Street – 5 minutes from Princes Street.
Surprisingly perhaps, Edinburgh does not have many town house hotels though its quiet Georgian terraces in the New Town lend themselves to the concept. The elegant and luxurious Howard Hotel therefore has its own place in the market. Within comfortable walking distance of Princes Street – though most of it uphill! – it is centrally located yet remote from the bustle of the main traffic routes. The hotel has been beautifully furnished and the high standards of the public areas are carried through to the kitchen from which skilful and creative young chefs present an interesting menu which should satisfy the most exacting diner. The Number Thirty Six Restaurant is not normally open at lunchtime, but by prior arrangement lunch can be provided there.
Open all year except Christmas
Rooms: 16 with private facilities
Dining Room/Restaurant Lunch – by prior arrangement only
Dinner 7.30 – 9.30 pm (e)
Dogs by arrangement
Bed & Breakfast £90 – £140
Dinner B & B – on request
Special Weekend Rates Oct to Apr
• *Fillet of Aberdeen Angus beef pan-fried in olive oil and parsley, served with a Madeira and shallot reduction. Fillet of Tay salmon and monkfish cooked in a lime and peppercorn butter, topped with a julienne of smoked salmon. Rich chocolate truffle cake laced with rum and served with white chocolate ice-cream.*
STB Commended 4 Crowns
Credit cards: 1, 2, 3, 5

IGG'S RESTAURANT

15 Jeffrey Street
Edinburgh EH1 1DR
Tel: 0131 557 8184

Off the Royal Mile.

This is a charming restaurant in a street just off the Royal Mile which has a reputation for its small interesting shops. The unusual name is derived from the first name of the proprietor, Ignacio Campos, who runs the restaurant personally. He has a wealth of catering experience behind him and this is a dignified yet relatively relaxed restaurant, with a bright interior and good standards of food preparation and presentation. The restaurant is an L shaped room, its pale yellow walls hung with classical artwork. The interesting three and four course table d'hote menus display the chef's skills to best advantage and offer an excellent choice of dishes. There are also some daily changing speciality items dependent on the fresh market produce available. At lunchtime and early evening until 7.30 pm (except Friday and Saturday) there is also a Tapas menu with a wide selection of fresh food items presented in the Spanish style. Spanish and French spoken. Children welcome.

Open all year
Dining Room/Restaurant Lunch 12 –
2.30 pm except Sun Mon (a-b)
Dinner 6 – 10.30 pm except
Sun Mon (c-d)
Closed Sun Mon
No smoking area in restaurant
Wheelchair access
• Roulade of smoked salmon and crab mousse with a watercress and lemon purée. Fillets of lemon sole and queenie scallops poached in white wine with a pink peppercorn and grapefruit sauce. Tournedos of Scottish beef brushed with chopped rosemary and mustard, served on a sweet pimento sauce.
Credit cards: 1, 2, 3, 5 + SWITCH
Proprietor: Ignacio Campos

JACKSON'S RESTAURANT

209-213 High Street
2 Jackson Close, Royal Mile
Edinburgh EH1 1PL
Tel: 0131 225 1793
Fax: 0131 220 0620

On the Royal Mile.

An interesting cellar restaurant on the Royal Mile that bustles from noon till late at night. Jackson's location attracts a great many tourists and locals who enjoy the Scottish emphasis in a number of dishes. The lunchtime menu is remarkably inexpensive and acts as a taster for the more serious eating in the evenings which is more realistically priced. Stone walls, pine tables and subtle lighting evoke a bistro style atmosphere. In addition to the cellar restaurant, there is a tastefully appointed private dining room which has air-conditioning and is available for parties of up to 45. The ambience of the place and the cheerful friendly service give Jackson's a special cachet.

Open all year except Christmas +
Boxing Days, 1 + 2 Jan
Dining Room/Restaurant Lunch 12 –
2 pm except Sun Sat (a)
Dinner 6 – 11 pm (d)
Extended hours during Edinburgh Festival
• Fricassé of wild game marinated with sloe gin presented in a strudel basket with pine mushrooms. Fillet of red snapper grilled gently with cardamon butter presented in a wild gooseberry and nutmeg sauce. Noisettes of tender spring lamb roasted with thyme, set on a mature port wine jus with courgette and carrot ribbons.
Credit cards: 1, 2, 3, 6
Proprietor: Lyn MacKinnon

KEEPERS RESTAURANT

13B Dundas Street
Edinburgh EH3 6QG
Tel: 0131 556 5707/0831 185792

Dundas Street (continuation of Hanover Street) is to north of Princes Street.

This is an unusual cellar restaurant in a Georgian basement in the New Town. There are three cellar rooms with their original stone floors and walls so there is always a pleasing element of intimacy and lack of distracting bustle. The menu is fairly straightforward with good wholesome cooking the order of the day rather than extravagant frills. Individual rooms or indeed the whole restaurant can be reserved for business or private functions.

Open all year except Boxing Day + 1 Jan
Dining Room/Restaurant Lunch 12 –
2 pm (a-b)
Dinner 6 – 10 pm (b-c)
Pre-theatre meals 6 – 7 pm (a)
No smoking area in restaurant
• Seafood chowder. Squat lobsters pan-fried in garlic butter. Aberdeen Angus fillet steak with a Drambuie, mushroom and cream sauce. Salmon filled with green butter and served with lobster sauce. Venison steak in a sauce of cranberry, port and mustard. Scotch

lamb chops on the bone with an elderberry and orange sauce.
Credit cards: 1, 2, 3, 5
Proprietor: Sheena Marshall

KELLY'S RESTAURANT

46 West Richmond Street
Edinburgh EH6 9DZ
Tel: 0131 668 3847

West Richmond Street is off Clerk Street (continuation of North Bridge from east end of Princes Street) convenient for the Queen's Hall and the new Festival Theatre.

This delightful and friendly little restaurant has established itself very firmly as a favourite eating place for discerning diners looking for something special in the way of food, and a warm comfortable atmosphere in which to enjoy it. The building was originally an old bakehouse which has been lovingly converted to create this small intimate restaurant. The Kellys are a charming couple, very much in evidence, who exercise close personal supervision of their restaurant. Jacque Kelly produces a small well balanced menu emphasising prime Scottish produce carefully prepared and beautifully presented. The fact that it is almost impossible to get a table without booking in advance reflects something of the restaurant's reputation for good food. Located as it is within a few minutes of the Festival Theatre, Kelly's makes an ideal venue for a pre-theatre supper.

Open all year except 1 to 3 Jan + 1 to 18 Oct
Dinner 6.30 – 9.30 pm except Sun Mon (d)
Closed Sun Mon

Diners requested not to smoke until after 9 pm
• Mull of Kintyre cheddar blended with goats cheese and Lowland malt whisky, served grilled over an apple croustade, with a crunchy salad. Suprême of chicken stuffed with a leek mousseline and roasted, served with a timbale of rice and poached prunes in a light cream sauce flavoured with truffle juice. A lemon cream covered with brambles and hot meringue.
Credit cards: 1, 2, 3
Proprietor: Jacque Kelly

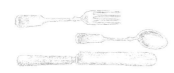

LE MARCHÉ NOIR
2/4 Eyre Place
Edinburgh EH3 5EP
Tel: 0131 558 1608
Fax: 0131 556 0798
Eyre Place is at northern end of Dundas Street (continuation of Hanover Street, north of Princes Street).
This charming little restaurant is situated in a peaceful area of the New Town. Proprietor Malcolm Duck presents the daily changing menus in French and his philosophy behind this is that it is a talking point and encourages a good rapport between the diners and his staff as they give each table an explanation of the menu items. Although the name may be French and the style of food may be French country cooking, there is strong evidence of the Auld Alliance. The brigade of Scottish chefs prepare and present interesting and innovative dishes using the best of fresh Scottish produce. The combination of good food and knowledgeable friendly staff makes for a very pleasing dining experience within the relaxed surroundings of this cosy and intimate restaurant.
Open all year except Christmas + Boxing Days
Dining Room/Restaurant Lunch 12 – 2.30 pm except Sun Sat (b-c)
Dinner 7 – 10 pm Mon to Thu: 7 – 10.30 pm Fri Sat: 6.30 – 9.30 pm Sun (c-d)

Facilities for disabled visitors
• Terrine of salmon and prawns. Warm salad of goats cheese. Black pudding with red wine. Suprême of Guinea fowl with a Calvados sauce. Escalopes of venison with mint and redcurrants. Delice of salmon grilled with orange butter.
Credit card: 1
Proprietor: Malcolm Duck

LIGHTBODY'S RESTAURANT & BAR
23 Glasgow Road
Edinburgh EH12 8HW
Tel: 0131 334 2300
On main Corstorphine road out of Edinburgh towards the airport and Glasgow.
A family run bar restaurant on the busy road out through Corstorphine towards Glasgow. It is a popular rendezvous for the local business community and for special evening-out groups. The dining area is cheerfully set out with fresh flowers and colourful napkins and many pictures on the walls. A special three course businessman's lunch is very good value and portions are generous. A much broader à la carte menu is also available and offers a wide range of choice.
Open all year except Christmas + Boxing Days, 1 + 2 Jan
Bar Lunch 12 – 2 pm except Sun (a)
Dining Room/Restaurant Lunch 12 – 2 pm except Sun (a-c)
Bar Supper 6 – 10 pm except Sun Sat (a)
Dinner 6 – 10 pm except Sun (c)
Closed Sun
• Smoked Scottish salmon. Lobster soup with sherry and cream. Haggis with Dijon mustard sauce. Fillet of trout in oatmeal. Aberdeen Angus beef with an interesting variety of sauces. Marinated haunch of venison casseroled with red wine, onion, mushroom and orange.
Credit cards: 1, 2, 3, 6
Proprietors: Malcolm &
      Norman Lightbody

MARTINS RESTAURANT
70 Rose Street North Lane
Edinburgh EH2 3DX
Tel: 0131 225 3106

Prestige Award Winner 1988

In the north lane off Rose Street between Frederick Street and Castle Street.
Martins is one of Edinburgh's premier restaurants – and one of its best kept secrets! Hidden away in a little cobbled service lane in the city centre, its unpretentious exterior belies the delightful style of the well appointed restaurant that is within. Subtle lighting seems to focus on the fresh flowers and crisp linen napery at each table. The atmosphere is intimate and unhurried, and there is a genuine warmth of welcome unsurpassed in the city. Martin and Gay Irons put a lot into the running of this delightful little restaurant which has earned innumerable awards and accolades. It has deservedly retained the three Rosettes awarded by the Automobile Association, reflecting the consistently high standard of food. Chef Forbes Stott's menus are well balanced and change daily according to the availability of prime quality ingredients, specialising in Scottish seafish, shellfish and game. The restaurant has an established reputation and is therefore popular, so it is best to book in advance.
Open all year except 24 Dec to 24 Jan, 1 wk late Jun + late Sep
Dining Room Lunch 12 – 2 pm except Sun Mon Sat (b-e) – booking essential
Dinner 7 – 10 pm except Sun Mon (d-e) – booking essential
Closed Sun Mon
No smoking in dining areas
• Home-made bread served with a daily changing fresh herb vinaigrette. Suprême of wild salmon baked with leeks and mustard. Grilled saddle of venison with beetroot and Puy lentils. Fillets of turbot and halibut pan-fried with chicory and a sweet pepper coulis. Whole roasted and boned quail stuffed with couscous, spinach and smoked bacon. Award winning cheeseboard.
Credit cards: 1, 2, 3, 5
Proprietors: Martin & Gay Irons

NORTON HOUSE HOTEL
Ingliston, Edinburgh
Midlothian EH28 8LX
Tel: 0131 333 1275
Fax: 0131 333 5305

Just off A8, 6 miles from Edinburgh city centre, ½ mile from airport, on the road to Glasgow.

Norton House is a grand old Victorian mansion set in acres of secluded parkland in what was once the estate of Sir John Usher of Norton and Wells who gave his name to the famous brewing company. The hotel is now part of Richard Branson's Virgin Group. Sympathetic upgrading of the original house has re-created the feeling of gracious living and opulence redolent of the earlier time in which it was built. Within the tranquil surroundings of the hotel set amid lawns and tall trees it is difficult to believe you are just on the outskirts of Edinburgh, minutes from the airport and the central Scotland motorway network.
Accommodation ranges from excellent standard rooms through to suites, all beautifully furnished and well equipped. There are rooms set aside for non-smokers. The Conservatory Restaurant has gained a reputation as one of the city's top eating places and has been awarded two AA Rosettes. Menus feature the finest local produce presented with creative skill by the experienced team of chefs. For more informal eating or a relaxed drink, there is the Norton Tavern which sits separate from the hotel within the converted old stable block. You will also find a walled garden, barbecue area and children's play area there.

Open all year
Rooms: 47 with private facilities
Bar Lunch 12 – 2.30 pm (b)
Dining Room/Restaurant Lunch 12 – 2.30 pm except Sat (b)
Bar Supper 5.30 – 9.30 pm (b)
Dinner 7 – 10 pm (d)
Facilities for disabled visitors
No smoking area in restaurant
Bed & Breakfast £99 – £165
Dinner B & B £55 – £205
• *Roast monkfish tail with a sauce of squat lobsters and fried leeks. Saddle of Scottish venison with a raspberry vinegar and bitter chocolate sauce. Fillet of Angus beef set on a potato scone served with a small Yorkshire pudding filled with roast garlic and shallots. Escalope of Scottish salmon topped with a salmon souffle, baked and served with Vermouth and chive butter.*
STB Highly Commended 5 Crowns
Credit cards: 1, 2, 3, 5, 6 + SWITCH

OVERTURES RESTAURANT
18-22 Greenside Place, Edinburgh
Midlothian EH1 3AA
Tel: 0131 557 8339
Fax: 0131 557 6520

At top of Leith Walk, entrance adjacent to Edinburgh Playhouse Theatre ticket office.

Overtures Restaurant is located on the first floor within The Playhouse Theatre. The interior of the restaurant is reminiscent of old Victorian splendour, lavishly – and theatrically – appointed in scarlets and golds, with brocade drapes, gilt-edged mirrors, fine ceramics and luxurious furnishings. These grand yet comfortable surroundings make for a truly memorable experience. The cuisine has its roots in fundamental cookery of various origins with classical French and Scottish dishes. Chef/manager Paul Rowan has put a lot of research into the compilation of the monthly changing table d'hôte menus to ensure a high quality dining experience. The menus offer a good choice and cater to a wide variety of tastes. Fine cuisine combined with high standards of service is the trademark of Overtures. The restaurant is open to the general public with its own entrance separate from the theatre, but it is also geared to cater for theatre-goers with pre- and post-performance suppers. In addition to the expansive dining room, there are two small party suites, catering for up to 16 guests offering the same menu as in Overtures.

Open all year except Christmas Eve, Christmas + Boxing Days
Dining Room/Restaurant Lunch 11.30 am – 3 pm except Sun (a)
Dinner 6 – 11 pm except Sun (b)
Closed Sun
No smoking area in restaurant
• *Partan bree – crab soup. Roasted Guinea fowl served with fried crumbs, redcurrants, jus and bread sauce. Chargrilled rump steak glazed with Stilton, garlic and Worcester sauce. Marinated salmon grilled in oatmeal with an anchovy butter. Roasted loin of lamb with a black pudding stuffing, roasted garlic and burgundy sauce.*
Credit cards: 1, 3, 6 + SWITCH, DELTA

ROCK CAFE RESTAURANT
18 Howe Street
Edinburgh EH3 6TG
Tel: 0131 225 7225

Howe Street (continuation of Frederick Street) is to north of Princes Street.
The Rock Cafe's decor may be reminiscent of the '60s and '70s with its huge murals of rock stars past and present, but this is

a serious eating place which will appeal to all age groups. There is a marked tendency towards modern day eating styles in some of the dishes on offer, but there are also excellent steaks served in a variety of interesting ways, specialities such as salmon en croûte and dishes of the day listed on the blackboard. The style of restaurant may be considered American, but the food is quality and superbly cooked. John Mackay is a charming and amiable host and his friendly personality adds to the whole dining experience. The good mix of background music fits in well with the atmosphere of the place.

Open all year except 24 Dec to 5 Jan
Open 12 – 11 pm Sat only
Dinner 5 – 11 pm except Sun Mon (b–c)
Closed Sun Mon
• *Smoked salmon. Aberdeen Angus beef steaks and burgers. Chargrilled Scottish salmon with basil butter. Chicken suprême filled with spinach, Gruyère and garlic. Fish of the day. Fresh pasta.*
Credit cards: 1, 3
Proprietor: John Mackay

THE ROUND TABLE
31 Jeffrey Street
Edinburgh EH1 1DH
Tel: 0131 557 3032

Off the Royal Mile and less than 5 minutes walk from Waverley Station.
The Round Table has the appearance and many of the attributes of a traditional cafe bistro. Money has not been wasted attempting to create a trendy theme or a pseudo atmosphere. The restaurant probably takes its name from the many round tables which seem to be a feature of it and these, with the assortment of stout wooden chairs on polished wooden floors, provide a simple but effective enough ambience. The menu leans heavily towards seafood but meat-eaters are not forgotten and there are some good value for money dishes. The benefit of this informal style of dining is that you are not restricted to 'lunchtime' to have lunch, the menu is available throughout the afternoon until dinner takes over in the evening. Downstairs is a small non-smoking private dining area called the Scullery Kitchen which can be reserved for up to 14 people. Here diners can watch the experienced chef at work and sample traditional Scottish fare.

Open all year except Christmas + Boxing Days, 1 Jan
Open from 10 am
Dining Room/Restaurant Lunch 12 –

5.30 pm except Sun (a)
Dinner 5.30 – 10 pm Tue to Sat (b)
*Closed Sun except during Edinburgh
Festival*
• *Smoked salmon and avocado gratin.
Cream dill fish soup. Mignons of beef
and venison with Drambuie onion
marmalade. Poached salmon. Smoked
haddock and trout fillet grilled and
topped with a leek cream sauce.
Raspberry cranachan with malt whisky.*
Credit cards: 1, 3, 6
Proprietors: Anne & Robert Winter

SHERATON GRAND HOTEL
1 Festival Square
Edinburgh EH3 9SR
Tel: 0131 229 9131 • Telex: 72398
Fax: 0131 229 6254

Prestige Award Winner 1993

*Lothian Road opposite Usher Hall and
only 5 minutes from Princes Street.*
International travellers are well aware that
the name Sheraton is a comforting
assurance of high quality standards in
every aspect, and the Sheraton Grand in
Edinburgh is no exception. In a prime
situation on Festival Square, it is
convenient for the Usher Hall, the Royal
Lyceum and Traverse Theatres, the King's
Theatre (a few minutes walk away) and
the new International Conference Centre
due to open soon. This is a modern hotel
– awarded five stars by the AA – and
grand in more than its name. The public
areas are sumptuously furnished in the
grand style with fine traditional materials
giving a warmth and richness to the
surroundings. An impressive staircase
joins the lower level of reception with the
comfortable lobby bar on the ground floor.
Bedrooms and suites are of a very high
standard with every degree of comfort and
commanding views. There are also
excellent function and conference suites.
The elegant Grill Room is a delightful
place for a special meal experience.
Executive Chef Jean Michel Gauffre's
enthusiasm for Scottish produce is
evident in the marked prominence he
gives on his menus to traditional Scottish
recipes. He also introduces a French
influence in his special treatment of some
of the prime produce he selects from
around the country. The Terrace
Restaurant adjacent to the Grill Room
looks out onto Festival Square and offers
a menu of light interesting meals and
snacks throughout the day. Children are
welcome. French, Italian, German and
Spanish spoken.

Open all year
Rooms: 261 with private facilities
Bar Meals 11 am – 6 pm (a)
Lunch (Terrace) 12 – 2.30 pm (b)
*Lunch (Grill) 12 – 2.30 pm except Sun
Sat (c-d)*
Dinner (Terrace) 6 – 11 pm (b)
Dinner (Grill) 7 – 10.30 pm except Sun (e)
*No smoking areas in restaurants +
lounge*
Bed & Breakfast £71 – £110
Dinner B & B £91 – £130
Room Rate £57.50 – £120
Special Rates available
• *Home-smoked Scottish salmon with
nettles and bacon. Loin of Ayrshire lamb
with stovies and garden vegetables.*
STB Deluxe 5 Crowns
Credit cards: 1, 2, 3, 5, 6 + SWITCH

THE WITCHERY BY THE CASTLE
Castlehill, Royal Mile
Edinburgh EH1 1NE
Tel: 0131 225 5613
Fax: 0131 220 4392
*Situated at the entrance to Edinburgh
Castle.*
The Witchery survives the tourist crush to
remain intimate, friendly and quite unique.
Already steeped in eight centuries of
history, it claims once to have been the
very centre of witchcraft and sorcery in the
Old Town and the Witchery captivates this
atmosphere. The Secret Garden restaurant
was formerly a school yard which has been
carefully converted to re-create the
atmosphere of bygone days, with ancient
tapestries upon the stone walls and huge
candles on the tables. The style of food
and presentation is contemporary offering
diners the opportunity to sample the top
quality produce of Scotland. One of the
Witchery's best kept secrets is the Inner
Sanctum, a sumptuously appointed suite
with its own private dining room in the
minstrel's gallery. Among the beautiful
antiques in the Victorian bedroom is a
19th century four poster bed and even the
luxurious bathroom is in keeping with
those times.
Open all year except Christmas Day
Rooms: 1 suite with private facilities
*Dining Room/Restaurant Lunch 12 –
4 pm (b)*
Dinner 4 – 11.30 pm (e)
Reservations advisable
Room Rate from £120
• *Mixed mushroom soup with walnut
croûtons. Grilled escalope of salmon on
a gooseberry and nutmeg cream. Loin of
lamb cutlets en papillote with garlic
potatoes and light pepper jus. Pan-fried*

*scallops, cooked with mussels and
shallots, topped with a pesto crust.
Bitter chocolate cup filled with lavender
ice-cream on a purée of blueberries.*
Credit cards: 1, 2, 3, 5 + SWITCH
Proprietor: James Thomson

Elgin

Location 83

MANSEFIELD HOUSE HOTEL
Mayne Road, Elgin
Moray IV30 1NY
Tel: 01343 540883
Fax: 01343 552491
*Just off A96 in Elgin. From Inverness,
drive towards town centre and turn right
at first roundabout. At mini-roundabout,
hotel on right.*
A gracious old Georgian town house which
has been tastefully converted to its
present role and stands amid beautifully
kept flower beds and garden. There is a
gymnasium and sauna room and
everywhere a high standard of decor and
comfort. The dining room is quite
sumptuous and a delightful place in which
to relax and enjoy some of Chef Robin
Murray's renowned cooking. There is a
very extensive menu but, rightly, a
concentration on the abundance of
excellent fish for which the north east is
noted. En suite bedrooms have all the
little accessories that are a feature of
good hotels nowadays. There are facilities
for conferences and private parties.
Open all year
Rooms: 17 with private facilities
*Dining Room/Restaurant Lunch 12 –
2.30 pm except Sun: 12.30 -2.30 pm
Sun (a)*
*Dinner 6.30 – 9.30 pm Sun to Thu: 6.30
– 10.30 pm Fri Sat (c)*
No dogs
Facilities for disabled visitors
No smoking in restaurant
Bed & Breakfast from £45
Dinner B & B from £62.50
• *Salmon and sole terrine studded with
North Sea prawns presented with
seasonal leaves and lemon dressing.
Pan-roasted quail on a compote of plums
and port. King scallops baked in a rich
cheese sauce. Lobster, steamed, then
grilled with garlic butter. Prime fillet
steak topped with bread croûton and
chicken liver parfait, finished in a rich
Madeira sauce.*
STB Highly Commended 4 Crowns
Credit cards: 1, 2, 3 + SWITCH
Proprietors: Ross & Kathleen Murray

MANSION HOUSE HOTEL & COUNTRY CLUB
The Haugh, Elgin
Moray IV30 1AW
Tel: 01343 548811
Fax: 01343 547916

Turn off main A96 in Elgin into Haugh Road.
In parkland and beautiful grounds by the River Lossie sits this old 19th century baronial mansion which was once owned by the Bibby Shipping Line and is now an elegant and welcoming hotel and country club. Within such tranquil surroundings it is easier to believe you are in the country than just a few minutes of walk of the centre of Elgin. The house has some interesting architectural features and period furnishings, gracious public rooms and individually styled four poster bedrooms. Within the Country Club there is a range of leisure facilities including a swimming pool and gymnasium. The restaurant is an elegant room where menus feature the best of local produce, offering a good variety of well balanced dishes with some interesting combinations of ingredients.
Open all year
Rooms: 22 with private facilities
Bar Lunch 12 – 5 pm (a)
Dining Room/Restaurant Lunch 12 – 2 pm (b)
Bar Supper 5 – 9 pm (a)
Dinner 7 – 9 pm (c)
No dogs
No smoking in restaurant
Bed & Breakfast £55 – £75
Dinner B & B £70 – £90
Special Rates available
• Light pastry pouch filled with a ragoût of local seafoods. Mushrooms in white wine and cream with home-made garlic bread. Smoked scampi and wild mushroom soup. Darne of salmon filled with creamed watercress and baked in filo pastry. Loin of venison with quail served with a blackcurrant and juniper sauce. Prime beef fillet wrapped in a horseradish pancake, with a rich gravy.
STB Highly Commended 5 Crowns
Credit cards: 1, 2, 3, 5 + SWITCH
Proprietors: Jim & Joan Stirrat

Elie

Location 84

BOUQUET GARNI RESTAURANT
51 High Street, Elie
Fife KY9 1BZ
Tel: 01333 330374

On main street through Elie.
A delightful little restaurant in the centre of this charming East Neuk town. With ample supplies of fresh fish and seafood on its doorstep the Bouquet Garni naturally specialises in high quality fish dishes but with a complementary range of other typical Scottish fare. The intimate and cosy candlelit dining room is almost certain to appeal to the connoisseur of good food. If you have tried to book and the restaurant was full, you will be delighted to learn that a new extension opens early in 1995 providing an additional dining room. The Bouquet Garni now also runs a courtesy vehicle for parties of four or more (maximum 11) coming to dine at the restaurant from the surrounding area. A little French spoken.
Open all year except 2 wks Nov + last 3 wks Jan
Bar Lunch 12 – 2 pm except Sun (a)
Dining Room/Restaurant Lunch 12 – 1.30 pm except Sun (b)
Dinner from 7 pm except Sun (d)
No smoking area in restaurant
• Pan-fried scallops in walnut oil, set on carrot and leek, served with Noilly Prat orange sauce. Sea bass set on fresh spinach with a hot tomato and garlic dressing. Loin of Scottish lamb, cooked pink, set on creamed celeriac, with wild mushrooms and rosemary jus. Brandy basket filled with a duo of chocolate mousse and tropical fruit with kummel and ginger cream sauce.
Credit cards: 1, 2, 3 + SWITCH, DELTA
Proprietors: Andrew & Norah Keracher

Erbusaig
by Kyle of Lochalsh

Location 85

THE OLD SCHOOLHOUSE RESTAURANT
"Tigh Fasgaidh," Erbusaig, Kyle
Ross-shire IV40 8BB
Tel: 01599 534369

Outskirts of Erbusaig on Kyle-Plockton road.
This is a charming old 19th century schoolhouse set in its own grounds which has been tastefully converted to form a small restaurant with rooms. Yet

the atmosphere of the past has been retained while providing the standard of comfort and surroundings to satisfy guests today. Imaginative cuisine makes full use of all the wonderful shellfish and fish so readily available locally, but meat-eaters and vegetarians are not forgotten. The menu is reasonably priced and well balanced, and there is obvious culinary skill in its execution. Booking advisable.
Open 1 Apr to 31 Oct
Rooms: 2 with private facilities
Dinner 7 – 10.30 pm (b-d)
Bed & Breakfast £18 – £30
Special Rates for 7+ nights
• Scallops marinaded in fresh herbs and citrus juices, sautéd in walnut oil. Prawns grilled with a fennel vinaigrette. Poached salmon served with elderflower wine and tarragon sauce. Monkfish braised in wine, finished with cream and fresh basil. Noisettes of lamb served with a mint and white wine sauce. Raspberry brûlée made with locally produced yoghurt.
STB Commended 3 Crowns
Credit cards: 1, 2, 3
Proprietors: Calum & Joanne Cumine

Fairlie

Location 86

FINS RESTAURANT
Fencefoot Farm, Fairlie
Ayrshire KA29 0EG
Tel: 01475 568989
Fax: 01475 568921

On A78, 1 mile south of Fairlie near Largs.
This delightful seafood restaurant has been created from a tastefully converted old 18th century barn. The white-washed walls and high beamed ceiling with roof windows create a lovely informal atmosphere for relaxed dining. Interesting old photographs of the farm and fishery scenes adorn the walls. The restaurant specialises in fresh locally caught seasonal fish and shellfish, some of which is beech or oak smoked in the traditional kilns of the smokehouse. Rainbow trout are farmed on site in spring water from the moors above and there is a shellfish purification plant containing live lobster, oysters and crabs. The philosophy behind Bernard and Jill Thain's venture is that fish and shellfish are the most wonderful foods in the world so long as they are fresh. But their menus cater for the non-fish eater and vegetarian equally well. Fins is a

popular place so it is advisable to book in advance.

Open all year except Christmas + Boxing Days, 1 Jan
Dining Room/Restaurant Lunch 12 – 2 pm except Mon (a)
Dinner 7 – 10 pm except Sun Mon (c)
Closed Mon
Facilities for disabled visitors
• *Woodland mushroom and vegetable terrine on a smooth sauce of tomato and sweet basil. Fillet of Atlantic salmon set on a pool of port wine, grape and root ginger sauce. Colonsay cod lightly poached and served with orange and lemon citrus butter sauce. Squat lobster and scallop sauted with shallots, garlic and tomato concassé. Prime Aberdeen Angus fillet of beef.*
Credit cards: 1, 2, 3, 5, 6 + SWITCH, DELTA
Proprietors: Bernard & Jill Thain

Falkirk

Location 87
INCHYRA GRANGE HOTEL
Grange Road, Polmont
Falkirk FK2 0YB
Tel: 01324 711911 • Telex: 777693
Fax: 01324 716134

Junction 4 or 5, M9 motorway. Situated on border of Polmont/Grangemouth.
A fine Scottish country house set in eight acres of private grounds. The old part of the house dates from as far back as the 12th century and has witnessed a great deal of history, in particular many battles during the dark ages which were fought on the land in front of it, including the Battle of Falkirk in 1298. Nowadays the original building has been much extended and modernised providing a high degree of comfort and modern amenity. There is a leisure club available to residents with swimming pool, spa bath, sauna, snooker room and solarium. The restaurant has a very comprehensive menu with some interesting and unusual dishes, including a vegetarian option.
Open all year

Rooms: 43 with private facilities
Bar Lunch 12 – 2 pm Mon to Sat: 12 – 2.30 pm Sun (b)
Dining Room/Restaurant Lunch 12.30 – 2 pm except Sat (b)
Bar Supper 6 – 10 pm Mon to Sat: 6.30 – 10 pm Sun (b)
Dinner 7 – 9.30 pm Mon to Fri: 7 – 10 pm Sat: 7.30 – 9.30 pm Sun (c)
Bed & Breakfast £50 – £75
Special Rates for 3+ nights
• *Salmon, scampi and scallops in a basil and cream sauce. Fillet steak stuffed with scallops and covered in a bernaise sauce. Poached salmon fillet with a delicate sauce of fresh dill, cream, onions and white wine. Roast fillet of Scottish lamb with a honey and rosemary glaze. Fillet of venison baked with a mushroom parfait and served on a red wine glaze.*
STB Commended 4 Crowns
Credit cards: 1, 2, 3, 5, 6 + SWITCH

Falkland

Location 88
COVENANTER HOTEL
The Square, Falkland
Fife KY7 7BU
Tel: 01337 857542/857224
Fax: 01337 857163

Centre of Falkland.
George and Margaret Menzies are well established hosts at this 17th century coaching inn almost opposite Falkland Palace. They have been running the Covenanter for over 15 years during which time it has steadily increased its profile and its reputation for good honest food, good service and warm hospitality. There is a choice of eating styles, either in the traditional restaurant or the informal bistro. Menus feature a selection of made to order dishes with the emphasis on home produce and vegetarian and special diets are catered for. In addition to the hotel accommodation, there is also a selection of self-catering cottages available in the village.
Open all year
Rooms: 4 with private facilities
Bar Lunch 12 – 2 pm except Mon (a)
Dining Room/Restaurant Lunch 12 – 2 pm except Mon (b)
Bar Supper 5.30 – 9.30 pm except Mon (a)
Dinner 6 – 9 pm except Mon (b)
(table d'hôte + à la carte dinner menus available)
Restaurants closed Mon
No dogs
Bed & Breakfast £25 – £37.50
Dinner B & B £37.50 – £50
Special Rates available
• *Scampi Falkland cooked in a cream sauce with sliced onions and mushrooms. Tay salmon steak grilled or poached. Sirloin steak auld alliance coated in French mustard, topped with soft brown sugar and grilled.*
STB Commended 3 Crowns
Credit cards: 1, 2, 3, 5, 6
Proprietors: George & Margaret Menzies

KIND KYTTOCK'S KITCHEN
Cross Wynd, Falkland
Fife KY7 7BE
Tel: 01337 857477

A912 to Falkland. Off main street in village.
Falkland must be one of Fife's most charming villages. Not only is it steeped in history but it has fascinating architecture and also seems to be a frequent winner of Best Kept Village Awards. It is a place to walk around and enjoy, and when you do so you will come across Kind Kyttock's right in the heart of the village. This delightful little restaurant and tearoom is something special, dedicated to delicious home-baking in the traditional Scottish manner. It is one of a vanishing breed, and you should not visit Falkland without enjoying the ambience of the place and the good things it has to offer. Kind Kyttock's has been a regular winner of The Tea Council's Award for Excellence.
Open 4 Jan to Christmas Eve
Food service 12 – 5 pm except Mon (a)
Closed Mon
No smoking throughout
• *Home-baked pancakes, scones, fruit squares, shortbread, wholemeal bread, stovies, cloutie dumpling. Locally grown vegetables used in Scotch broth and at salad table. Selection of teas available.*
Credit cards: 1, 3
Proprietor: Bert Dalrymple

Fintry

Location 89

CULCREUCH CASTLE
Culcreuch Castle Country Park, Fintry
Stirlingshire G63 0LW
Tel: 0136 086 228/555
Fax: 0136 086 555

From Stirling, A811 west for 10 miles to junction with B822. Turn left to Fintry – 6 miles. From Glasgow, A81 to Killearn then turn right on B818 to Fintry – 6 miles.

There are castles aplenty in Scotland and while some may lay claim to individual distinction, here is one with it all! Culcreuch has romance – in its close proximity to that most romantic of lochs, Loch Lomond, which is a 20 minutes drive away; history – in its 700 years of existence as a fortress home for the Clan Galbraith; ghosts – human, animal and musical – but be re-assured, they are benevolent; and grace, beauty and dignity in the way in which it has been restored to the elegant country house hotel it is today. Set in a tranquil 1600 acre estate, there are log fires, a cosy dungeon bar, four poster beds and candlelit dinner; and the chef responds to the atmosphere by basing his menus on traditional Scottish fare.

Open all year except 1 Jan
Note: Residents only 1 Jan + no bar meals Christmas Day
Rooms: 8 with private facilities + 16 lodge bedrooms
Bar Lunch 12.30 – 2.30 pm (a-c)
Bar Supper 5 – 9 pm (a-c)
Dinner 7 – 8.30 pm (d) 4 course menu
Bed & Breakfast £35 – £60
Dinner B & B £55 – £80
• Smoked mackerel mousse with a cream cheese and spring onion coulis. Escalope of venison pan-fried and served with a black cherry and red wine sauce. Paupiettes of lemon sole stuffed with prawns, poached in a white wine and lobster cream. Sirloin steak au poivre.
STB Commended 3 Crowns
Credit cards: 1, 2, 3, 5

Fochabers

Location 90

BAXTERS VISITOR CENTRE
Fochabers
Moray IV32 7LD
Tel: 01343 820393
Fax: 01343 821790

Situated on A96 Aberdeen-Inverness, 1 mile west of Fochabers.

Within the famous Baxters Visitor Centre at Fochabers, is the Spey Restaurant, an excellent example of a well run self-service restaurant. It is a spacious attractive room laid out with pine furniture and on warm days visitors may dine outside at tables on the patio. The whole experience is extremely good value for money and of the quality expected of the Baxter name. Naturally their own products are featured on the menu, in the form of the famous soups and jams, but in addition there are daily changing freshly made hot main meal dishes utilising local produce, served over lunchtime. The aroma of hot pancakes freshly baked on the open griddle is enough to tempt anyone, and the selection of delicious home-baking is not to be missed. This is a very popular place frequented by many just dropping in for something to eat as well as those there for the Baxter Experience.

Open all year
Open 9.30 am – 5 pm
Lunch 11 am – 3.30 pm: traditional roast Sun (a)
Table Licence
No smoking area in restaurant
• A choice of Baxters famous soups. Rollmop herring with salad. Pâté and oatcakes. Highland cheeseboard. Two daily changing main meal dishes, one vegetarian. Filled baked potatoes. Salads and sandwiches. Selection of home-baking. Pancakes cooked to order on open griddle.
Credit cards: 1, 3 + SWITCH, DELTA

Forres

Location 91

KNOCKOMIE HOTEL
Grantown Road, Forres
Moray IV36 0SG
Tel: 01309 673146
Fax: 01309 673290

On A940 just south of Forres on Grantown road.

Just on the outskirts of the Royal Burgh of Forres, Knockomie Hotel is set back half a mile from the main road and commands lovely views over the Moray Firth. There is some fine wood panelling in the foyer and a beamed ceiling in the dining room. The accommodation is very pleasingly furnished and there is now one ground floor bedroom suitable for disabled guests. Both table d'hôte and à la carte menus are normally available in the dining room and offer a fine choice of some classic and regional dishes. The hotel has earned a fine reputation for its high standards of food preparation and presentation, complemented by good service from the smart well trained and polite staff.

Open all year except Christmas Day
Rooms: 14 with private facilities
Bar Lunch 12 – 2 pm except Sun (a-b)
Dining Room/Restaurant Lunch 12 – 2 pm (b)
Dinner 7 – 9 pm (d-e) 4 or 5 course menu
Bed & Breakfast £37.50 – £80
Dinner B & B £62 – £104
• Feuilleté of Hebridean mussels. Fillet of smoked haddock topped with Welsh rarebit served on a tomato salad. Boned quail with a raspberry vinaigrette. Fillet of local salmon with a prawn sauce. Noisette of spring lamb on a bed of ratatouille. Aberdeen Angus rib-eye steak with a red wine sauce.
STB Commended 4 Crowns
Credit cards: 1, 2, 3, 5
Proprietor: Gavin Ellis

RAMNEE HOTEL
Victoria Road, Forres
Moray IV36 0BN
Tel: 01309 672410
Fax: 01309 673392

A96 Inverness-Aberdeen, off bypass at roundabout at eastern side of Forres – 500 yards on right.

The Royal Burgh of Forres is famous for its award winning gardens in Grant Park, and just across from the park is the Ramnee Hotel set in its own two acres of well manicured lawns and garden. Ramnee was built in 1907 as a private house for Richard Hamblin on his retirement from the Indian Civil Service. It retains much of the opulence and grandeur of that period but has been completely and sensitively refurbished. The en suite bedrooms have all the little extras to be found in a quality hotel and the food is of an extremely high standard, with excellent value table d'hôte lunch and dinner menus augmented by an imaginative à la carte menu. Lighter and more informal meals are also served in Tipplings cocktail lounge. An impressive hotel with smart well trained staff.

Open all year except Christmas Day +
1 to 3 Jan
Rooms: 18 with private facilities
Bar Lunch 12 – 2 pm (a)
Dining Room/Restaurant Lunch 12 –
2 pm (a)
Bar Supper 6 – 9 pm (b)
Dinner 7 – 9 pm (c)
Bed & Breakfast £35 – £55
Dinner B & B £52.50 – £75
Special Weekend Rates available
• Smoked mackerel and creamed
beetroot. Breast of Guinea fowl in apricot
sauce. Medallions of beef fillet with
shallots, mushrooms, tomato concassé,
white wine and herbs. Breaded lamb
cutlets with a whisky and tomato cream
sauce.
STB Commended 4 Crowns
Credit cards: 1, 2, 3, 5 + SWITCH, DELTA

Fort Augustus

Location 92

THE BRAE HOTEL

Bunoich Brae, Fort Augustus
Inverness-shire PH32 4DG
Tel: 01320 366289
Fax: 01320 366702

200 yards off A82.
This former Victorian built church manse
stands in its own attractive grounds in an
elevated position overlooking Fort
Augustus, with wonderful views of the
Caledonian Canal, River Oich and Loch
Ness. It is now a family run hotel where
Andrew and Mari Reive aim to ensure
their guests feel most welcome,
comfortable and at home. Subtle classical
music enhances the atmosphere of the
dining room where Mari presents an
interesting and innovative four course
table d'hôte dinner menu. This changes
daily and is a fine example of good fresh
Scottish produce being prepared and
cooked with international flair and skill. A
carefully selected wine list complements
the food. The hotel has a pair of mountain
bikes for hire and there are many
pleasant walks in the area. Also available
locally are golf, pony trekking, fishing and
skiing in the winter. Fort Augustus makes
an ideal base for touring the north and
western Highlands.
Open 1 Mar to 31 Oct
Rooms: 8 , 5 with private facilities
Dinner 7 – 8.30 pm (d) 4 course menu
Children over 7 years welcome
No smoking in dining room
Bed & Breakfast £21 – £28
Dinner B & B £36 – £47

Special Rates available
• Prawns en croûte with a minted orange
sauce. Smoked and fresh salmon
rillettes. Grilled duck breast with plum
and ginger, and an apple and chive
crêpe. Venison fillet with spiced
cranberry sauce and cumin rice timbale.
Salmon baked with ginger, garlic and
lime. Fillet steak with red wine and
mushrooms. Home-made bread, ice-
creams and desserts.
STB Highly Commended 3 Crowns
Credit cards: 1, 2, 3
Proprietors: Andrew & Mari Reive

LOVAT ARMS HOTEL

Fort William Road, Fort Augustus
Inverness-shire PH32 4DU
Tel: 01320 366206/4
Fax: 01320 366677

A82 Fort William-Inverness.
Set back from the main Fort William-
Inverness road, almost exactly half way
between these two famous Highland
towns, is the Lovat Arms, a spacious old
Victorian hotel standing in 2½ acres of
beautifully kept grounds in a dominant
position overlooking the town and the
canal. The original 18th century Fort
Augustus barracks were erected in what
are now the hotel's grounds and
remnants remain in the huge wall
alongside the car park. The restful
unhurried atmosphere of the Lovat Arms
is redolent of a more leisurely age and
Hector and Mary MacLean are caring and
welcoming hosts. In the restaurant with
its high ceilings and wood panelling, a
touch of Victorian grandeur remains. The
menus offer a selection of dishes –
some quite innovative and some more
traditional – using a wide range of west
coast fish and shellfish together with
local game and beef, prepared to a high
standard by highly experienced chefs.
There is also a bar meal menu served in
the spacious lounge bar.
Open all year
Rooms: 21 with private facilities
*Bar Lunch 12.30 – 2 pm: 12.30 –
2.30 pm Jun to Sep (a-b)*
*Dining Room/Restaurant Lunch – by
arrangement groups only*
*Bar Supper 6.30 – 8.30 pm: 6.30 –
9 pm Jun to Sep (a-b)*

*Dinner 7 – 8.30 pm: 7 – 9 pm Jun to
Sep (c)*
Bed & Breakfast £26.50 – £33.50
Special Rates available
• Scallops in beurre blanc sauce.
Mussels, langoustines and salmon.
Pâtés, fish and game terrines. Saddle of
venison. Noisettes of lamb. Angus beef.
Vegetarian dishes.
STB Commended 3 Crowns
Credit cards: 1, 3
Proprietors: Hector & Mary MacLean

Fort William

Location 93

AN CRANN

Seangan Bridge, Muirshearlich
Fort William
Inverness-shire PH33 7PB
Tel: 01397 772077

*From A830 at Banavie, take B8004 for
2½ miles. From A82 at Commando
Memorial take B8004 for 8 miles.*
This little restaurant sits on the banks of
the Seangan Burn, just 100 yards from
the Caledonian Canal. This old stone
barn was originally built as the Seangan
steading for Sine Ross's great-
grandmother's uncle back in 1896 and
has been in the family ever since. The
building was converted in 1993 to form
An Crann – which is Gaelic for 'The
Plough'- retaining the original stonework
and enhancing it with large arch windows
to create a bright airy interior. High stone
walls, a beamed vaulted ceiling and old
prints and photographs of the original
steading all add to the rustic charm.
Snacks and home-baking are available
throughout the day and the blackboard
menu highlights the specialities available
at lunchtime. The restaurant specialises
is creatively prepared high quality local
produce and this is displayed at its best
in the evening dinner menus.
Open Easter to end Oct
*Soup, sandwiches + home baking
available 10.30 am – 5 pm*
*Dining Room/Restaurant Lunch 12.30 –
2.30 pm Sun only (a)*
Dinner 6.30 – 9.30 pm (c)
Table Licence
Facilities for disabled visitors
• Local scallops with coriander and lentil
sauce. Venison with red wine and rowan
jelly sauce. Scottish lamb with rosemary
and Madeira. Bread and butter pudding
with rum and raisin syrup.
Credit cards: 1, 3
Proprietor: Sine Ross

CRANNOG SEAFOOD RESTAURANT
Town Pier, Fort William
Inverness-shire PH33 7NG
Tel: 01397 705589/703919
Fax: 01397 705026

Fort William town pier – off A82 Fort William town centre bypass.

This is the original Crannog Seafood Restaurant, a little red roofed octagonal building which sits on the pier at Fort William. It is a really special little restaurant where diners can watch the fishing boat's catch being off-loaded directly into the kitchen and shortly afterwards enjoy some of the finest and freshest shellfish imaginable. From the same pier you can then set off on a cruise to Seal Island. This is a speciality restaurant concentrating on wonderfully good seafood and there is such a variety of dishes from which to choose. The decor is simple – white walls, smooth wooden tables and comfortable chairs – to suit the Crannog philosophy of offering the finest and freshest seafood in simple friendly surroundings. From its vantage point on the pier, the restaurant has some wonderful views over Loch Linnhe. Crannog is extremely popular so it is advisable to book.

Open all year except Christmas Day + 1 Jan
Dining Room/Restaurant Lunch 12 – 2.30 pm (b-c)
Dinner 6 – 9.30 pm: 6 – 10.30 pm May to Sep (c)
Note: opening times may vary in winter months
No smoking area in restaurant
• Crannog bouillabaisse made from a variety of finfish and shellfish. Salmon fillet in filo pastry with a rich prawn sauce. Wing of skate in foamed lemon butter with capers. Langoustine prawns served cold with three mayonnaises – garlic, spicy and parsley remoulade. Walnut tart and cream. Cranachan whipped cream, raspberries, toasted oats and whisky.
Credit cards: 1, 3 + SWITCH, DELTA

THE MOORINGS HOTEL
Banavie, Fort William
Inverness-shire PH33 7LY
Tel: 01397 772797
Fax: 01397 772441

Situated off A830, 3 miles from Fort William at Banavie.

The Moorings is an attractive white-painted hotel which stands just above Neptune's Staircase by the Caledonian Canal. The interior is beautifully designed on a nautical theme, with wooden fittings and memorabilia from old ships and photographs of famous boats on the Canal. The hotel was awarded AA Hotel of the Year for Scotland 1994 as well as two AA Rosettes in recognition of its standard of food, and an RAC Merit and Hospitality award. Each of the bedrooms is individually designed offering high standards of comfort and facilities. In the comfortably elegant Jacobean Restaurant, with its beamed ceiling and rich colourful ambience, the menus are well balanced and carefully compiled. Naturally in such a location they concentrate on the best of local west coast seafood, Highland game and other prime produce. There is much evidence of skill and expertise in the kitchen with careful combinations of flavour and pleasing presentation. Smart well trained young staff add to the enjoyment of the dining experience.

Open all year except Christmas + Boxing Days
Rooms: 24 with private facilities
Bar Lunch 12 – 2 pm (b)
Dining Room Lunch (b-c) – by arrangement
Bar Supper 6 – 9.30 pm (b)
Dinner 7 – 9.30 pm (d)
Bed & Breakfast £30 – £40
Dinner B & B £65 – £85
Special Rates for 3+ nights
• Casserole of Mallaig scallops and Loch Linnhe prawns with a dill cream sauce. Loin of Mamore lamb with rhubarb chutney and a rosemary sauce. Roast Mallaig monkfish tail topped with tomato and served with a red wine and basil sauce. Grilled fillet of fresh local salmon with lentils and bacon, and a white wine and chive sauce. Steamed date pudding with sticky toffee sauce.
STB Highly Commended 4 Crowns
Credit cards: 1, 2, 3, 5
Proprietor: Norman Sinclair

Gairloch

Location 94
CREAG MOR HOTEL
Charleston, Gairloch
Ross-shire IV21 2AH
Tel: 01714 452068
Fax: 01714 452044

A9 north from Inverness, then A835 and A832 through Garve and Achnasheen and on via Loch Maree to Gairloch. Hotel on south side of Gairloch.

The Creag Mor is an impressive looking modern hotel set in landscaped gardens on the outskirts of Gairloch, with fine views over Old Gairloch Harbour to the Isle of Skye and the Outer Isles. Through the arched picture windows of the Gallery Lounge guests can appreciate the full benefit of these marvellous views. This lounge also features an exhibition of interesting water colour paintings by a local artist. The tastefully appointed bedroom accommodation is of a high standard providing the range of facilities guests expect today. Up a few steps from the lounge is the main dining room – the Mackenzie Room – where dinner menus offer a good range of well prepared and presented dishes, with the emphasis on seafood straight from Gairloch pier. For more informal eating there is the Buttery where there is an all day service of bar meals, snacks and coffee.

Open 1 Mar to 15 Nov
Rooms: 19 with private facilities
All day menu 8 am – 10 pm (b)
Dinner 6.30 – 9.30 pm (d)
Bed & Breakfast £25 – £39
Dinner B & B £48   £63
Special Rates available end/early season
• Smoked salmon. Haggis with a creamy tarragon and Glayva sauce. Medallions of Slattadale venison with sage and onion on a pool of game sauce flambéd with cognac. Darne of salmon with a parsley and lemon butter. Highland sirloin steak sautéed with garlic and black pepper. Cranachan.
STB Highly Commended 5 Crowns
Credit cards: 1, 3
Proprietors: Larry & Betty Nieto

Credit Card Code		Meal Price Range	
1.	Access/Mastercard/Eurocard	(a)	under £10
2.	American Express	(b)	£10 – £15
3.	Visa	(c)	£15 – £20
4.	Carte Bleu	(d)	£20 – £25
5.	Diners Club	(e)	£25 – £30
6.	Mastercharge	(f)	over £30

quince and mint. Breast of chicken marinated and baked with lime, fresh ginger root and sherry. Wild salmon with spinach and orange purée sauce. Pear and stem ginger custard tart. Highland raspberry brûlée.
STB Highly Commended 3 Crowns
No credit cards
Proprietors: Di Johnson & Inge Ford

LITTLE LODGE
North Erradale, Gairloch
Wester Ross IV21 2DS
Tel: 01445 771237
Take B8021 from Gairloch towards Melvaig, situated ¼ mile beyond turning to North Erradale.
The charm of Little Lodge starts with its stone and pine-lined walls, tasteful furnishings, burning logs and gracious hospitality, but there is much more to it than that. The rest of the special atmosphere of the place is created by its proprietors, Di Johnson and Inge Ford, whose personal charm, interest in their guests and superb cuisine have earned much praise. This white-washed crofthouse with its domestic hens, sheep and goats, is set on a moorland peninsula north of Gairloch, with fine views to the Torridon Mountains and Skye, and is an idyllic retreat. Dinner is served in a small conservatory room where guests can combine the delights of the superb food and the magnificent outlook. Di's imaginative marinades and sauces enhance excellent local produce, fish from the harbour and vegetables from the garden, while Inge's home-made bread, oatcakes, yoghurt and preserves, make the Scottish breakfast memorable and put the crowning seal on the excellent food and service.
Open Feb to mid Dec
Rooms: 3 with private facilities
Dinner at 7 pm (b-c)
Residents only
Unlicensed – guests welcome to take own wine + spirits
No children
No dogs
Wheelchair access to ground floor bedroom
No smoking throughout
Dinner B & B £35 – £42
• Goujons of monkfish with garlic mayonnaise. Avocado and locally smoked salmon salad. Noisettes of local lamb in port wine sauce with a jelly of

THE STEADING RESTAURANT
Achtercairn, Gairloch
Ross-shire IV21 2BP
Tel: 01445 172449
On A832 at junction with B802 in Gairloch.
Coffee shop/restaurant adjoining the prize winning Gairloch Museum of West Highland Life and located in converted 19th century farm buildings and retaining their old world atmosphere, with stone floors, white-washed walls and open rafters. Local produce, seafood fresh from the loch, home-baked cakes and scones are on offer and there are special dishes for children. Self-service by day and waitress service in evenings. As the complete menu is available all day it is possible to choose what is wanted when it is wanted. The price ranges shown are therefore what a smaller (lunch) or a larger (dinner) meal might cost. Some French spoken. Dogs not allowed in restaurant but may be tied up outside in courtyard with water and shade.
Open Easter to end Sep
Food service all day 9.30 am – 5 pm except Sun; 9.30 am – 9 pm Jul Aug Sep except Sun (b)
Dinner 7 – 9 pm Jul Aug Sep except Sun (d)
Closed Sun
• Flowerdale Bay whole crab. Munro venison casserole cooked in red wine and served with dumplings. Sirloin steak served with a choice of herb and garlic, lemon or prawn butter. Salmon steak marinated in white wine and green peppercorns. Cloutie dumpling.
Credit cards: 1, 3

Galashiels

Location 95

WOODLANDS HOUSE HOTEL & RESTAURANTS
Windyknowe Road, Galashiels
Selkirkshire TD1 1RQ
Tel: 01896 754722
Fax: 01896 754722
Just off A7, take A72 towards Peebles. Turn left up Hall Street – Windyknowe Road is second on right.
This large Victorian gothic mansion is set amidst well kept grounds and mature woodland overlooking the town of Galashiels, with views over the surrounding hills. Inside the stonework and architecture are reminiscent of a castle, all beautifully restored and decorated with stags heads, heraldic shields and ancient coats of arms. The large windows are all set in carved stonework, and ceilings in the public rooms feature ornate plasterwork. Kevin and Nicki Winsland have taken great care with the refurbishment of this fine old house to preserve its original ambience and character. The dining room is elegant and comfortable and has a good reputation for fine food and interesting menus. In addition there is Sanderson's – a steak-house restaurant – for a less formal dining style. This hotel makes a good base for visiting the beautiful Scottish Border countryside, and yet is within an hour of Edinburgh.
Open all year except Boxing Day
Rooms: 9 with private facilities
Bar Lunch 12 – 2 pm (a)
Dining Room/Restaurant Lunch 12 – 2 pm except Mon (b)
Carvery 12 – 7 pm Sun (a-b)
Bar Supper 6 – 9.30 pm (b)
Dinner 6 – 9.30 pm (c)
Bed & Breakfast £34 – £47
Dinner B & B £45 – £55
• Marinated duck with an apple and honey dressing. Lobster bisque. Smoked salmon layered over a bed of Waldorf salad with a lime dressing. Fillet of pork filled with apple and Stilton cheese served with a cider cream sauce. Lamb cutlets accompanied with a minted chasseur sauce. Prime sirloin steaks.
STB Commended 4 Crowns
Credit cards: 1, 3
Proprietors: Kevin & Nicki Winsland

Garve

Location 96

INCHBAE LODGE HOTEL
by Garve
Ross-shire IV23 2PH
Tel: 019975 269

On A835 Inverness-Ullapool, 6 miles west of Garve village.

In the very heart of the northern Highlands, Inchbae Lodge is ideally located for exploring this beautiful unspoilt part of Scotland. A former Victorian hunting lodge on the banks of the River Blackwater, it is surrounded by forests and mountains but while secluded it is only six miles from Garve village and gives easy access to all areas north of Inverness. Since taking over the business, Patrick and Judy Price have maintained the Inchbae Lodge's reputation for variety and high standards of food, showing imagination in the treatment of locally procured produce. Menus are very reasonably priced for the composition, preparation and care with which they are presented. There is free trout fishing at the bottom of the garden and clay pigeon shooting in the grounds – and a special deal for families, children are welcomed and accommodated free.

Open all year except Christmas + Boxing Days
Rooms: 12 with private facilities
Bar Lunch 12 – 2 pm (a)
Bar Supper 5 – 8.30 pm (a)
Dinner 7.30 – 8.30 pm (d)
No smoking in restaurant
Bed & Breakfast £28 – £33
Dinner B & B £49 – £54
Special Rates for 2+ nights
• Thin slices of prime beef marinated in olive oil, served with shavings of parmesan. Oven-baked monkfish with black peppercorns, served with a mustard and white wine sauce. Gressingham duck served off the bone with a lemon and tarragon sauce. Roast haunch of wild venison with a port and rowan sauce. Caramel and almond roulade.
STB Commended 3 Crowns
No credit cards
Proprietors: Patrick & Judy Price

Gatehouse-of-Fleet

Location 97

CALLY PALACE HOTEL
Gatehouse-of-Fleet
Dumfries & Galloway DG7 2DL
Tel: 01557 814341
Fax: 01557 814522

1 mile from Gatehouse-of-Fleet exit off A75 Dumfries-Stranraer, 30 miles west of Dumfries.

The Cally Palace is aptly named for it is truly a regal looking establishment. Approached by a long sweeping drive through woodland, this palatial four star hotel stands overlooking its own loch and 18 hole golf course in an idyllic setting within 100 acres of magnificent grounds. Marble pillars, floors and tables combine with gilt and exquisite plasterwork to reflect the grandeur of this old 18th century mansion. The elegant public rooms are spacious and grand in every sense of the word, and every window has delightful views of the grounds. The bedrooms, suites and family rooms are tastefully and comfortably appointed, with colour TV, trouser press, hairdryer etc and en suite facilities. There is a splendid traditional dining room with flowers and candles on the tables and silver service. The large windows look out over the lawns and in the evening the atmosphere is enhanced with background music from the grand piano. Menus concentrate on selecting and presenting good local produce with style, offering a daily changing table d'hôte menu as well as à la carte. There are excellent indoor leisure facilities of swimming pool and sauna etc, and outdoors there is putting, tennis and croquet as well as the hotel's own recently opened 18 hole par 70 golf course. The hotel is superbly managed by Jennifer Adams who selects and trains staff to be alert and responsive to guests' every need and probably few other hotels attract quite as much repeat business as does the Cally Palace from its ever-growing list of satisfied guests.

Open 3 Mar to 3 Jan
Rooms: 56 with private facilities
Snacks only 12.30 – 2 pm
Dining Room/Restaurant Lunch 12.30 – 2 pm (c)
Dinner 6.15 – 9.30 pm (d) – 4 course menu
No smoking in dining room
Dinner B & B £58 – £98
Special Rates available
• Prawn bisque. Roast sirloin of beef with

baby vegetables. Roast cannon of venison seasoned in five spice with a juniper berry jus-lie. Steamed suprême of salmon in a light saffron velouté served with spinach flavoured noodles. Ecclefechan butter tart with hazelnut sauce.*
STB Deluxe 4 Crowns
Credit cards: 1, 3 + SWITCH

Isle of Gigha

Location 98

GIGHA HOTEL
Isle of Gigha
Argyll PA41 7AA
Tel: 01583 505 254
Fax: 01583 505 244

A83 Lochgilphead-Campbeltown, c. 18 miles south of Tarbert turn into Tayinloan. Follow Gigha ferry sign.

This traditional white-painted building is the original old inn of the island which sits looking out over the Sound of Gigha to the hills of Kintyre. A combination of old world charm and modern comfort makes this a delightful place to stay. The island of Gigha is only a 20 minute ferry trip from the Mull of Kintyre but in some respects it is a century or two distant. Life is gentle and unhurried and flows at a pace that visitors can adjust to their needs whether they be walking, fishing, golfing, bird-watching or enjoying Achamore Gardens. There are bicycles for hire at the local store and post office, so the more energetic can visit some of the lovely little beaches further afield. As much of island life seems to revolve around the Gigha Hotel, you will find both locals and visitors in the bar swapping stories of their day's activities. The bedrooms are well appointed and the restaurant takes full advantage of freshly delivered seafood from the local fishing boats.

Open Mar to mid Oct
Rooms: 13, 11 with private facilities
Bar Lunch 12 – 2.30 pm (a)
Bar Supper 6 – 8.30 pm (a)
Dinner 7 – 9 pm (c) 4 course menu
Bed & Breakfast £30 – £36
Dinner B & B £45.50 – £49.50

Special Rates for 3+ nights
• Gigha lobster and clams. Seafood in a fennel sauce on a bed of tagliatelle. Roast beef with red wine and mushroom sauce. Grilled stuffed rainbow trout. Chicken coated with cinnamon and lemon butter.
STB Commended 3 Crowns
Credit cards: 1, 3
Proprietors: William & Sandra Howden

Glasgow

Location 99
THE BRASSERIE
176 West Regent Street
Glasgow G2 4RL
Tel: 0141 248 3801
Fax: 0141 248 8917
Approach via Bath Street from city centre; turn left into Blythswood Street then left into West Regent Street. From outwith city, follow one way systems via Blythswood Square to West Regent Street.

The name Brasserie seems quite a modern concept to be associated with the solid classic style of building in which it is situated. An imposing pillared entranceway leads you into the dining area which exudes an instant air of quality rather like an exclusive club. In all respects this is a first class restaurant where food is presented with skill and flair and there are some interesting combinations of ingredients to be found on the menus. Courteous and attentive well trained staff ensure that diners are well looked after. At lunchtime The Brasserie is a firm favourite with the business community while in the evening it appeals to a wider section of the population out to enjoy imaginative food in a pleasing atmosphere. It is worth noting that both restaurant and bar meals are available throughout the day.
Open all year except public holidays
Bar Meals 12 – 11 pm except Sun (a)
Dining Room/Restaurant Meals 12 – 11 pm except Sun (b-c)
Closed Sun
• Langoustine bisque. Isle of Seil oysters. Lamb noisettes, rosemary jus. Grilled salmon with leeks. Scallop and monkfish skewers. Prime fillet of Aberdeen Angus with a peppercorn sauce. Summer pudding, crème anglaise. Prune pastry, cognac sabayon.
Credit cards: 1, 2, 3, 5, 6 + SWITCH, DELTA

THE BUTTERY
652 Argyle Street
Glasgow G3 8UF
Tel: 0141 221 8188
Fax: 0141 204 4639
Junction 19, M8 – approach by St Vincent Street and Elderslie Street.

The Buttery is a perennial favourite and continues to be one of Glasgow's premier restaurants. The appearance of the old tenement building gives no inkling of the different world you will discover inside and the unique character of the place. Bits and pieces of old church furniture and lots of touches of Victoriana combine to create an ambience without equal in the city and an oasis of comfort and elegance. Polite and unobtrusive service characterise The Buttery. Jim Wilson who manages the restaurant has carefully selected the waiting staff. Efficient and well informed, they take great pride in their contribution to the whole dining experience. Interesting menus and beautifully presented food reflect much credit on the kitchen brigade headed by Chef Stephen Johnson. For less formal dining there is the Belfry which – contrary to what its name might suggest – is in the basement, with its own separate entrance from the car park. Food has a more bistro style but follows the same quality standards as are to be found in the rest of this interesting establishment.
Open all year except bank/public holidays
Bar Lunch 12 – 2.30 pm except Sun Sat (b)
Dining Room/Restaurant Lunch 12 – 2.30 pm except Sun Sat (d)
Dinner 7 – 10.30 pm except Sun (e)
Closed Sun
• Wild pigeon and blackberry pie with a toasted oatmeal glaze. Home-smoked fillet of salmon on a light beetroot and parsley cream. Highland venison layered with a home-made strawberry and raisin chutney on an Arran mustard jus. Sliced pork fillet on honey glazed apples with a rosemary and bee's pollen cream.
Credit cards: 1, 2, 3, 5, 6 + SWITCH, DELTA

THE CITY MERCHANT RESTAURANT
97 Candleriggs
Glasgow G1 1NP
Tel: 0141 553 1577
Facing City Halls in Candleriggs, in Glasgow's Merchant City. Candleriggs on right going east along Ingram Street.

Situated in the heart of Glasgow's Merchant City in a little cobbled street, is The City Merchant Restaurant created in the form of a traditional Victorian oyster bar. The premises were originally a post office and the Fruit Market Tearoom was in the basement in the days before the market moved to its current site at Blochairn. Now the basement houses The Oyster Bar which is most often in use as a function room. The Restaurant on the ground floor specialises in seafood and the policy is good Scottish produce, freshly prepared at value for money prices, served in a relaxed atmosphere. You may taste oysters and Loch Sween mussels taken from the sea the same morning, which arrive in Glasgow on the bus from Oban and are collected by Tony Matteo himself. However diners are not restricted to choosing fish and shellfish – meat-eaters are catered for as well. The blackboard menu highlights a selection of local and exotic seafoods delivered daily from the market. Children over six years welcome.
Open all year except first wk Jan + last 2 wks Jul
Dining Room/Restaurant Lunch 12 – 2.30 pm except Sun (a)
Dinner 5.30 – 10.30 pm except Sun (c) – booking advised
Closed Sun
Facilities for disabled visitors
• Partan bree – a creamy crab soup. Steamed Loch Sween mussels. Venison with chanterelles, red wine and redcurrant gravy, served with a skirlie tart. Queen scallops with dulse in a light shellfish sauce. Fillet of salmon baked in oatmeal with parsley and lemon butter. Roast pheasant with mead, port and juniper berries.
Credit cards: 1, 2, 3, 5, 6 + SWITCH
Proprietors: Tony & Linda Matteo

Credit Card Code		**Meal Price Range**	
1.	Access/Mastercard/Eurocard	(a)	under £10
2.	American Express	(b)	£10 – £15
3.	Visa	(c)	£15 – £20
4.	Carte Bleu	(d)	£20 – £25
5.	Diners Club	(e)	£25 – £30
6.	Mastercharge	(f)	over £30

CRANNOG SEAFOOD RESTAURANT
28 Cheapside Street
Glasgow G3 8BH
Tel: 0141 221 1727
Fax: 0141 221 1727

Off Broomielaw by River Clyde. At north end of Kingston Bridge. Accessible from Clydeside expressway.

Tucked away inconspicuously in Cheapside Street, Finnieston, the Crannog is not a restaurant that you chance upon, but it is indeed a joy to find. The location is as different as Glasgow from Fort William, where the original Crannog restaurant is to be found, but the same philosophy and quality of food prevail. The interior is almost spartan – white-washed walls decorated with interesting pieces of driftwood, and pine tables and chairs – but within these simple friendly surroundings you can experience the finest and freshest of Scottish seafoods. The menus concentrate on presenting interesting dishes using really fresh fish and shellfish, prepared using traditional cooking methods and combining complementary flavours. There is also a separate blackboard menu which highlights specialities of the day. Crannog's own smokehouse in Fort William supplies the smoked salmon, mussels, trout etc featured in the restaurant menus, and many of these items are now available by mail order.
Open all year except Christmas Day + 1 Jan
Dining Room/Restaurant Lunch 12 – 2.30 pm except Sun Mon (a-c)
Dinner 6 – 9.30 pm Tue to Thu: 6 – 10.30 pm Fri Sat (c)
Note: Pre-theatre meals available 5.30 – 7 pm
Closed Sun Mon
• Crannog bouillabaise – a hearty soup made from a variety of finfish and shellfish. Salmon marinated in brandy and dill, with a mustard sauce. Langoustine prawns served cold with three mayonnaises – garlic, spicy and

parsley rémoulade. Sole fillets rolled with smoked salmon, in a light sherry sauce. Walnut tart. Cranachan – whipped cream, raspberries, toasted oats and whisky.
Credit cards: 1, 3 + SWITCH, DELTA

GLASGOW HILTON INTERNATIONAL
Camerons Restaurant
1 William Street
Glasgow G3 8HT
Tel: 0141 204 5555
Fax: 0141 204 5004

Access from M8 to hotel, or via Waterloo Street and Bishop Street from city centre.

Camerons is the premier restaurant within the luxury five star Glasgow Hilton International. The restaurant has been beautifully designed and decorated on the theme of a Highland shooting lodge, with subtly separated dining areas set out in the style of the lodge's dining room, library etc. Within these surroundings it is hard to believe that you are actually dining in such a modern hotel. There is that quiet dignified air of gracious living which you would expect to find in a Highland lodge. The menu echoes the theme and presents a fine selection of prime Scottish produce in imaginative dishes created by the kitchen team headed by Executive Chef Michael Mizzen. The waiting staff dressed in their traditional Cameron tartan trews have the attentive confidence that goes with the knowledge that they are serving the best of good food. As is befitting of a deluxe grading, the hotel is luxuriously appointed and has an excellent standard of accommodation. There is also an outstanding range of facilities, including a swimming pool and gymnasium.
Open all year
Rooms: 319 with private facilities
Dining Room/Restaurant Lunch 12 – 2.30 pm except Sun Sat (c)
Dinner 7 – 11 pm (f)
No dogs
Facilities for disabled visitors
No smoking area in restaurant
Bed & Breakfast £127.50 – £362
Dinner B & B £132 – £367
Room Rate £115 – £350
• Warmed Loch Buie oysters with a fennel spaghetti and a savora mustard sabayon. Light broth of Western Isles seafood and summer vegetables with pastry twists. Grilled supreme of halibut with samphire and a rich clam nage. Lightly smoked fillet of Borders lamb with

polenta, charred aubergine and fresh vegetable dips. Medley of Highland game with forest mushrooms on a rich game jus.
STB Deluxe 5 Crowns
Credit cards: 1, 2, 3, 5, 6 + SWITCH

MOAT HOUSE INTERNATIONAL
Congress Road
Glasgow G3 8QT
Tel: 0141 204 0733 • Telex: 776244
Fax: 0141 221 2022

Prestige Award Winner 1992

Situated on the banks of the River Clyde, next to the SECC.

The award winning Moat House International has one of Glasgow's most desirable sites right on the banks of the River Clyde, adjacent to the Scottish Exhibition Centre, and with generous parking. The interior layout is dramatically different rather in the style of an ocean liner and the views from the huge windows on to the river complete this effect. Towering over this open plan area is a magnificent mural of Clydeside Glasgow. Beyond the marbled entrance foyer there is a small but well equipped leisure centre with swimming pool. Bedrooms and suites are luxuriously equipped and have splendid panoramic views. The hotel has two restaurants both of which are within the atrium on the ground floor and offer two levels of dining. Top of the range is The Mariner, set on a raised central area, where food of exceptional quality and style is presented. In recognition of the outstanding standard this restaurant has been awarded two AA Rosettes. Adjacent is the Pointhouse Restaurant which offers a carvery as well as an à la carte menu with a good range of all day dining in a more informal setting. The Moat House is very well managed and deserves its prominence as one of the city's very best hotels.
Open all year
Rooms: 283 with private facilities
All day dining 6.30 am – 10.45 pm (Pointhouse)
Dining Room/Restaurant Lunch 12 – 2.30 pm (Mariner) (c)
Dinner (Mariner) 7 – 11 pm (d)
No dogs
Facilities for disabled visitors
No smoking areas in restaurants
Bed & Breakfast £35 – £45
Dinner B & B £55 – £65
Room Rate from £50
• Fillet of sea bass with asparagus

soufflé, spiced spaetzle and vanilla fumet. Medallions of salmon with herb noodles, vegetable pearls and dill. Tournedos of Angus fillet with shallots, baby leeks, wild mushrooms and tarragon essence. Peppered loin of lamb with haricot beans, savoy cabbage, smoked garlic, tomato and basil sauce. STB Highly Commended 5 Crowns
Credit cards: 1, 2, 3

ROGANO RESTAURANT & CAFE ROGANO
11 Exchange Place
Glasgow G1 3AN
Tel: 0141 248 4055
Fax: 0141 248 2608
Glasgow city centre, near Buchanan Street precinct and Queen Street/George Square.
Restaurants come and go but those that are really good survive and Rogano has been around the Glasgow scene for as long as anyone can remember. It was re-modelled in 1935 in "art deco" style with wood panelling inset with mermaids and giant seashell carvings. The restaurant still retains the appeal, the ambience and the high standards on which its reputation was founded. It concentrates primarily on serving superb fish and shellfish for which it has always been noted and it does so with style, but there are several other interesting alternatives to fish for those who prefer them. The main restaurant on the ground floor has an air of luxury and elegance, and downstairs the Cafe Rogano is much more liberal with a busy bistro atmosphere and equally good food.

Open all year except public holidays
Bar Meals 12 – 6 pm except Sun (a)
Cafe Rogano 12 – 11 pm Mon to Thu: 12 – 12 midnight Fri Sat: 6 – 10 pm Sun (c)
Dining Room/Restaurant Lunch 12 – 2.30 pm except Sun (c-f)
Dinner 6.30 – 10.30 pm Mon to Sat: 6 – 10 pm Sun (f)
No smoking requested before 2 pm (Lunch) and 9 pm (Dinner)
• Crisp-fried salmon with redcurrants and coriander. Feuilleté of mussels and monkfish on a chive cream. Fillets of halibut with a champagne and oyster broth. Iced caramel parfait. Mousse brûlée.
Credit cards: 1, 2, 3, 5 + SWITCH, DELTA

THE UBIQUITOUS CHIP
12 Ashton Lane
Glasgow G12 8SJ
Tel: 0141 334 5007
A secluded lane off Byres Road in the heart of Glasgow's West End.
The Ubiquitous Chip is more than a restaurant, it is almost an institution in Glasgow which everyone seems to know and of which everyone has heard. The setting is unlikely, a white-washed Victorian mews stable down an old fashioned cobbled street, but a restaurant with a style all its own. There is a selection of areas in which to eat, from the glass roofed ground floor with its lush green plants and trees, to the small mezzanine restaurant which overlooks this, and then there is the adjoining spacious dining room with white-washed walls covered in modern art hangings. The menus emphasise and concentrate on the wealth of good regional produce and the chefs present meals with inspired originality and combination of flavours. 'Upstairs at the Chip' serves light inexpensive lunches and evening meals. Dinner in the restaurant is something to be taken seriously and prices reflect this though they are still good value for money. 'The Chip' boasts one of the UK's most celebrated, extensive and modestly priced wine lists.
Open all year except Christmas Day, 31 Dec + 1 Jan
Upstairs Restaurant 12 – 11 pm (a)
Dining Room Lunch 12 – 2.30 pm (b-c)
Dinner 5.30 – 11 pm (d)
• Oban landed squid cooked in its own ink with balsamic onion and lemon zest vinaigrette. Pan-fried marinaded fillets of venison with a green peppercorn and

Drambuie sauce. Aberdeen Angus steak with onion and leek marmalade. Seil Island scallops served on a roasted potato cake with stewed garlic.
Credit cards: 1, 2, 3, 5
Proprietor: Ron Clydesdale

VICTORIA & ALBERT
159 Buchanan Street
Glasgow G1 2JX
Tel: 0141 248 6329
Approach via Buchanan Street pedestrian precinct towards St Vincent Street or from West George Street, short distance from George Square.
A much patronised and very popular establishment with the business community of Glasgow city centre, the Victoria and Albert is primarily an up market bar restaurant, situated beneath Glasgow's Stock Exchange. There is a Victorian charm and elegance about it which is very appealing and the dining areas are entirely harmonious. Its central location near the Royal Concert Hall and the Theatre Royal, make it a suitable rendezvous for dining before or after performances. You can also enjoy coffee from ten in the morning and the restaurant/bar menu is available throughout the day.
Open all year except Christmas + Boxing Days, 1 + 2 Jan, public holidays
Coffee/Snacks from 10 am except Sun (a)
Restaurant/Bar Menu 11.30 am – 10.30 pm except Sun (a-b)
Closed Sun
Children welcome in restaurant only
• Salad of smoked chicken, feta cheese, capers and crispy bacon. Steamed fillets of sole with a crab mousse on a dill and lemon cream. Terrine of citrus sorbets set on mango purée.
Credit cards: 1, 2, 3, 5, 6 + SWITCH, DELTA

WESTERWOOD HOTEL, GOLF & COUNTRY CLUB

St Andrews Drive
Cumbernauld G68 0EW
Tel: 01236 457171
Fax: 01236 738478

A80 Cumbernauld, 13 miles north-east of Glasgow. Take Wardpark exit. Follow to roundabout, take Dullatur exit. At mini roundabout, turn right – road leads to hotel entrance.

This spacious and luxurious hotel nestles into the Kilsyth Hills. It is a modern building which has been magnificently furnished in an elegant traditional style. The 18 hole golf course was designed by Seve Ballesteros and Dave Thomas and is of course the principal recreational feature of the hotel, but excellent leisure facilities are also available such as a swimming pool and gymnasium, tennis and squash courts, snooker etc. The hotel offers a range of dining in its two restaurants and has established a high reputation for the excellence of its food. Whether you eat in the Club House or the upmarket Old Masters Restaurant, you can expect to experience and enjoy well prepared and presented food from the enthusiastic kitchen brigade. There is an interesting wine list to complement your menu choice. French, German and Spanish spoken.

Open all year
Note: accommodation closed 23 to 28 Dec
Rooms: 49 with private facilities
Bar Lunch 12 – 2.30 pm (a)
Dining Room/Restaurant Lunch (Club House) 12 – 2.30 pm (b)
Bar Supper (Club House) 7 – 10 pm (c)
Dinner (Old Masters) 7 – 9.30 pm except Sun Mon (d)
Facilities for disabled visitors
Bed & Breakfast £50 – £60
Room Rate £55 – £95
• *Smoked haddock chowder with saffron and horseradish, garnished with green lentils and bacon. Canon of lamb set on a bed of creamed aubergine with a whisky and pickled walnut sauce. Fillet of turbot garnished with ruby grapefruit, presented with a warm coriander, honey and olive oil dressing. Medallion of beef fillet topped with a horseradish crust, set on a burgundy truffle essence.*
STB Highly Commended 5 Crowns
Credit cards: 1, 2, 3, 5, 6

Glenelg

Location 100

GLENELG INN

Glenelg Bay, Glenelg, nr Shiel Bridge
Ross-shire IV40 8AG
Tel: 0159 982 273
Fax: 0159 982 373

Access to Glenelg via unclassified road west of A87 at Shiel Bridge, 1 mile from Kylerhea-Skye ferry which runs April to October.

Situated at the closest point to Skye on the Scottish mainland, the village of Glenelg can be reached by ferry from Skye or by a single track road from Shiel Bridge which must be one of the most spectacular routes in Scotland. The Glenelg Inn stands in its own extensive grounds overlooking the bay. It has been skilfully converted from old coaching mews to retain the traditional character of an inn, yet offering the utmost in comfort in its six individually styled bedrooms. The dining room offers fine Scottish cuisine using local seafood, game, lamb and other seasonally fresh produce. In its friendly bar, guest, crofter and fisherman alike relax in the genuine atmosphere of the ceilidh. Cruises can be arranged around the sea lochs to unspoilt beaches, islands and hidden coves on the inn's own boats, weather permitting.

Open Easter to Oct + New Year
Rooms: 6 with private facilities
Bar Lunch 12.30 – 2.15 pm (a)
Bar Supper 6.30 – 9 pm except Sun (a)
Dinner 7.30 – 9 pm (c)
No smoking in dining room
Facilities for disabled visitors
Dinner B & B £45 – £75
Special Rates for 4+ nights
• *Locally smoked seafood platter. Fresh Loch Hourn scallops. Locally bred hill lamb, roasted with fresh mint and gravy. Scotch sirloin steak, pan-fried and finished in a brandy sauce. Poached fillet of local salmon with a hollandaise sauce.*
No credit cards
Proprietor: Christopher Main

Glenfinnan

Location 101

THE PRINCE'S HOUSE

Glenfinnan
Inverness-shire PH37 4LT
Tel: 01397 722 246
Fax: 01397 722 307

15 miles west of Fort William on A830 'Road to the Isles' ½ mile on right past Glenfinnan Monument.

Since 1990 when they took over the hotel known as The Stage House, Robert and Carole Hawkes have been continuously upgrading the building and improving standards throughout. To reflect these changes they decided to rename this old 17th century coaching inn The Prince's House so still maintaining its connections with the Jacobite history of the area, for Glenfinnan is the place where Bonnie Prince Charlie landed from France in 1745 to claim the Scottish throne. He may even have taken a dram at the inn since this was the only building in the immediate area at that time! Under the supervision of the present owners, the hotel has been thoroughly modernised and now provides a very good standard of comfortable accommodation, including five deluxe bedrooms. Chef/proprietor Carole Hawkes has established an enviable reputation for providing an excellent menu making extensive use of fresh and smoked local produce, in particular game and shellfish. There is a choice of dining, either in Flora's Restaurant where an à la carte menu is offered, or more informally in the lounge bar. Lovely log fires in winter enhance the peaceful and relaxed atmosphere of the inn. This makes a good base for lots of outdoor pursuits like fishing and walking. Boats and mountain bikes may be hired, and there are beaches nearby.

Open 1 Apr to 30 Nov + New Year
Rooms: 9 with private facilities
Bar Lunch 12.30 – 2.30 pm (a)
Bar Supper 5 – 9 pm (a)
Dinner 6.30 – 8.30 pm (c)
No smoking in restaurant or rooms
Bed & Breakfast £25.95 – £37.95
Dinner B & B £45.95 – £57.95
Special Rates for 3+ nights
• *Local wild salmon steak lightly poached and served with butter and chive sauce. Lamb cutlets chargrilled and accompanied by a gooseberry and mint sauce. Chargrilled prime Scotch beef steaks. Venison steak with a game and onion gravy with rowanberry jelly.*

Cranachan. Selection of Scottish cheeses served with oatcakes.
STB Commended 3 Crowns
Credit cards: 1, 2, 3, + SWITCH, DELTA
Proprietors: Robert & Carole Hawkes

Glenlivet
Location 102

MINMORE HOUSE
Glenlivet, Ballindalloch
Banffshire AB37 9DB
Tel: 01807 590 378
Fax: 01807 590 472

On B9136, off B9008, 9 miles from Tomintoul. Adjacent to The Glenlivet Distillery.

Minmore House is tucked away in four acres of landscaped gardens adjacent to the Glenlivet Distillery, with fine open views across the River Livet and excellent local walks which are well maintained by the Crown Estate. Originally the home of the founder of the distillery, the house is comfortably and appropriately furnished throughout with period furniture. In the oak-panelled bar with its log fires, there is a selection of nearly 100 malt whiskies from which to choose, and guests can enjoy delicious afternoon tea in the spacious drawing room. Belinda Luxmoore is a hostess par excellence. The descriptions on the daily changing menus are simple but her cooking is traditional and superb. This is a wonderful retreat for those who enjoy the countryside and wholesome good food.

Open 1 May to 25 Oct
Rooms: 9 with private facilities
Bar + Picnic Lunches can be arranged for residents
Dinner at 8 pm (d) 5 course set menu
No smoking in dining room
Bed & Breakfast £35 – £37
Dinner B & B £45 – £55
Special Rates for 3+ nights
• Home-made soups e.g. pea and mint, Cullen skink. Grilled monkfish provençale. Aberdeen Angus chateaubriand. Roast rack of Highland lamb with fresh mint and honey glaze.

Fresh raspberry cheesecake. Lochin Ora burnt cream. Scottish cheeses.
STB Commended 4 Crowns
Credit cards: 1, 3
Proprietor: Belinda Luxmoore

Glenrothes
Location 103

BALBIRNIE HOUSE HOTEL
Balbirnie Park, Markinch
by Glenrothes
Fife KY7 6NE
Tel: 01592 610066
Fax: 01592 610529

Prestige Award Winner 1991

Off A92 on B9130, follow directions to village of Markinch and Balbirnie Park.
Balbirnie is a delightful Georgian country house dating from 1777, now Listed Grade 'A' – of architectural and historical importance. Privately owned, the house has been caringly restored and converted to a quite magnificent small luxury hotel which is situated in a beautiful landscaped estate and country park of 400 acres. Internally it is superb, the unique long gallery, old library and drawing room being noteworthy. The restaurant looks over formal gardens and ancient yew hedges. This is an establishment of which the entire staff seem to be proud and anxious to maintain standards. Chef Ian MacDonald presides in the kitchen and upholds the hotel's reputation for fine food and interesting dishes that use, whenever possible, the natural larder that is Scotland. Balbirnie was named Scotland on Sunday 'Word of Mouth' Restaurant of the Year 1993/94. Geographically the hotel is ideally situated in the heart of the Kingdom of Fife, within easy reach of St Andrews, the quaint fishing villages and countryside of Fife, as well as Edinburgh, the capital, which is about 30 minutes drive away.

Open all year
Rooms: 30 with private facilities
Bar Lunch 12 – 2.30 pm (b)
Dining Room/Restaurant Lunch 12 – 2.30 pm (c)
Dinner 7 – 9.30 pm (e) 4 course menu
Bed & Breakfast £85 – £97.50
Dinner B & B £112.50 – £125
Special Rates available
• Cock-a-leekie soup. Chargrilled fillet of Shetland salmon with a sauce of virgin olive oil, balsamic vinegar, coriander and tomato. Loin of lamb baked in a puff

pastry lattice, served with broad beans and a natural essence flavoured with basil. Collops of Perthshire venison, served with poached pear, roasted baby onions and pickled walnut red wine sauce.
STB Deluxe 5 Crowns
Credit cards: 1, 2, 3, 5
Proprietors: The Russell Family

RESCOBIE HOTEL & RESTAURANT
Valley Drive, Leslie
Glenrothes
Fife KY6 3BQ
Tel: 01592 742143
Fax: 01592 620231

8 miles from M90 – just off A911 at west end of the village of Leslie.
This is a warm and friendly little country house hotel of the 1930s, with many original features and appropriate period furniture, and set in immaculate grounds. There are two comfortable and uncrowded dining rooms and a lovely lounge with deep armchairs and a log fire. The table d'hôte menu changes daily and there is a supplementary à la carte extending the choice, and always a full vegetarian menu. The food is excellent, of a far higher standard than is normally associated with a two star hotel, and has been recognised by the award of a Rosette from the Automobile Association. Perhaps because it is off the beaten tourist track Rescobie has to try harder and it certainly seems to do so, attracting much repeat business from the business community in Glenrothes as well as local residents. Children are very welcome with appropriate reductions. French and German spoken.

Open all year except 24 to 26 Dec
Rooms: 10 with private facilities
Bar Lunch 12 – 2 pm (a)
Dining Room/Restaurant Lunch 12 – 2 pm (a)
Dinner 7 – 9 pm (c)
No dogs
Bed & Breakfast £30 – £50
Dinner B & B £38 – £56
Special Rates for 3+ nights
• Crab bisque. Monkfish tail wrapped in bacon, set on a bed of vegetables and coated with a tarragon butter sauce. Prime fillet of lamb with basil and wholegrain mustard, wrapped in puff pastry and baked, served on a sauce of red wine and shallots. Raspberry cranachan.
STB Commended 4 Crowns
Credit cards: 1, 2, 3, 5
Proprietors: Tony & Wendy Hughes-Lewis

Grange
by Errol

WATERYBUTTS LODGE
Grange, by Errol
Perthshire PH2 7SZ
Tel: 01821 642894
Fax: 01821 642523

*A85 Perth-Dundee, 9 miles out of Perth
take road for Grange. Then after
1½ miles turn left, immediately
before railway crossing.*

The original building was a 15th century friary attached to Coupar Angus Abbey though the lectern style doocot and small turreted stone stair are all that remains. The main Georgian building was erected in 1802 and later added to in the Victorian era. It is a beautiful old Georgian lodge set in lovely grounds where there is a unique herb garden, providing fresh herbs for the kitchen, which was formed originally from Dutch soil shipped as ballast on boats returning from Holland after delivering potatoes. The atmosphere at Waterybutts is distinctly 'house party' and guests wine and dine in style around a 16 foot Charles I refectory table, enjoying good conversation, good food, and an ambience of yesteryear.

*Open all year
Rooms: 7 with private facilities
Dinner 7 – 10 pm (b) 4 course menu
Non-residents – by prior arrangement
Restricted Licence
No children
Bed & Breakfast £27.50 – £35
Dinner B & B £42.50 – £50*
• *Cullen skink. Fresh trout pâté. Moules marinière. Roast haunch of venison. Tay salmon poached in herbs. All game in season.*
*STB Highly Commended 3 Crowns
Credit cards: 1, 2, 3
Proprietors: Barry & Rachel
Allenby-Wilcox*

Grantown-on-Spey

ARDCONNEL HOUSE
Woodlands Terrace, Grantown-on-Spey
Moray PH26 3JU
Tel: 01479 872104
Fax: 01479 872104

On A95, south-west entry to town.
Well kept gardens and neatly trimmed lawns round this splendid Victorian villa on the southern edge of Grantown-on-Spey, give an immediate indication that this is a well tended property in which high standards prevail. The interior more than lives up to expectation as a recent programme of refurbishment has just been completed. Public rooms are pleasingly furnished and attractive and the spacious bedrooms are tastefully appointed. James and Barbara Casey express their philosophy as providing quality food and accommodation in a relaxed and friendly atmosphere – and at realistic prices. The menu changes daily in order to utilise the best available produce and the standard of food is high and of interesting variety.

*Open 1 Mar to 31 Oct + New Year
Rooms: 7 with private facilities
Dinner at 7 pm (b)
Residents only
Restricted Licence
Children over 10 years welcome
No smoking throughout
Bed & Breakfast £21 – £30
Dinner B & B £34 – £43*
• *Home-made soup e.g. wild mushroom; carrot, leek and ginger. Buckie haddock in a mornay sauce. Venison in a wine and cream sauce. Wild Spey salmon. Roasts of beef, lamb, pork. Chicken and herbs. Sticky toffee pudding. Clootie dumpling. Fudge cake with foaming orange sauce.*
*STB Deluxe 3 Crowns
Credit cards: 1, 2, 3
Proprietors: James & Barbara Casey*

THE ARDLARIG
Woodlands Terrace
Grantown-on-Spey
Moray PH26 3JU
Tel: 01479 873245

From A9 Perth-Inverness follow signs for Grantown-on-Spey. On entry to town, one of first houses on left.
The Ardlarig is an imposing blue whinstone villa set in its own gardens. Before conversion to a guest house, it was the private residence of Sir Thomas Shankland – a notable local figure who was Britain's Commissioner to Nigeria. Mike and Sue Greer are proud of their standards of food and every dish is home-made, using local produce whenever possible, and presented with care in a pleasantly furbished dining room. The entire operation is based on offering affordable accommodation and food in a relaxed comfortable atmosphere where the emphasis is on friendly, courteous service. Children welcome.

*Open all year except 23 to 29 Dec
Rooms: 7, 1 with private facilities
Dinner at 7 pm (b)
Residents only
Restricted Licence
No smoking in dining room
Bed & Breakfast £17.50 – £18.50
Dinner B & B £28 – £29
Special Rates for 3+ nights*
• *Smoked haddock chowder served with warm rolls. Fricassée of Scotch lamb in a cream sauce with mushrooms and onions. Strathspey salmon steak with a chive sauce. Roasted silverside of Scotch beef with Yorkshire pudding. Plums in shortcrust pastry served with fresh cream. Raspberry brûlée.*
*STB Commended 2 Crowns
No credit cards
Proprietors: Sue & Mike Greer*

CULDEARN HOUSE
Woodlands Terrace, Grantown-on-Spey
Moray PH26 3JU
Tel: 01479 872106
Fax: 01479 873641

On A95, south-west entry to Grantown-on-Spey.
A fine Victorian house on the outskirts of the town with a solid permanent air to it and a distinctly Scottish atmosphere. Alasdair and Isobel Little are very welcoming and genuinely concerned to ensure that their guests enjoy their stay. Culdearn House was named AA Guest House of the Year 1994 for Scotland. There is a high standard of decor and furnishing throughout and the bedrooms are all en suite looking out over well kept lawns and mature trees. The menu changes daily and concentrates on producing a selection of good food based on some regional specialities and some old favourites. Grantown-on-Spey is increasingly recognised as a good base from which to tour the Highlands and has lots of appeal to walkers, anglers, bird-watchers and golfers.

Open 1 Mar to 31 Oct

Rooms: 9 with private facilities
Picnic Lunches to order
Dinner 6.45 – 7.30 pm (c)
Residents only
Restricted Licence
No dogs
No smoking in dining room
Dinner B & B from £48
Special Rates for 3+/7+ nights
• Carrot and coriander soup. Roast Moray lamb served with redcurrant, mint and orange jelly. Poached fillets of Strathspey salmon in a butter sauce. Wild Highland venison gently cooked in red wine. Prime Angus fillet steak pan-fried with mushrooms in cream and Drambuie. Plum and cinnamon crumble. Chocolate roulade.
STB Deluxe 3 Crowns
Credit cards: 1, 3, 5, 6
Proprietors: Alasdair & Isobel Little

GARTH HOTEL
The Square, Grantown-on-Spey
Moray PH26 3HN
Tel: 01479 872836/872162
On the Square of Grantown-on-Spey.
The Garth Hotel commands a view of the picturesque Square of Grantown-on-Spey and sits amidst four acres of landscaped gardens. This three star hotel dates from the 17th century and offers old world charm with every modern comfort and convenience. Fourteen individually furnished bedrooms – all en suite – with direct dial telephone, colour TV and tea/coffee-making facilities. Extensive and selective menu with an accent on fresh local produce. French and German spoken.
Open all year
Rooms: 14 with private facilities
Bar Lunch 12 – 2 pm (a)
Dining Room/Restaurant Lunch 12 – 1.30 pm (b)
Dinner 7.30 – 8.30 pm (d)
No dogs
No smoking in restaurant
Bed & Breakfast £38 – £47
Dinner B & B from £60
Special Rates available
• Buchan farmhouse broth. Fillet of Spey salmon poached and served with a fresh cucumber sauce. Local spring lamb roasted with garlic and rosemary, served with Madeira sauce, roast gravy and mint sauce.
STB Highly Commended 4 Crowns
Credit cards: 1, 2, 3, 5
Proprietor: Gordon McLaughlan

KINROSS HOUSE
Woodside Avenue, Grantown-on-Spey
Moray PH26 3JR
Tel: 01479 872042
Fax: 01479 873504
Proceeding up High Street from south on A95 turn right at traffic lights, then right at first crossroads – 200 yards on left.
An attractive Victorian villa in a quiet residential area of the town with a tidy garden in front and car parking at the side. There is a lovely homely and friendly atmosphere. Bedrooms are warm bright and cheerful, with welcome tray and colour TV. A no smoking rule applies throughout the house. The set menu of good wholesome fare changes daily, is well balanced and good value and attracts favourable guest comments. Mr Elder dons his kilt for the occasion and is an attentive and caring host. Children over seven years welcome.
Open 1 Apr to 31 Oct
Rooms: 6, 5 with private facilities
Dinner at 7 pm (b) 4 course menu
Residents only
No dogs
Facilities for disabled visitors
No smoking throughout
Bed & Breakfast £21 – £27
Dinner B & B £32 – £38
• Daily changing menu using local produce. Speyside smoked salmon. Fresh fish, venison, beef, lamb. Rumbledethumps. Home-made desserts. Scottish cheeseboard.
STB Highly Commended 3 Crowns
No credit cards
Proprietors: David & Katherine Elder

RAVENSCOURT HOUSE HOTEL
Seafield Avenue, Grantown-on-Spey
Moray PH26 3JG
Tel: 01479 872286
Fax: 01479 873260
Just off main Square.
Ravenscourt is a delightful town house hotel with more of the atmosphere of a country house in its quiet quality and elegance. The drawing room has some fine original oil paintings and water colours and is sumptuously furnished. Dinner is served in the tastefully appointed Orangery Restaurant. The menus are well balanced and the standard of cooking and presentation is excellent, as is the service. A good wine list features a selection for all tastes at all price levels and there are especially chosen house wines to complement the food. Comments in the visitors book clearly indicate that many guests return again and again to enjoy Ravenscourt.

Open all year
Rooms: 9 with private facilities
Dining Room Lunch 12 – 2 pm (b)
Dinner 7 – 10 pm (c-d) 4 course set menu
No dogs
No smoking area in restaurant
Bed & Breakfast £29.50 – £39.50
Dinner B & B £51.50 – £61.50
• Mixed platter of Scottish smoked halibut and salmon paupiette stuffed with avocado fromage. New season's rack of Scottish lamb. Half honey roast duckling with ripe cherries and wine. Aberdeen Angus sirloin steak au poivre. Local salmon steak with a lemon grass sauce.
STB Deluxe 3 Crowns
Credit cards: 1, 3

Gullane

Location 106

GOLF INN HOTEL
Main Street, Gullane
East Lothian EH31 2AB
Tel: 01620 843259
Fax: 01620 842066
18 miles east of Edinburgh, 4 miles west of North Berwick.
Originally an old coaching house, the Golf Inn Hotel is now an established family run business, catering both for the golfer and non-golfer. The emphasis is on personal and friendly service coupled with excellent food and good beer! The hotel has been refurbished to a high standard and offers facilities for weddings, conferences, dinner dances etc. For the resident, golf packages can be tailored to requirement. The Carriage Lounge has an interesting range of light snack dishes and the Saddlers Restaurant menu, for the serious diner, has just the right touch of choice and quality.
Open all year except Christmas Day
Rooms: 18, 11 with private facilities
Restricted parking
Bar Meals 12 – 10 pm (a-b)
Dining Room/Restaurant Lunch 12 – 6 pm Sun only (c)
Dinner 6.30 – 10 pm (c)
Dogs by arrangement
Bed & Breakfast £32 – £42
Dinner B & B £45 – £55
• Quenelles of Scottish salmon with a lobster sauce. Medallions of venison with an essence of rosehip and juniper. Prime fillet steak stuffed with pâté and covered with a port and cream sauce.
STB Commended 2 Crowns
Credit cards: 1, 3, 5
Proprietors: Tom & Kathleen Saddler

GREYWALLS

Muirfield, Gullane
East Lothian EH31 2EG
Tel: 01620 842144
Fax: 01620 842241

Prestige Award Winner 1992

Signposted (Historic Building) in Gullane, off A198 Musselburgh-North Berwick – a few miles from A1.
This exquisitely proportioned country house was designed at the turn of the century by the renowned architect Sir Edwin Lutyens and retains all of the grace and grandeur of the times. It sits amidst magnificent formal gardens on the very edge of the famous Muirfield Golf Course. The house is almost a time capsule, yet incorporating the elegance of the Edwardian era with modern comfort and amenities. The cuisine is outstanding and Chef Paul Baron's deft touch makes every meal a special occasion. The whole atmosphere of Greywalls is of luxury and relaxation.
Open 13 Apr to 31 Oct
Rooms: 22 with private facilities
Bar Lunch 12.30 – 2 pm except Sun (b)
Dining Room/Restaurant Lunch 12.30 – 2 pm (c)
Dinner 7.30 – 9.15 pm (f)
No smoking in dining room
Facilities for disabled visitors
Bed & Breakfast £75 – £95
• Loin of venison served with a selection of wild mushrooms and a red wine sauce. Steamed fillet of Scottish salmon with a champagne sauce garnished with cucumber noodles. Brandy snap basket filled with fresh fruit marinated in peach liqueur with an orange and Earl Grey sorbet.
STB Highly Commended 4 Crowns
Credit cards: 1, 2, 3, 5, 6 + SWITCH
Proprietors: Giles & Ros Weaver

Haddington

Location 107

MAITLANDFIELD HOUSE HOTEL

24 Sidegate, Haddington
East Lothian EH41 4BZ
Tel: 0162 082 6513
Fax: 0162 082 6713

Turn off A1 Edinburgh-Newcastle at Haddington. Follow signs for town centre then for Gifford. Hotel is 400 yards after Gifford turn-off on the right.
Maitlandfield House is set in beautifully landscaped gardens within minutes of the centre of Haddington. The hotel has been completely redeveloped and fully refurbished in recent years to provide high standards of accommodation and facilities. Of the 22 en suite rooms, three are master bedrooms with four poster beds, and all are tastefully appointed. It is claimed that this small East Lothian town has been visited by no less than 16 kings since 1124, so it is very appropriate that the hotel has used this theme in The Sixteen Kings Restaurant. One wall of this small and intimate room is decorated with paintings depicting the visiting kings. Under its canopied ceiling, guests dine by candlelight at highly polished dark wood tables, savouring the delights of the menus based on French and Scottish cuisine. For more informal dining there is the spacious and very popular Conservatory which offers a bistro style menu, but equally you can enjoy drop in for a snack or just a drink. There is also a beer garden and children's play area. Other facilities include a ballroom and three suites suitable for meetings or private parties. A courtesy coach is available for groups of six or more visiting The Sixteen Kings Restaurant within a 20 mile radius.
Open all year
Rooms: 22 with private facilities
Bar Meals 10 am – 9.30 pm (a)
Dinner 7 – 10 pm except Sun Mon (c)
Facilities for disabled visitors
Bed & Breakfast £37.50 – £65
Dinner B & B £50 – £75
Special Breaks available
• Breast of goose sliced onto a port and berry sauce. Fillet of seacat stuffed with smoked haddock on a butter sauce. Scottish salmon filled with fresh oysters and topped with a chive sauce.
Credit cards: 1, 2, 3 + SWITCH
Proprietor: Alan Berry

Isle of Harris

Location 108

ALLAN COTTAGE GUEST HOUSE

Tarbert
Isle of Harris PA85 3DJ
Tel: 01859 50 2146

Upper road overlooking ferry road, c. 600 yards from ferry.
An attractive old building at the side of the road which was formerly a telephone exchange and which has preserved some of the best features. It has been extended to form a house of unusual charm and character, quiet, homely and welcoming. Rooms are all beautifully furnished in cottage style and all bedrooms have private facilities. Bill and Evelyn Reed look after their guests well and their likes and dislikes in food are noted when the daily changing dinner menu is discussed each morning. For such a small place the food is interesting and imaginative and attracts favourable comment.
Open 23 Mar to 28 Oct
Rooms: 3 with private facilities
Dinner at 7 pm (b-c)
Residents only
Unlicensed
No smoking in dining room + bedrooms
Bed & Breakfast from £21
Dinner B & B from £35
• Aberdeen Angus beef stuffed with smoked oysters served with cucumber sauce. Local venison in port and Guinness with cassis sauce. Wild salmon with prawns and dill sauce. Pheasant with claret and orange sauce.
STB Highly Commended 3 Crowns
No credit cards
Proprietors: Bill & Evelyn Reed

ARDVOURLIE CASTLE

Aird A Mhulaidh
Isle of Harris PA85 3AB
Tel: 01859 50 2307

On A859 10 miles north of Tarbert.
Ardvourlie Castle stands in a spectacular position on the shores of Loch Seaforth, surrounded by the hills of Harris. This fine old building has been carefully restored by Derek Martin and his family. Though modestly described as a guest house, this is really much more than that, with features such as oak panelling, some gas lighting and rare high tester beds. The best of Scottish produce is carefully sourced and the food is good home cooking at its best, with

plentiful portions and even home-baked bread. Ardvourlie has its own special atmosphere and is an unusual yet lovely place to stay while visiting Harris and Lewis.

Open all year except over Christmas period
Rooms: 4
Dinner by arrangement (e) 4 course menu
Residents only
Restricted Licence
Bed & Breakfast £40 – £45
Dinner B & B £65 – £70
Special Rates for 5+ nights
• *Trout in mayonnaise with capers and tarragon, served in avocado halves. Fillet steak flamed in brandy, served with green peppercorn sauce. Half roast duck basted with honey and crisped, served with an orange liqueur sauce.*
No credit cards
Proprietor: Derek Martin

SCARISTA HOUSE
Isle of Harris PA85 3HX
Tel: 01859 550 238
Fax: 01859 550 277
On A859, 15 miles south-west of Tarbert (Western Isles).
Scarista House is a charming Georgian dwelling and occupies an imposing position overlooking a three mile long shell-sand beach on the magnificent Atlantic coast of Harris. The eight bedrooms, all with views over the sea, are comfortably and traditionally furnished, with bathrooms en suite. There are two lawned gardens, a walled herb garden and a vegetable garden. With no television or radio, but an extensive library, the hotel offers an atmosphere of complete tranquillity, complemented by excellent cuisine – noted in guides worldwide – in which local fish and shellfish feature prominently. There is also an extensive wine list. Children over eight years welcome.
Open May to Sep

Rooms: 8 with private facilities
Dinner at 8.15 pm (e)
Residents Licence
No smoking in dining room
Bed & Breakfast £43 – £62
Dinner B & B £68 – £86
• *Razor-shell clams. Prawn soufflés. Fillet of wild venison with a blackcurrant and cassis sauce. Vegetables from the garden. Praline ice-cream with raspberry and almond biscuits. Various Scottish cheeses. Home-made oatcakes, bread, scones etc.*
No credit cards
Proprietors: Ian & Jane Callaghan

TWO WATERS GUEST HOUSE
Lickisto
Isle of Harris PA85 3EL
Tel: 01859 530 246
From Tarbert take road signed to Roghadal (Rodel), then fourth road on left C79 single track. Between Stockinish and Geocrab.
A modern comfortable bungalow situated just 15 yards from the sea in wild mountainous scenery. If you are lucky you may well spot otters and seals nearby. John and Jill Barber have concentrated on making this a home from home and guests look forward eagerly to the imaginative evening meals which feature local seafoods and some of John's own smoked products. The choice of fish for breakfast is quite exceptional but standard normal breakfast fare is of course also available. All rooms are en suite with tea/coffee-making facilities and thoughtful little touches like home-made biscuits. There is free trout fishing. A lovely spot from which to indulge in some hill-walking, angling, sailing or bird-watching.
Open 1 May to 30 Sep
Rooms: 4 with private facilities
Dinner at 7 pm (b) 4 course menu
Residents only
Unlicensed
No children
No smoking in dining room
Bed & Breakfast £25 – £27
Dinner B & B £39 – £41
• *Hot smoked salmon roulade. Lamb with apricots and fresh herbs. Vegetable medley cake. Apple and pear tarte tatin with cinnamon yoghurt.*
STB Highly Commended 3 Crowns
No credit cards
Proprietors: Jill & John Barber

Hawick

Location 109

MANSFIELD HOUSE HOTEL
Weensland Road, Hawick
Roxburghshire TD9 8LB
Tel: 01450 373988
Fax: 01450 372007
On A698 Hawick-Jedburgh, c. 1 mile from centre of Hawick.
The Scottish Borders are famed for their knitwear and Hawick is the centre of the area's textile industry. Mansfield House was built in 1870 for a well established local family and is set in ten acres of gardens overlooking the town. This former mansion house has been tastefully converted into a fine hotel retaining many distinctive architectural features. Ornate ceilings with rose and thistle motifs, classical friezes and cornices have been carefully restored. The hotel has been recently refurbished and during the past year a large function room and extended bar/bistro facilities have been added. Mansfield House has earned an outstanding reputation for good food and wines.
Open all year
Rooms: 12 with private facilities
Bar Lunch 12 – 2 pm (a)
Dining Room/Restaurant Lunch 12 – 2 pm except Sun Sat (c)
Bar Supper 5.30 – 9 pm (a)
Dinner 7 – 9 pm except Sun (c)
No smoking area in restaurant
Bed & Breakfast £30 – £52
Dinner B & B £45 – £70
Room Rate £46 – £66
Special Weekend Rates available
• *Loch Fyne smoked salmon. Haunch of venison sautéed with mussels and flavoured with nutmeg, anchovies and red wine. Salmon oven-poached in white wine with a cream butter sauce. Border beef steaks. Ginger baked sponge pudding with ginger sauce and honey ice-cream.*
STB Commended 3 Crowns
Credit cards: 1, 2, 3, 5
Proprietors: Sheila & Ian MacKinnon

THE OLD FORGE RESTAURANT
Newmill-on-Teviot, by Hawick
Roxburghshire TD9 0JU
Tel: 01450 85 298

*A7, 4 miles south of Hawick, 18 miles
north of Langholm. (Edinburgh 54 miles)*
This attractive roadside licensed
restaurant was once the local
blacksmith's and all the character of the
old 19th century buildings have been
retained. Exposed brick walls, beamed
ceilings, genuine working bellows and
even the original anvil, give the place
special appeal. Chef/proprietor Simon
Findlay is an award winning chef and this
is demonstrated in the skill with which
he draws on the local produce and
transforms it into interesting dishes for
his menus, which represent good value
for money. Simon's wife Judith looks
after the restaurant and its customers
with great charm and courtesy. The Old
Forge has earned a high reputation for
fine food so is very popular and it is
advisable to book in advance.
*Open all year except first wk Nov,
Christmas + Boxing Days
Restaurant Lunch 12 – 2 pm Tue to Sat:
12.30 – 2 pm Sun (b)
Dinner 7 – 9.30 pm Tue to Sat: High Tea
4 – 6 pm Sun (c)
Closed Mon
Facilities for disabled visitors
No smoking area in restaurant
• Smoked trout coated with a lobster
and chive sauce. Medallions of beef with
red wine and horseradish. Chocolate
cups filled with chestnut and honey ice-
cream.
Credit card: 1, 3 + SWITCH
Proprietors: Simon & Judith Findlay*

WHITCHESTER CHRISTIAN GUEST HOUSE
Borthaugh, Hawick
Roxburghshire TD9 7LN
Tel: 01450 77477
Fax: 01450 371080

*¼ mile off A7, 2 miles south of Hawick
on B711 to Roberton.*
A former Dower House of the Buccleuch
Estate set in this quiet and beautiful
spot within almost four acres of garden.
The house has been refurbished in a
comfortable and relaxing style. All food
including the bread is cooked on the
premises and local produce is widely
used. Full board includes a traditional
Scottish afternoon tea. A wide range of
soups are made such as carrot and
coriander and lemon and yoghurt, sweets
include brûlées, pavlovas, sorbet

concoctions and many others, a large
Scottish cheese board is kept.
*Open 1 Feb to 29 Dec
Rooms: 8, 4 with private facilities
Dining Room/Restaurant Lunch 12.30 –
1.30 pm Mon to Sat: at 1 pm Sun (a)
Full Afternoon Tea 4.30 – 5 pm
Dinner 6.30 – 8 pm Mon to Sat: at 7 pm
Sun (b)
Unlicensed
No smoking in dining room, bedrooms +
conservatory
Bed & Breakfast £22 – £25
Dinner B & B £30 – £35
• Home-made soups, pâtés and bread.
Salmon. Poached trout. Grouse,
pheasant, venison. Local fruit
cranachans, syllabubs. Crunchy almond
gâteau, walnut roll. Vegetarian dishes a
speciality, using home-grown vegetables.
STB Commended 3 Crowns
Credit cards: 1, 3 + DELTA
Proprietors: David & Doreen Maybury*

Helmsdale

Location 110
NAVIDALE HOUSE HOTEL
Helmsdale
Sutherland KW8 6JS
Tel: 01431 821258

On A9, ½ mile north of Helmsdale.
A former Victorian shooting lodge of the
Dukes of Sutherland, Navidale is now a
comfortable country house hotel. It
stands in seven acres of garden on a
cliff top overlooking the North Sea. There
is an air of spacious elegance about the
well appointed public rooms which have
superb panoramic views and open fires.
The bedrooms are furnished to a high
standard and overlook the sea and
gardens. Additional accommodation is
available in the lodge house in the
gardens. Chef/proprietor Marcus
Blackwell prepares menus which make
good use of the fine supply of local
seafish and shellfish as well as Highland
lamb, Caithness beef and game in

season.
*Open 1 Feb to 15 Nov
Rooms: 15 with private facilities
Bar Lunch 12 – 2 pm (a)
Dining Room/Restaurant Lunch – by
arrangement
Dinner 7 – 9 pm (c)
No smoking in restaurant
Bed & Breakfast £30 – £35
Dinner B & B £50 – £56
Room Rate £30 – £70
Special Rates for 3+ nights
• Half melon filled with smoked salmon
and langoustine. Fillet of venison served
with red wine and blackcurrant sauce.
Lamb's sweetbreads with a cream and
mushroom sauce served in a pastry
case.
Credit cards: 1, 3
Proprietor: Marcus Blackwell*

Humbie
nr Edinburgh

Location 111
JOHNSTOUNBURN HOUSE HOTEL
Humbie
East Lothian EH36 5PL
Tel: 01875 833696
Fax: 01875 833626

*From A68 Edinburgh-Jedburgh 2 miles
south of Pathhead, turn at Fala (hotel is
signposted) – 2 miles on right.*
A beautifully kept large country mansion,
approached by a long tree-lined drive and
surrounded by acres of lawns, gardens
and picturesque farmland at the foot of
the Lammermuir Hills. The visitor to
Johnstounburn would hardly imagine that
he or she is only 15 miles away from
bustling Edinburgh. And once inside the
17th century stone walls, warmed by the
open fires and treated to an interesting
menu made with fresh local produce, one
begins to appreciate the depth of
Scotland's heritage. Johnstounburn has
20 well appointed bedrooms, conference
rooms for as many delegates, an
exquisite pine-panelled dining room, and
a singularly relaxing wood-panelled
lounge.
*Open all year
Rooms: 20 with private facilities
Bar Lunch 12 – 2 pm (b)
Dining Room/Restaurant Lunch 12 –
2 pm (c)
Dinner 7 – 9 pm (e)
Bed & Breakfast £47.50 – £110
Dinner B & B £75 – £137.50
Special Weekend Rates available*

• Poached délice of Scottish salmon with a tomato and dill cream sauce. Roast noisettes of Border lamb with a mint and cucumber sauce. Pan-fried medallions of prime Aberdeen Angus beef with a coarse grain mustard sauce.
STB Commended 4 Crowns
Credit cards: 1, 2, 3, 5

by **Huntly**
Location 112
THE OLD MANSE OF MARNOCH
Bridge of Marnoch
by Huntly AB54 5RS
Tel: 01466 780873
Fax: 01466 780873
On B9117, 1 mile off A97 midway between Huntly and Banff.
A secluded Georgian country house set in three acres of splendid gardens on the River Deveron. Well appointed en suite bedrooms, elegant lounges, and the dining room set with silver and crystal, combine to provide an experience of true Scottish hospitality. Keren Carter produces fine Scots cooking in both traditional and contemporary dishes. The set four course dinner changes daily and everything is prepared in The Old Manse kitchen, whilst the herb parterre and walled kitchen garden supply fresh produce in season. At breakfast there is an outstanding and award winning selection of items to set you up for the day. A destination for the discerning traveller. Fluent German spoken. Dogs welcome, but not in the dining room.
Open all year except 2 wks Nov
Rooms: 5 with private facilities
Picnic lunch – as requested (a)
Dining Room/Restaurant Lunch – residents only by request (b)
Afternoon tea – residents only (a)
Dinner 7.30 for 8 pm (d) 4 course menu
Reservations essential for non-residents
No smoking in dining room
Bed & Breakfast from £35
Dinner B & B from £55
Special Rates for 7+ nights
• Meg Dods' high-flavoured onion soup. Fresh pea soup with dill. Baby haggis with a mustard and oatmeal dip. Smoked Loch Etive trout with horseradish cream. Darne of Deveron salmon poached in white wine. Venison collops with a blackcurrant and chocolate sauce. Bitter orange curd tart. Raspberry damask.
STB Deluxe 3 Crowns
Credit cards: 1, 3 + DELTA
Proprietors: Patrick & Keren Carter

Innerleithen
Location 113
TRAQUAIR ARMS HOTEL
Traquair Road, Innerleithen
Peeblesshire EH44 6PD
Tel: 01896 830229
Fax: 01896 830260
On A72 midway between Peebles and Galashiels. Midway along Innerleithen High Street take B709 Yarrow. Hotel 150 yards on left.
Traquair Arms is an attractive traditional 19th century Scottish inn just half an hour from Edinburgh and ten minutes from Peebles in the quiet country town of Innerleithen which lies in a delightful Borders valley. Hugh and Marian Anderson run it as a relaxing, friendly, family run hotel with genuine concern for the comfort of their guests. Imaginative menus utilise the best local produce and, in appropriate weather, can be enjoyed beside a blazing log fire in the dining room or al fresco in the secluded garden. The bar prides itself in its real ales and there is an interesting selection of light dining dishes available throughout the day.
Open all year except Christmas + Boxing Days, 1 + 2 Jan
Rooms: 10 with private facilities
All day menu 12 – 9 pm (a)
Dining Room/Restaurant Lunch 12 – 6 pm (b)
Dinner 7 – 9 pm except Mon Tue (c)
Bed & Breakfast £28 – £37
Dinner B & B £44 – £48
Special Rates available
• Border lamb cutlets served on a sauce of bramble and fresh mint. Thin slices of Scottish salmon baked in a pool of fresh chive sauce. Medallions of Aberdeen Angus fillets flamed in whisky, in a rich sauce of cream and Scottish mustard, garnished with walnuts.
STB Commended 3 Crowns
Credit cards: 1, 2, 3 + SWITCH
Proprietors: Hugh & Marian Anderson

Inverkeilor
by Arbroath
Location 114
GORDON'S RESTAURANT
Homewood House, Main Street
Inverkeilor, by Arbroath
Angus DD11 5RN
Tel: 01241 830364
Just off A92 Arbroath-Montrose, at north end of Main Street.
A cosy little village restaurant, Gordon's occupies the end of a row of terraced properties forming Main Street and dates back to 1850. The restaurant is attractively decorated in a traditional cottage style and the two bedrooms are tastefully appointed and have en suite showers. Chef/proprietor Gordon Watson's cooking is imaginative and unpretentious making full use of quality fresh ingredients from the locality and fresh herbs from their own garden. His wife, Maria, looks after the customers and sets a tone of friendly and efficient service. Booking is advisable.
Open all year except last 2 wks Jan
Rooms: 2 with private facilities
Bar Lunch 12 – 2.30 pm except Mon (a)
Dining Room/Restaurant Lunch 12 – 2.30 pm except Mon (a)
Bar Supper 6 – 9.15 pm except Mon Sat (a)
Dinner 7 – 9.15 pm except Mon (b-c)
Closed Mon
Facilities for disabled visitors
No smoking area in restaurant
Bed & Breakfast £20.50 – £27.50
Dinner B & B £36.50 – £46.50
• King scallops served in shell with white wine sauce and sliced mushrooms. Scampi poached in Noilly Prat and cream sauce, served with pilaff rice. Chicken with cider, apples and cream flamed in Calvados. Sirloin steak grilled and served with wild rosemary butter.
STB Commended 2 Crowns
Credit cards: 1, 3 + DELTA
Proprietors: Gordon & Maria Watson

Credit Card Code		Meal Price Range	
1.	Access/Mastercard/Eurocard	(a)	under £10
2.	American Express	(b)	£10 – £15
3.	Visa	(c)	£15 – £20
4.	Carte Bleu	(d)	£20 – £25
5.	Diners Club	(e)	£25 – £30
6.	Mastercharge	(f)	over £30

Invermoriston

Location 115

GLENMORISTON ARMS HOTEL
Invermoriston, Glenmoriston
Inverness-shire IV3 6YA
Tel: 01320 51206

*At junction of A82 and A887 in
Invermoriston.*

This traditional old coaching inn nestling
at the foot of Glenmoriston has been
around for some 200 years and is as
well sited and popular as a stopping
place now as it no doubt was in earlier
times. It is well placed at the junction of
the main routes to Inverness and Kyle of
Lochalsh and just a few minutes from
world famous Loch Ness. This is a family
run typically Scottish hostelry which is
furnished and decorated simply but
pleasingly. The restaurant serves a good
variety of national and regional
specialities on its seasonally changing
menus and there is an impressive range
of malt whiskies in the bar.

Open all year except Christmas Day
Rooms: 8 with private facilities
Bar Lunch 12 – 2 pm (a)
Dining Room/Restaurant Lunch 12 –
2 pm Sun only (a)
Bar Supper 5 – 8.30 pm (a)
Dinner 6.30 – 8.30 pm (c)
Bed & Breakfast £30 – £45
Dinner B & B £47 – £60
Special Rates for 3+ nights
*• Smoked breast of chicken with a mixed
salad and tarragon vinaigrette. Roast
rack of lamb with a light port wine gravy.
Baked salmon served with hollandaise
sauce.*
STB Commended 4 Crowns
Credit cards: 1, 3
Proprietor: Alan Draper

Inverness

Location 116

BUNCHREW HOUSE HOTEL
Bunchrew
Inverness IV3 6TA
Tel: 01463 234917
Fax: 01463 710620

*On A862 Inverness-Beauly, c. 10
minutes from centre of Inverness.*

Bunchrew House is a very fine 17th
century mansion spectacularly situated
on the shores of the Beauly Firth, within
18 acres of landscaped gardens and
woodlands. Careful restoration and
refurbishment has been carried out over
the years to preserve the heritage of this
historic old building while providing the
high standards of accommodation and
amenities expected by guests today.
Bedrooms and suites are individually
decorated, very comfortable and
luxuriously appointed, and some feature
canopied four poster or half tester beds.
Log fires blaze in winter in the charming
wood-panelled drawing room where
guests relax over drinks before dinner in
the candlelit Mackenzie Room with its
view out over the Firth to the Black Isle.
The chef presents an interesting
selection of dishes on the thoughtfully
compiled four course dinner menus. A
new bistro style restaurant is due to
open during 1995 which will offer a more
informal style of eating and complement
the existing dining room. In their first two
years at Bunchrew, Stewart and Lesley
Dykes have proved themselves caring
and friendly hosts who put a great deal
of effort into maintaining the high
standards for which Bunchrew House is
renowned.

Open all year
Rooms: 11 with private facilities
Bar Lunch 12 – 2 pm (b)
Dining Room/Restaurant Lunch 12 –
2 pm (b)
Bar Supper 7 – 9 pm (b)
Dinner 7 – 9 pm (d)
Facilities for disabled visitors
No smoking in dining room
Bed & Breakfast £40 – £70
Dinner B & B £65 – £95
*• Highland game terrine served with a
pear and rosemary jelly. Home-made
pies. Baked fillet of wild salmon topped
with a herb crust and served with a
tomato and basil sauce. Pan-fried fillet of
beef topped with wild mushrooms and
finished with a tomato and red wine jus.
Bread and butter pudding served with a
light crème anglaise.*
STB Commended 4 Crowns
Credit cards: 1, 2, 3
Proprietors: Stewart & Lesley Dykes

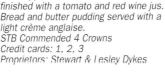

CULLODEN HOUSE HOTEL
Culloden
nr Inverness IV1 2NZ
Tel: 01463 790461
Fax: 01463 792181
Toll-free fax from USA: 1 800 373 7987

*A96, 3 miles south of Inverness, take
road signed to Culloden. 5 miles from
Inverness Airport.*

There must be few who can pass
through the entrance gates leading to
this magnificent building without being
impressed by the symmetry, the
elegance and the enduring quality of this
architectural gem. It has historical and
romantic associations with Bonnie
Prince Charlie and the Battle of Culloden
which was fought nearby. There are fine
lawns and acres of parkland around this
oasis of quiet dignity and charm. In the
late 18th century the house was
remodelled as a Palladian mansion and
the splendid marble fireplaces and
classical plasterwork reliefs of the
period still feature in the magnificent
public rooms. In addition to the
excellently appointed spacious
bedrooms and suites of this lovely old
house – several of which have four
poster beds – there are four luxurious
suites within the adjacent Garden
Mansion built recently in the Palladian
style in a secluded area of garden. Chef
Michael Simpson presents menus for
the Adam Dining Room which are a
delightful blend of classical and Scottish
country house cooking and offer a good
range of skilfully prepared interesting
dishes. The food presented is of the
same order of excellence which marks
every aspect of this special
establishment.

Open all year
*Rooms: 23 with private facilities +
4 Garden Suites*
*Dining Room/Restaurant Lunch 12.30 –
2 pm (b-c)*
Dinner 7 – 9 pm (f)
Bed & Breakfast £87.50 – £120
*• Warm filo pastry parcel of scallops
and smoked salmon served with a
creamed dill sauce. Medallions of fillet
of beef coated with a Lanark Blue
cheese sauce, topped with forestière
mushrooms. Paupiettes of salmon with
julienne of vegetables on a creamed
chervil sauce. Baked hot sorrel and
onion tart.*
STB Deluxe 5 Crowns
Credit cards: 1, 2, 3, 5, 6 + SWITCH
Proprietors: Ian & Marjory McKenzie

DUNAIN PARK HOTEL
Dunain Park
Inverness IV3 6JN
Tel: 01463 230512
Fax: 01463 224532

A82, 1 mile west of Inverness.
Ann and Edward Nicoll have established a very high reputation for their delightful country house hotel secluded in six acres of garden and woodland just a mile out of Inverness. As one would expect, the public rooms, bedrooms and suites are extremely well furnished and equipped; the suites particularly being the last word in comfort and elegant living. But it is for the food that Dunain is renowned. Ann Nicoll's cooking is something special and has earned high praise from discerning food writers and brings guests back time and time again. There is a hint of French influence in her deft light touch, especially with fish, but her prowess is also displayed in fine home-cooking and a mouth-watering range of desserts. Fresh herbs and vegetables for the kitchen come from the two acre walled garden. In the grounds of the house there is an indoor heated swimming pool and a sauna in a log cabin and two delightful family suites in the coach house.
Open all year except 3 wks Jan/Feb
Rooms: 14 with private facilities
Dining Room/Restaurant Lunch 12.30 – 1.30 pm (c) 5 course menu – booking essential
Dinner 7 – 9 pm (d) 5 course menu
No smoking in dining room
Bed & Breakfast £45 – £75
Dinner B & B £65 – £95
Special Rates for 3+/7+ nights Oct to Apr
• Mousseline of smoked haddock and whiting served with a sabayon sauce. Millefeuille of wild mushrooms in a white wine cream sauce. Fillet of salmon baked in sea salt and served with a white port, lime and ginger sauce. Ragoût of hare and rabbit served with a port and juniper berry sauce.
STB Deluxe 4 Crowns
Credit cards: 1, 2, 3, 5 + SWITCH, DELTA
Proprietors: Ann & Edward Nicoll

GLEN MHOR HOTEL & RESTAURANT
Ness Bank
Inverness IV2 4SG
Tel: 01463 234308
Fax: 01463 713170

On river bank below castle.
As locations go Glen Mhor is hard to beat – in a prime site on the south bank of the River Ness near the town centre. There is a choice of dining styles on offer. The spacious Riverview Seafood Restaurant, its tables set with classic crisp white linen, offers an à la carte dinner menu concentrating on fresh fish and seafood, complemented by a range of daily changing non-fish dishes emphasising the restaurant's modern Taste of Scotland approach to beef, lamb and game etc. Alternatively you may choose the more informal style of Nico's, a charming Victorian oak-panelled bistro bar which specialises in traditional Scottish food as well as international favourites such as pasta, chargrills, ethnic and vegetarian options. There is also a range of snacks available at lunchtime.
Open all year except 31 Dec to 2 Jan
Rooms: 30 with private facilities
Bistro Lunch 12 – 2.15 pm (a)
Dining Room/Restaurant Lunch 12.30 – 2 pm Sun only (b-c)
Bistro Supper 5 – 10.30 pm (a-c)
Dinner 6.30 – 9.30 pm (d)
Note: Restaurant closed Sun evenings from Oct to Apr
Bed & Breakfast £35 – £60
Dinner B & B £49 – £75
Special Rates available Oct to Apr
• Loch Fyne oysters with a red wine shallot vinegar. Whole Lybster crab. Parcel of wild salmon baked with dill potatoes and vegetable julienne. Lobster. Lamb cutlets with a watercress and rosemary butter. Venison fillet in a pink peppercorn sauce.
STB Commended 4 Crowns
Credit cards: 1, 2, 3, 5, + SWITCH
Proprietors: Nicol & Beverley Manson

GLENDRUIDH HOUSE HOTEL
by Castle Heather
Old Edinburgh Road South
Inverness IV1 2AA
Tel: 01463 226499
Fax: 01463 710745

2 miles from Inverness centre. Half mile south of Inverness southern distributor road.
Glendruidh House is a comfortable small hotel set amidst several acres of rolling lawns and woodlands, with its own lochan. It is a quite unique building which developed from two small cottages in 1850 to become a large family residence. The drawing room is completely circular, its doors and windows shaped to the contour of this restful and comfortably furnished room. There is a good choice of interesting dishes in the carefully compiled menus presented in the dining room overlooking the beautifully kept garden. Christine Smith enjoys working with the very best fresh produce available in the Highlands of Scotland and specialises in a traditional style of cuisine. Michael Smith is a friendly and welcoming host who is always ready to offer advice on the best places to visit whether your interests are historical sites, wildlife areas or cultural events.
Open all year
Rooms: 7 with private facilities
Dining Room/Restaurant Lunch 12.30 – 2.30 pm (c)
Dinner 6 – 8 pm (c) – or later if required
Residents only
No dogs
Facilities for disabled visitors
No smoking throughout
Bed & Breakfast £36.50 – £50
Dinner B & B £53.50 – £69.50
Special Rates available
• Melon with smoked Coignafearn Hill venison and wild rowan jelly. Grilled fillet of Strathconon salmon with asparagus sauce. Braised Black Isle chicken with raisin and nut stuffing. Grilled Highland lamb chops with quince and orange sauce. Queen of puddings. Drambuie spiced peaches.
STB Commended 3 Crowns
Credit cards: 1, 2, 3, 5
Proprietors: Christine & Michael Smith

MOYNESS HOUSE

6 Bruce Gardens
Inverness IV3 5EN
Tel: 01463 233836
Fax: 01463 233836

*From A9 (north + south) and A862
Beauly, follow signs for A82 Fort William
holiday route. Through Tomnahurich
Street to Glenurquhart Road (A82), turn
into Bruce Gardens diagonally opposite
Highland Regional Council offices.*
A detached Victorian villa built in 1880,
Moyness House was for a short time the
home of one of Scotland's best known
authors, Neil Gunn. It is located in a
quiet residential area within 10 minutes
walk of the town centre. This carefully
converted house still retains the charm
and elegance of a Victorian home, yet
also offers the amenities expected of a
modern hotel. The comfortable bedrooms
are fitted out to a high standard. It is a
truly family run concern with four Joneses
involved in the day to day management
of the hotel. The principal in the kitchen
is Nonna Jones who is responsible for
the creativity of the menus. Being in the
same ownership for 10 years, Moyness
House has built up an established and
loyal clientele. However dining facilities
are only available to residents and their
guests. A large garden is available for
guests to enjoy and there is plenty of car
parking space at the back of the house.
*Open all year except 23 Dec to 4 Jan
Rooms: 7 with private facilities
Dinner 6.30 – 7.30 pm (b)
Residents only
Restricted Licence
No smoking in restaurant
Bed & Breakfast £25 – £29
Dinner B & B £40 – £44
Special Rates for 3+ nights*
• Medallions of venison with port wine
sauce. Monkfish with a sweet red pepper
sauce. Poached fillet of salmon with sun-
dried tomato sauce and cucumber
spaghetti. Noisettes of lamb with
rosemary gravy. Roulade of sole, salmon
and spinach with lobster sauce. Warm
apricot and almond cake served with
cream. Strawberry shortcake with orange
syllabub.
*STB Deluxe 3 Crowns
Credit cards: 1, 2, 3 + DELTA
Proprietors: Nonna & Michael Jones*

Inverurie

Location 117

THAINSTONE HOUSE HOTEL

Thainstone Estate, Inverurie
Aberdeenshire AB51 5NT
Tel: 01467 621643
Fax: 01467 625084

*On A96 north of Aberdeen (8 miles from
airport).*
The impressive facade of Thainstone
House remains unchanged, but behind it
has been completely transformed and
has become a sumptuous and luxurious
hotel and leisure centre. Architects and
designers have done a wonderful job in
retaining the character of the old
palladian building whilst introducing
gracious new public rooms and well
equipped bedrooms. International award
winning chef Bill Gibb won the Taste of
Scotland Scotch Lamb Challenge in
1992 and over the following years of the
competition two of his sous-chefs have
been placed in the finals. The food
presented at Thainstone is of an
exceptional standard of excellence,
contributing to the hotel's high ranking
within the quality country house hotels of
Scotland.
*Open all year
Rooms: 48 with private facilities
Bar Lunch 12 – 2.30 pm except Sun (a)
Dining Room/Restaurant Lunch
(Simpsons) 12 – 2.30 pm (a)
Bar Supper 6 – 9.30 pm (a)
Dinner (Simpsons) 7 – 9.30 pm (e)
4 course menu
No smoking in restaurant
No dogs
Bed & Breakfast £34.50 – £60
Dinner B & B £54 – £89
Room Rate £69 – £125
Special Rates available*
• Smoked salmon bavarois with prawn
tails, marinated salmon and keta caviar
vinaigrette dressing. Pavé of beef glazed
with shallot purée and Arran mustard
sabayon on a Madeira sauce with button
onions, flageolets, turned carrots and
seasonal mushrooms. Fillet of turbot
with a horseradish crust in a lemon
grass sauce with langoustine, cucumber
and tomato concasse.
*STB Highly Commended 5 Crowns
Credit cards: 1, 2, 3, 5, 6 + SWITCH*

Isle of Islay

Location 118

GLENMACHRIE FARMHOUSE

Port Ellen, Isle of Islay
Argyll PA42 7AW
Tel: 01496 30 2560

*Midway on A846 between Port Ellen and
Bowmore.*
Glenmachrie is a large traditional
farmhouse set in a large walled garden
by the river and surrounded by 450 acres
which support Scottish blackface sheep,
Highland ponies and Highland cattle. The
house has been completely refurbished
to high standards throughout to provide
very comfortable accommodation. Rachel
Whyte is the perfect host, making
everyone feel very much at home and
producing wonderful meals in the
evening from local and farm produce.
There is a lovely homely atmosphere in
the dining room which is candlelit at
dinner and has views out towards the
sea. Guests are offered free fishing for
wild brown trout on the loch, which is
overlooked by the famous Machrie Golf
Links. Children over 5 years welcome.
*Open all year
Rooms: 5 with private facilities
Dinner 6.30 – 7.30 pm
Residents only
Unlicensed – guests welcome to take
own wine
Dogs accepted – by prior agreement only
Facilities for disabled visitors (ground
floor bedroom)
No smoking throughout
Bed & Breakfast £25 – £28
Dinner B & B £34 – £38*
• Scotch tomatoes stuffed with home-
made haggis spiked with Islay malt
whisky. Mussels and prawns in an Islay
cheese sauce. Collops of Glenmachrie
lamb in a rowan and rosemary sauce.
Dunlossit Estate venison and prune
casserole. Glenmachrie salmon poached
in white wine and served with Islay
parsley butter. Glenmachrie beef
casseroled with home-made herb
dumplings.
*STB Commended 3 Crowns
No credit cards
Proprietor: Rachel Whyte*

KILCHOMAN HOUSE RESTAURANT
by Bruichladdich, Isle of Islay
Argyll PA49 7UY
Tel: 0149 6850382
Fax: 0149 6850277

At end of B8018, off A847 Bridgend-Bruichladdich. Beyond Kilchoman Church, on the Atlantic side of the Rhinns of Islay, 6 miles from Bruichladdich.

A Listed Georgian building, formerly a manse, Kilchoman House sits in a little hollow, overlooked by majestic crags and open farmland, and is the Taylor family's home. Their attractive and relaxed 20 seat dining room is admirably hosted by Stuart whilst Lesley applies imagination in creating daily changing menus with the help of superior local produce. A very pleasant way to spend an evening. The five self-catering cottages are open all year, minimum three nights stay, early booking advised. B & B accommodation available locally.

Open Apr to Oct, Christmas/New Year + booked parties by arrangement
Dinner 7.30 – 9 pm except Sun Mon (c) – reservation essential
Closed Sun Mon
• *Islay venison braised with vegetables. Poached salmon with garden herbs. Lobster thermidor (pre-ordered). Special diet and vegetarian dishes on request.*
No credit cards
Proprietors: Stuart & Lesley Taylor

KILMENY FARMHOUSE
Ballygrant, Isle of Islay
Argyll PA45 7QW
Tel: 0149 684 0668

3 minute drive up private road, ½ mile south of Ballygrant.

A most attractive white-painted traditional farmhouse commanding spectacular views across the valley. The stables attached to the farmhouse have been very tastefully converted to two charming en suite bedrooms, with some lovely antique French furniture. At dinner guests can experience superb home-cooking by Margaret Rozga who uses only the best local produce from the farm and the estates on Islay. A simple three course menu is served at the large polished table in the small beautifully furnished dining room, where little paintings by local artists hang on the wall. There is a great welcome at Kilmeny and comfort, friendliness and peace abound.

Open all year except Christmas/New Year
Rooms: 3 with private facilities
Dinner 6.30 – 8 pm (b)
Residents only
Unlicensed

Dogs by arrangement
No smoking throughout
Bed & Breakfast £25 – £30
Dinner B & B £40 – £45
• *Home-made bread. Roast sirloin of Islay beef and Yorkshire puddings. Islay scallops poached in white wine and cream. Steak in a peppercorn sauce. Wild rabbit and leek pie. Hot Islay cheese soufflé. Bread and butter pudding.*
STB Highly Commended 3 Crowns
No credit cards
Proprietor: Margaret Rozga

Jedburgh

Location 119

WILLOW COURT
The Friars, Jedburgh
Roxburghshire TD8 6BN
Tel: 01835 863702

From Market Place, Jedburgh, take Exchange Street – The Friars is first road on right.

In a peaceful setting overlooking the town sits Willow Court, a charming modern guest house, within its own immaculately kept gardens and lawns. The public rooms and some bedrooms look out across the valley to the wooded hillsides beyond. Dinner is served in the bright dining conservatory from which guests can appreciate the panoramic view. Bedrooms are pleasingly decorated with a cheerful airy feel to them. Jane McGovern and her husband put a lot of effort into ensuring the comfort and satisfaction of their guests and to establishing a personal rapport with them. Jane's cooking is much acclaimed: her menus change regularly and include some enterprising dishes. The garden provides much of the fruit and vegetables needed in the kitchen, and fresh flowers for the house.

Open all year except Christmas Eve + Christmas Day
Rooms: 4 with private facilities
Dinner at 6.30 pm (b) – guests are requested to select their menu by 6 pm
Restricted Licence
Facilities for disabled visitors
No smoking in restaurant + bedrooms
Bed & Breakfast £14 – £28
Dinner B & B £25 – £39
• *Home-made soups. Dill marinated Orkney herring with cucumber and yoghurt dip. Local roe venison braised in red wine with juniper berries. Border lamb chops with fruit jelly. Chicken fillet with honey and mustard sauce. Salmon steak poached in butter and dry cider. Home-grown fruit and vegetables.*

Speciality home-made ice-creams e.g. Drambuie and lemon, brown bread.
STB Highly Commended 3 Crowns
No credit cards
Proprietor: Jane McGovern

Kelso

Location 120

EDNAM HOUSE HOTEL
Bridge Street, Kelso
Roxburghshire TD5 7HT
Tel: 01573 224168
Fax: 01573 226319

Off town square of Kelso, on right hand side of street leading to the bridge.

Standing on the banks of the River Tweed, Ednam House is an exceptionally fine example of Georgian architecture (built 1761) and is even considered to be the finest Georgian mansion in Roxburghshire. It was turned into a hotel in 1928 by Ralph Brooks, and has been in the family ever since. Indeed today after more than 65 years, a fourth generation of Brooks has joined the family business. Although the original house has been extended and modernised through the years there is still an aura of olde worlde charm. Many magnificent features remain, the ceilings, fireplaces and woodwork being worthy of particular note. Beautifully tended gardens and lawns stretch down to the riverside, and the dining room, lounges and bars take advantage of this view. Although within yards of the centre of Kelso, this is really a country house and sporting hotel in the best tradition. The menus focus on fresh local produce, in a subtle blend of traditional and creative Scottish cooking.

Open 10 Jan to 23 Dec
Rooms: 32 with private facilities
Bar Lunch 12.30 – 2 pm except Sun (a)
Dining Room/Restaurant Lunch 12.30 – 2 pm Sun only (a)
Dinner 7 – 9 pm (a-c)
Bed & Breakfast £32.50 – £44.50
Dinner B & B £43.25 – £55 (min 2 nights)
• *Smoked haddock baked in a cheese sauce. Border lamb chops with a thyme gravy. Pan-roasted Scottish salmon with sorrel sauce. Pot-roasted Guinea fowl with a red wine gravy. Collops of wild venison served with a cranberry and honey sauce. Cloutie dumpling with whipped cream and toasted flaked almonds. Whisky shortcake with coffee sauce. Home-made ice-creams. Scottish cheeseboard.*
STB Commended 4 Crowns
Credit cards: 1, 3 + SWITCH
Proprietors: R Alastair Brooks & Ralph Brooks

FLOORS CASTLE

Kelso
Roxburghshire TD5 7RW
Tel: 01573 223333/223866

A699 west of Kelso.

Floors is the magnificent and imposing Border home of the Duke of Roxburghe much of which is open to the public. The self-service restaurant which caters for visitors is plainly but comfortably furnished and has a well sheltered open courtyard in which you may eat out in good weather. The restaurant makes good use of available fresh produce from the castle gardens, salmon from the River Tweed, and there is some good home-baking.

Open Easter weekend then end Apr to end Oct
Note: open Sun to Thu Apr to Jun + Sep: daily Jul Aug: Sun Wed only Oct
Food service 10.30 am – 5 pm (a)
No smoking area in restaurant
• Floors kitchen pheasant pâté, Tweed salmon, smoked Tweed salmon, home-baking from Floors Castle kitchens.
Credit cards: 1, 3 + SWITCH

SUNLAWS HOUSE HOTEL

Heiton, Kelso
Roxburghshire TD5 8JZ
Tel: 01573 450331
Fax: 01573 450611

On A698 Kelso-Jedburgh in the village of Heiton.

The origins of Sunlaws go back many hundreds of years and the present 18th century mansion, owned by the Duke of Roxburghe, is magnificent both inside and out. This delightful country house hotel sits surrounded by lovely grounds and gardens within hundreds of acres of park and woodland by the banks of the River Teviot. The bedroom accommodation and public rooms are very comfortable and extremely well appointed. Standards throughout are very high and the food is excellent both in quality and in value, bar lunches in particular being quite exceptional. Chef David Bates presents interesting and well balanced menus for the dining room, which highlight the abundance of good Borders produce. This is a luxurious country house with charm, comfort and style, and with plenty of outdoor recreational activities readily available.

Open all year
Rooms: 22 with private facilities
Bar Lunch 12.30 – 2 pm (a-b)
Dining Room Lunch 12.30 – 2 pm (b)
Dinner 7.30 – 9.30 pm (d-e)

No smoking in dining room
Bed & Breakfast £70 – £95
Dinner B & B £100 – £125
Special Rates available
• Smoked Tweed salmon with a potato and parsley compote. Roast loin of Borders lamb with black pudding and minted lamb jus. Wild salmon with a tomato fondue. Collops of Angus beef fillet with a mushroom, cognac and cream sauce. Warm rhubarb and lemon flan with rhubarb cream.
STB Highly Commended 4 Crowns
Credit cards: 1, 2, 3, 5, 6 + SWITCH

Kenmore

Location 121

CROFT-NA-CABER

Garden Restaurant, Kenmore
Perthshire PH15 2HW
Tel: 01887 830236
Fax: 01887 830649

A827 to Kenmore, then take unclassified road along south shore of the loch for ½ mile.

An attractive old stone building originally a manse which has been extended and improved to provide a restaurant still in keeping with the original building. It overlooks Loch Tay and a busy water sports complex. All bedrooms have en suite facilities. The Swiss trained chef introduces an intriguing element of continental cooking and combines this with the best of traditional and modern Scottish fare to present interesting menus.

Open all year
Rooms: 5 with private facilities plus 17 chalets
Bar Meals 12 – 10 pm high season: 12 – 2 pm low season (a)
Dining Room/Restaurant Lunch 12 – 2 pm Mon to Fri: 12 – 4 pm Sun (b)
Bar Supper 6 – 10pm low season (a)
Dinner 7 – 9 pm (b)
Taste of Scotland applies to Garden Restaurant
Facilities for disabled visitors

No smoking in restaurant
Bed & Breakfast £25 – £35
Dinner B & B £39.50 – £49.50
• Home-made soup and pâté. Baked rainbow trout with brown butter and almonds. Poached salmon in a white wine and herb sauce. A rich stew of venison, mushrooms and bacon. Pheasant in a cream sauce garnished with grapes. Grilled lamb cutlets with a savoury butter.
Credit cards: 1, 3
Proprietor: A C Barratt

Kentallen of Appin

Location 122

ARDSHEAL HOUSE

Kentallen of Appin
Argyll PA38 4BX
Tel: 0163 174 227
Fax: 0163 174 342

On A828, 4 miles south of Ballachulish Bridge.

There are some lovely features in this old house once the home of the Stewarts of Appin and set in 900 acres of woods and meadows overlooking Loch Linnhe. The impressive oak staircase and the oak-panelled reception lounge with its unique barrel window are especially noteworthy. The dining room with its conservatory area is a pleasant place to enjoy some really first class food cooked to perfection and well presented. Local game and seafood feature strongly on the menu, bread is baked fresh each day and herbs and fruits come from the hotel's two acre garden. An excellent wine list and wide choice of malt whiskies add to the enjoyment of a meal. There are beautiful gardens, a billiard room and a tennis court.

Open all year
Rooms: 13 with private facilities
Light Lunch (a)
Dining Room/Restaurant Lunch 12 2 pm (c)
Dinner at 8.30 pm (f) 5 course menu
No smoking in restaurant
Dinner B & B £64 – £90
Special Winter Rates available
• Ramekin of salmon, gravadlax and pink grapefruit with coarse grain mustard and dill dressing. Warm tartlet of quail with oyster mushrooms and lentils. Rosette of beef fillet with chervil mousse and pink peppercorn sauce. Hot mixed berries soufflé with rum crème anglaise.
STB Highly Commended 3 Crowns
Credit cards: 1, 2, 3 + SWITCH

Kilchrenan

Location 123

ARDANAISEIG HOTEL

Kilchrenan, by Taynuilt
Argyll PA35 1HE
Tel: 0186 63 333
Fax: 0186 63 222

Prestige Award Winner 1990

A85 to Taynuilt, then B845. At Kilchrenan take road signed for hotel (3½ miles).

Ardanaiseig is a lovely old house set in acres of renowned shrub and woodland gardens on the shores of Loch Awe. It was built in the early 19th century for a member of the Clan Campbell. This fine country house has a very special atmosphere and is beautifully appointed throughout its elegant public rooms and very comfortable bedrooms. The dining room looks out over the gardens to the loch. Food is imaginative and well presented, reflecting the same high standards that prevail everywhere in this peaceful haven.

Open Apr to mid Oct
Rooms: 14 with private facilities
Light Lunch 12 – 2 pm (a)
Dining Room/Restaurant Lunch 12 – 2 pm (b)
Dinner 7.30 – 9 pm (e)
No smoking in dining room
Bed & Breakfast £42 – £80
Dinner B & B £72 – £110
• Smoked salmon salad with a dill and mustard dressing. Medallion of beef fillet on a light horseradish flavoured jus. Darnes of monkfish served under a brioche crust, set on a pimento vinaigrette. Grand Marnier savarin. Hot hazelnut soufflé with poached fig and ginger sorbet. Selection of Scottish cheeses.
STB Highly Commended 4 Crowns
Credit cards: 1, 2, 3, 5, 6
Proprietor: James Smith

TAYCHREGGAN HOTEL

Kilchrenan, by Taynuilt
Argyll PA35 1HQ
Tel: 018663 211/366
Fax: 018663 244

Leave A85 at Taynuilt on to B845 through village of Kilchrenan to the loch side.

In a relatively short time at Taychreggan, Annie Paul has worked wonders in establishing new and higher standards of comfort and cuisine in this delightful small hotel. The location of this charming old drovers inn has everything going for it – a secluded site with splendid views across Loch Awe and the spot at which sturdy Highland cattle came to shore after being made to swim across the loch on their way to market. The cobbled courtyard is a pleasant place in which to sit out on a summer's evening and enjoy a cool drink and there are comfortable and well equipped public rooms and a delightful dining room. Annie and Euan Paul have personally selected the house wines on one of their many visits to Provence and the 'Enthusiasts' wine list is comprehensive with flair. Perhaps the character of Taychreggan can best be summed up in the words of a guest who wrote to Taste of Scotland – "It is very rare in this day and age to find an hotel of this standard...The combination of location, service, decor and ambience of Taychreggan....make it superior to most of the leading hotels. Add to this the quality of food prepared by the two young but experienced and committed chefs whose imagination, presentation and cooking skills produce meals of equal quality to any of the UK's most distinguished chefs...cannot wait to return."

Open all year
Rooms: 15 with private facilities
Bar Lunch 12.30 – 2.15 pm (b-c)
Dinner 7.30 – 9 pm (e) 5 course menu
Bed & Breakfast £34 – £50
Dinner B & B £60 – £75
Room Rate £30 – £40
Special Spring/Autumn Rates
• Ragoût of west coast seafood in a pastry tartlet with Reisling, basil and lime sauce. Seasonal salad pan-fried wood pigeon and poached quails eggs. Roasted fillet of Angus beef on a bed of oyster mushrooms with a bordelaise sauce. Medallions of monkfish steamed with ginger and spring onions on a tomato sauce. Bitter chocolate truffle cake with blueberry coulis.
STB Commended 4 Crowns
Credit cards: 1, 2, 3
Proprietors: Euan & Annie Paul

Kildrummy

Location 124

KILDRUMMY CASTLE HOTEL

Kildrummy, by Alford
Aberdeenshire AB33 8RA
Tel: 019755 71288
Fax: 019755 71345

On A97 Ballater-Huntly, 35 miles west of Aberdeen.

A grand and impressive mansion house overlooking the ruins of the original 13th century castle nearby. It has superb grounds – acres of beautiful gardens and woodland on which it is a joy to meander. The interior is very imposing with a grand staircase, what looks like acres of wood panelling, and tapestries dating from the turn of the century. The whole building abounds in character and atmosphere and Tom Hanna the proprietor maintains the highest of standards in all aspects of the hotel. Bedrooms are spacious and have every modern comfort and convenience, and the food is of the same high level of excellence that is demonstrated throughout. There is a superb wine list including – and full marks to Kildrummy – about 40 different half bottles.

Open 10 Feb to 31 Dec
Rooms: 16 with private facilities
Dining Room/Restaurant Lunch 12.30 – 1.45 pm (b)
Dinner 7 – 9 pm (e)
No smoking in dining room
Bed & Breakfast £55 – £70
Dinner B & B £59 – £96
Special Rates available
• Feuilleté of salmon fillet and mushroom slices, served in a Pernod flavoured cream sauce. Medallions of venison fillet served with a tarragon flavoured carrot, leek and celery sauce. Breast of pheasant wrapped in bacon, served with a peach and hazelnut sauce. Walnut and butterscotch flan.
STB Deluxe 4 Crowns
Credit cards: 1, 2, 3, 6
Proprietor: Thomas Hanna

Kilfinan

Location 125

KILFINAN HOTEL
Kilfinan, nr Tighnabruaich
Argyll PA21 2EP
Tel: 0170 082 201
Fax: 0170 082 205

On B8000 between Tighnabruaich and Otter Ferry on eastern side of Loch Fyne. Best access from north B886/B8003 via Tighnabruaich; from east – from Dunoon B836/A8003 via Tighnabruaich.

A truly delightful old coaching inn dating back to the 17th century and most tastefully and comfortably modernised. It is set in lovely countryside on the eastern shore of Loch Fyne and is a real haven of relaxation. Lynne and Rolf Mueller make their guests feel specially welcome and their attitude of caring attention is reflected in other members of staff. The dining room is a timeless characterful room of dark wood and low ceilings set out with fine china, glassware, fresh flowers and good table linen. The food is first class as one would expect from Chef Mueller who is a member of the Master Chefs of Great Britain.

Open 1 Mar to 31 Jan
Rooms: 11 with private facilities
Bar Lunch 12 – 2 pm (b)
Dining Room/Restaurant Lunch 12 – 2 pm Sun only (b)
Bar Supper 6 – 7 pm (c)
Dinner 7.30 – 9 pm (e) 4 course menu
Bed & Breakfast £36 – £46
Dinner B & B £61 – £71
Special Rates available
• *Hot-smoked Alba salmon with fennel and honey vinaigrette. Fish terrine wrapped in smoked halibut. Strips of venison with wild mushrooms served on a bed of noodles. Suprême of Gressingham duck with lemon sauce. Entrecôte steak with hazelnut and basil butter. Langoustine tails served in a lobster sauce. Raspberry and blueberry sable. Honey and poppyseed parfait.*
STB Highly Commended 3 Crowns
Credit cards: 1, 2, 3

Killiecrankie

Location 126

KILLIECRANKIE HOTEL
Killiecrankie, by Pitlochry
Perthshire PH16 5LG
Tel: 01796 473220
Fax: 01796 472451

On old A9, 3 miles north of Pitlochry.
This former Dower House is set in four acres of well kept gardens and wooded grounds overlooking the River Garry and the historic Pass of Killiecrankie. The hotel is furnished to a high standard and conveys the atmosphere expected of a small country house. Bedroom accommodation includes one suite and all the rooms are individually and tastefully decorated, providing every comfort requirement for the most fastidious guest. The dining room is renowned for its high standard of food. Head Chef John Ramsay and his team demonstrate their culinary skills to best advantage in the interesting and imaginative dinner menus, using the best of local produce.

Open all year except 3 Jan to 5 Mar
Rooms: 10 with private facilities
Bar Lunch 12.30 – 2 pm (b)
Bar Supper 6.30 – 9.30 pm (b)
Dinner 7 – 8.30 pm (d) 5 course menu
No smoking in dining room
Dinner B & B £69 – £79
Special Rates available
• *Arbroath smokie terrine wrapped in smoked salmon. Grilled fillet of halibut on a bed of braised fennel with a dill hollandaise sauce. Fillet of lamb topped with venison pâté, baked in puff pastry, with a redcurrant, wine and mint sauce. Baked rainbow trout with a cucumber and thyme stuffing, and a light lemon sauce. Blueberry tart with crème anglaise.*
STB Commended 4 Crowns
Credit cards: 1, 3 + SWITCH, DELTA
Proprietors: Colin & Carole Anderson

Kilmarnock

Location 127

THE COFFEE CLUB
30 Bank Street, Kilmarnock
Ayrshire KA1 1HA
Tel: 01563 522048

In town centre.
Situated in one of the oldest streets in Kilmarnock opposite the Laigh Kirk, The Coffee Club offers something for everyone – quick service, snack meals and a large varied menu including grills and vegetarian dishes. There is also the Executive Room menu. All food is produced to order using fresh produce where practicable and bakery items are a speciality. The ambience is relaxed, informal and friendly.

Open all year except Christmas Eve + Christmas Day, 1 + 2 Jan
Coffee + meals served 9.30 am – 10 pm except Sun (a-b)
Closed Sun for meals but coffee lounge open 12 – 5 pm
Unlicensed – guests welcome to take own wine
No smoking area in air-conditioned restaurant
• *Sandwiches, salads, omelettes etc. Children's menu. Vegetarian dishes. Grilled salmon steak with hollandaise sauce. Sole with almonds in a rich cream sauce. Duck breast fillet served with a hot cherry compote. Steaks with a variety of sauces.*
Credit cards: 1, 2, 3
Proprietors: Svend Kamming & William MacDonald

Kilmelford

Location 128

CUILFAIL HOTEL
Kilmelford
Argyll PA34 4XA
Tel: 01852 200 274
Fax: 01852 200 264

A816 midway between Oban and Lochgilphead, at top of Loch Melfort.
An old drovers inn and now a very comfortable traditional Scottish country hotel with a good West of Scotland atmosphere. It is a very popular overnight or meal time stopping place on the Oban-Lochgilphead road. A good base for touring or exploring the Firth of Lorn and well known to hill-walkers, fishermen and sailors. There is lots of character about the place and a major refurbishment and renovation programme

Credit Card Code		Meal Price Range	
1.	Access/Mastercard/Eurocard	(a)	under £10
2.	American Express	(b)	£10 – £15
3.	Visa	(c)	£15 – £20
4.	Carte Bleu	(d)	£20 – £25
5.	Diners Club	(e)	£25 – £30
6.	Mastercharge	(f)	over £30

over recent years has done much to improve the standard of bedrooms and public rooms. There are several cosy areas in which to dine and one of the lounges has a collection of over 600 whisky miniatures on display.

Open all year
Rooms: 12 with private facilities
Bar Lunch 12 – 2.30 pm (a)
Bar Supper 6.30 – 9.30 pm (b)
Dinner 6.30 – 9 pm (c)
Bed & Breakfast £25 – £35
Dinner B & B £35 – £40
Special Rates for 3+ nights
• *Home-made pies with crisp puff pastry. Chicken in pastry with various fillings and sauces. Local salmon. Prawns and lobster. All dishes freshly prepared.*
STB Commended 3 Crowns
Credit cards: 1, 3 + DELTA
Proprietor: David Birrell

Kilmun

Location 129

FERN GROVE
Kilmun
Argyll PA23 8SB
Tel: 01369 84 334
Fax: 01369 84 334

6 miles from Dunoon on A880 on the side of the Holy Loch.
The former family home of the 'Campbells of Kilmun' is on a site overlooking the Holy Loch. The welcoming warm hospitality of hosts Ian and Estralita Murray creates a very comforting and friendly atmosphere in this attractive Victorian house. It is not a large building and it emanates an air of relaxation and cosy family living. Estralita presides in the kitchen and uses fresh local and home-grown produce to create interesting and appealing meals for both bistro and à la carte menus. There is also a private dining room available.

Open all year except Nov + Feb
Rooms: 3 with private facilities
Bistro Menu 11 am – 9 pm (a)
Restaurant (à la carte) 11 am – 9 pm (b-c)
No dogs
No smoking in restaurant + bedrooms
Bed & Breakfast £18 – £22
Dinner B & B £33 – £38
• *Home-baked breads. Carrot and ginger soup. Spinach mousse with spicy tomato*

sauce. Local wild venison steak in a mustard sauce. Lemon sole in a goat cheese and cream sauce. Loin of lamb in a red wine gravy. Baked Argyll ham with orange and honey sauce. Monkfish tails in Pernod. Apple and almond tarts with home-made honey ice-cream. Crème brûlée. Sticky toffee pudding.
Credit cards: 1, 3
Proprietors: Ian & Estralita Murray

Kilwinning

Location 130

MONTGREENAN MANSION HOUSE HOTEL
Montgreenan Estate, Torranyard
Kilwinning
Ayrshire KA13 7QZ
Tel: 01294 557733
Fax: 01294 850397

Off A736 Glasgow-Irvine near Torranyard, c. 5 miles north of Irvine.
A stay at this lovely old mansion house is a journey back in time to an age of elegance and gracious living. Although its origins go back to the 14th century the present building is primarily 18th century and attractive features from that time have been retained. Stately rooms, decorative ceilings, marble and brass fireplaces spell out the inherited character of the place, yet outside is a heliport facility for those whose schedules are much more exciting than was the case when Montgreenan was first built. Bedrooms are excellent and the newly refurbished sitting room is ultra comfortable. In the kitchen Chef Alan McCall creates an exciting menu based on the best raw materials. The overall experience is very satisfying.

Open all year
Rooms: 21 with private facilities
Bar Lunch 12 – 2.30 pm (b)
Dining Room/Restaurant Lunch 12 – 2.30 pm (b)
Dinner 7 – 9.30 pm (d)
Bed & Breakfast £46 – £77
Dinner B & B £56 – £96
Room Rate £60 – £146
• *Poached fillet of sole with mushroom and champagne sauce. Haunch of venison in a port, redcurrant and pickled walnut sauce. Baked salmon stuffed with crab in a light mustard sauce. Poached chicken stuffed with sweet chestnuts and tarragon cream.*
STB Highly Commended 4 Crowns
Credit cards: 1, 2, 3, 5, 6
Proprietors: The Dobson Family

Kincraig

Location 131

MARCH HOUSE GUEST HOUSE
Feshiebridge, Kincraig
Kingussie
Inverness-shire PH21 1NG
Tel: 01540 651 388
Fax: 01540 651 388

Off A9 at Kincraig. Follow B970 for 2 miles to Feshiebridge. Past red telephone box, turn right. Half mile on left down gravel drive.
This very comfortable family run guest house is situated in the tranquillity of beautiful unspoilt Glenfeshie. Surrounded by mature pine trees it enjoys outstanding views of the Cairngorm Mountains. This is an ideal place for all outdoor pursuits, including skiing, gliding, watersports and golf (six courses within easy reach) and it is a naturalist and bird-watcher's paradise. Mountain bike hire available. Local attractions include the Wildlife Park, Highland Folk Museum and Inchriach Alpine Nursery. The bedrooms at March House are all en suite and have tea/coffee making facilities. In the dining room, recently extended by the addition of a conservatory, home-baking and imaginative cooking are the order of the day. Caroline Hayes creates her menus using the best of local produce including salmon, trout, lamb, Angus beef and venison, and fresh herbs from the garden. The whole atmosphere is friendly and relaxed.

Open 15 May to 1 Nov + 27 Dec to 15 Apr
Rooms: 6 with private facilities
Dinner at 7 pm (b)
Reservations essential for non-residents
Unlicensed – guests welcome to take own wine
Bed & Breakfast £18 – £24
Dinner B & B £27 – £33
Room Rate £32 – £50
Special Rates for 3+/5+ nights + weekends
• *Broccoli and asparagus soup. Wholemeal soda bread rolls with walnuts. Venison with pickled walnuts and red wine. Local trout, grilled and served with cucumber and yoghurt. Carbonnade of beef. Raspberry and apple pie. Hot light lemon sponge pudding served with cream.*
STB Commended 2 Crowns
No credit cards
Proprietors: Caroline & Ernie Hayes

Kingussie

Location 132

COLUMBA HOUSE HOTEL
Manse Road, Kingussie
Inverness-shire PH21 1JF
Tel: 01540 661402

Turn off A9 Kingussie/Kincraig. Manse Road second on left on B9152 (High Street).

This 19th century former manse sits on a small hill within its own grounds and delightful gardens, overlooking the Cairngorm and Monadhliath Mountains. It is now a small family run hotel which provides a tranquil and homely setting in which to relax. Guests can take a stroll along the woodland path or have a friendly game of putting or croquet in the extensive grounds. There are magnificent views from the bedrooms which are very comfortably appointed with colour TV, tea/coffee-making facilities, direct dial telephone and mini bar. The resident proprietors are on hand to ensure that guests are well looked after and their comfort and enjoyment is a priority. In the cosy restaurant which overlooks the secluded walled garden, Myra Shearer presents delicious food made with fresh home-grown produce from the kitchen garden and local salmon, trout, venison, lamb, beef etc. Vegetarians are well catered for as well. There is an extensive well balanced wine list and a good selection of fine malt whiskies and liqueurs.

Open all year
Rooms: 7 with private facilities
Bar Lunch 10.30 am – 4.30 pm (a)
Dining Room/Restaurant Lunch 11.30 am – 3.30 pm (a)
Bar Supper 5 – 9 pm (a)
Dinner 7 – 9 pm (c)
Facilities for disabled visitors – ground floor rooms
No smoking in restaurant

Bed & Breakfast £19 – £31
Dinner B & B £34 – £48
Special Rates for 3+ nights
• A rich coarse pâté marinaded in wine and brandy served with warm brown toast. Chunks of tender local venison cooked in a fruity sauce. Roast leg of lamb with Cumberland sauce. Ecclefechan butter tart. Home-made petit fours.
STB Commended 3 Crowns
Credit cards: 1, 3
Proprietor: Myra Shearer

THE CROSS
Tweed Mill Brae, Ardbroilach Road
Kingussie PH21 1TC
Tel: 01540 661166
Fax: 01540 661080

Prestige Award Winner 1989

From traffic lights in centre of village, travel uphill along Ardbroilach Road for c. 200 yards, then turn left down private drive (Tweed Mill Brae).

Tony and Ruth Hadley could not have made a better choice of location when they moved their award winning restaurant to the idyllic waterside setting of this old tweed mill. The old grey stone building has been converted with imagination and flair to provide nine simple but stylish bedrooms and a spacious restaurant full of character with a pleasant terrace overlooking the River Gynack. Naturally the main emphasis at The Cross is on the food which is of an outstanding standard. Ruth Hadley is still the mastermind behind the imaginative menus and that promises an excellent dining experience, something really special.

Open 1 Mar to 1 Dec + 27 Dec to 5 Jan
Rooms: 9 with private facilities
Dining Room/Restaurant Lunch 12.30 – 2 pm except Tue Wed (b)
Dinner 7 – 9 pm except Tue (e-f)
Closed Tue
No smoking in bedrooms
Dinner B & B from £75
Special Rates for 3+ nights
• Roasted quail with tarragon, with quail egg and salad leaves. Shetland salmon lightly sautéed with an olive oil and basil dressing. Duck breast well roasted, with cranberries and ginger. Fillet of Aberdeen Angus beef lightly cooked with shallots and red wine.
Credit cards: 3, 6 + SWITCH
Proprietors: Tony & Ruth Hadley

THE OSPREY HOTEL
Ruthven Road, Kingussie
Inverness-shire PH21 1EN
Tel: 01540 661510
Fax: 01540 661510

In Kingussie village, on corner of main road.

An attractive small Highland hotel in the middle of the village, where the owners, Robert and Aileen Burrow, put great emphasis on personal service and providing a relaxing and informal atmosphere for their guests. The imaginative menu features the best of local produce, home-baking and interesting vegetarian dishes, and the standard of cooking has earned The Osprey an AA Rosette. An ideal base from which to tour, or for those wishing to take advantage of the numerous sporting and outdoor pursuits in the area.

Open all year except 2 wks Nov
Rooms: 8 with private facilities
Dinner 7.30 – 8 pm (c)
No smoking in dining room
Bed & Breakfast £22 – £36
Dinner B & B £39 – £54
Special Rates for 3+ nights
• Smoked salmon and dill parcels. Orange and coriander soup. Pheasant pie. Pork fillet with redcurrant and port sauce. Mascarpone meringue roulade. Caramelised orange and chocolate mousse gâteau.
STB Commended 3 Crowns
Credit cards: 1, 2, 3
Proprietors: Robert & Aileen Burrow

Kinloch Rannoch

Location 133

BUNRANNOCH HOUSE
Kinloch Rannoch
Perthshire PH16 5QB
Tel: 01882 632407

Turn right after 500 yards on Schiehallion road, just outside Kinloch Rannoch off B846.

Bunrannoch House is a family run former hunting lodge, set amid mature trees on a little knoll nestled at the foot of the 'sleeping giant' mountain close by Loch Rannoch. There is an easy informality within this comfortable family home, making guests feel completely at ease and totally relaxed. The cosy lounge, log fires and uninterrupted Highland views complement the delicious aromas from the kitchen. It is lovely to relax and savour the delights of Jennifer

Skeaping's cooking after the day's activities, perhaps walking in the mountain glens, rambling on Rannoch Moor or catching trout in the loch.
Open all year except Christmas + New Year
Rooms: 7, 5 with private facilities
Dinner 7 – 8.30 pm (c)
No smoking in dining room
Bed & Breakfast £18 – £20
Dinner B & B £30 – £32
Special Family Rates available
• *Home-made soup. Smoked Tay salmon served with salmon mousse and melba toast. Fillet of venison in redcurrant and port. Chicken marinated in white wine, capers, olives, garlic and herbs, baked in the oven and served with its marinade. Shortcrust pastry topped with cream cheese filling and strawberries.*
STB Commended 2 Crowns
Credit cards: 1, 3
Proprietor: Jennifer Skeaping

CUILMORE COTTAGE
Kinloch Rannoch
Perthshire PH16 5QB
Tel: 01882 632218

Small is Beautiful Award 1990

100 yards from east corner of Loch Rannoch.
Anita Steffen has made a tremendous success of this cosy little 18th century croft and the standard and style of her food has been lauded and publicised to a degree that is remarkable for such a small establishment. Much of the produce is grown in the cottage garden and the rest is carefully sourced to ensure freshness and quality. Thereafter Anita displays her own skill and flair to the great satisfaction of her diners. And it is not just residents who may enjoy the experience of dining at Cuilmore. Dinners are served at the candlelit table in the intimate dining room of the cottage. Cuilmore is delightfully secluded and guests have the complimentary use of mountain bikes, dinghy and canoe to explore the locality.
Open 1 Feb to 31 Oct
Rooms: 2 with private facilities
Dinner 7 – 9 pm (d)
Prior booking essential for non-residents
Unlicensed – guests welcome to take own wine
No children
No smoking in dining room
Bed & Breakfast from £20
Dinner B & B from £40
• *Apple and beech smoked salmon*

slices on crisp salad leaves with hazelnut oil. Seasonal soups. Baked fillet of hake folded in smokey bacon with chervil and lime sauce. Roast best end of lamb crusted with herbs and rosemary jus. Crispy magret of duck glazed with honey, with rose petal vinegar. Local cheeseplate and home-made biscuits.
STB Deluxe 3 Crowns
No credit cards
Proprietor: Anita Steffen

WEST TEMPAR HOUSE
Kinloch Rannoch, by Pitlochry
Perthshire PH16 5QE
Tel: 01882 632338
Fax: 01882 632338

1½ miles from Kinloch Rannoch village, on unclassified road to Schiehallion and Aberfeldy.
Perched on a little knoll above the main road is West Tempar House. It was built in 1904 as the "smallest possible grand house" to accommodate both shooting parties and servants. Tempar is an anglicisation of 'Teamhar' which means an eminence with a wide view. Apart from its superb views its main features are the local Scots pine panelling and fireplaces downstairs. These were made by ships' panellers from Wearside employed by Henry Heath Cochrane, the shipowner-cum-builder who commissioned the house. Built originally for sporting purposes, the house would have seen only a few months occupation in the year. Andrew and Janet Mineyko are the first year-round inhabitants of over 10 years' standing. It is Janet who does the vast majority of the cooking, while Andrew provides most of the game for the table. Dinner is served at a large oval marble table in the dining room which looks onto the garden and the hill. For those interested in the great outdoors, Andrew can take guests on guided tours of the natural history of the estate, which rises from wetland at 600 feet to

high tops at 3,400 feet. Spanish, French and Italian spoken.
Open all year except 14 Feb to 16 Mar + 3 days over Christmas
Rooms: 3 with private facilities
Dinner at 8 pm (c)
Packed lunches available
Residents only
Unlicensed – guests welcome to take own wine
No smoking in dining room
Bed & Breakfast from £20
Dinner B & B £30 – £35
Special Rates for 4+ nights
• *Home-made soups. Pan-fried venison fillet with herbs, served with rowan jelly and coarse grain mustard. Chicken with broccoli in a cream mayonnaise. Various game and fish dishes. Chocolate brandy cake. Upside-down gingerbread. Home-made ice-creams.*
No credit cards
Proprietors: Andrew & Janet Mineyko

Kinlochbervie

Location 134

THE KINLOCHBERVIE HOTEL
Kinlochbervie, by Lairg
Sutherland IV27 4RP
Tel: 01971 521275
Fax: 01971 521438

On B801, via A838 from Lairg.
In the remoteness of Sutherland this is a surprisingly modern hotel set on top of a hill with superb views of Kinlochbervie harbour and Loch Clash. Kinlochbervie is a major fishing port and the hotel takes full advantage of this by featuring really fresh locally caught seafood on its menu in the candlelit dining room. There is also a bistro for informal eating. The hotel is well appointed with comfortable bedrooms and good standards.
Open 1 Mar to 31 Oct
Rooms: 14 with private facilities
Bar Lunch 12 – 1.45 pm (b)
Bar Supper 6.30 – 8.30 pm (b)
Dinner 7.30 – 8.30 pm (e) 4 course menu
No smoking in dining room
Bed & Breakfast £45 – £55
Dinner B & B £70 – £80
• *Scottish salmon smoked in own smokehouse. Tomato, bacon and garlic soup. Cullen skink. Steamed fillet of halibut with Noilly Prat sauce. Pan-fried calves liver with fresh herb butter.*
STB Commended 4 Crowns
Credit cards: 1, 2, 3, 5, 6
Proprietors: Rex & Kate Neame

Kinnesswood

THE LOMOND COUNTRY INN

Kinnesswood, by Loch Leven
Perthshire KY13 7HN
Tel: 01592 840253
Fax: 01592 840693

4 miles from Kinross. From south, M90 Junction 5, B9097 via Scotlandwell. From north, M90 Junction 7, A911 via Milnathort.

Situated in the historic village of Kinnesswood, by the Lomond Hills, this cosy family run hotel offers magnificent views over Loch Leven. Only fresh food is served – simply prepared and very tasty – good wines and real ale. Twelve en suite bedrooms all with colour TV, telephones, tea and coffee-making facilities. Only 45 minutes from Edinburgh, Perth and St Andrews, and at the hub of all the sporting, leisure and cultural opportunities that abound in the area.

Open all year
Rooms: 12 with private facilities
Light snacks (scones, sandwiches and tea) served all day
Bar Lunch 12 – 2.30 pm (a)
Dining Room/Restaurant Lunch 12 – 2.30 pm (b)
Bar Supper 6 – 9 pm (a)
Dinner 6 – 9 pm (b)
Bed & Breakfast £27.50 – £35
Dinner B & B £35 – £45
• Terrine of Perthshire game with redcurrant and orange jelly. Puff pastry parcel of wild salmon with vermouth sauce. Roast local pheasant with red wine and rosemary. Pan-fried Highland venison with port and cranberries. Poached lemon sole on Largo Bay crab cream. Peppered fillet steak. Sticky ginger pudding. Raspberry cranachan. Summer fruit brûlée.
STB Commended 3 Crowns
Credit cards: 1, 2, 3, 5, 6 + SWITCH
Proprietors: David Adams & Neil Hunter

Kinross

CROFTBANK HOUSE HOTEL & RESTAURANT

30 Station Road, Kinross
Fife KY13 7TG
Tel: 01577 863819

Junction 6, M90 on approach to Kinross. Croftbank is an old Victorian house on the edge of Kinross, not more than half a mile off the motorway. This is a very popular small and friendly hotel renowned for the high standard of its food, for which it has been awarded an AA Rosette. Chef/proprietor Bill Kerr is a chef of distinction and the menus he presents for his restaurant are imaginative and creative. His wife Diane looks after the front of the house with great charm and attention. Kinross is well placed for Fife's famous golf courses or for fishing, shooting or just sight-seeing as it is very convenient for Edinburgh, Perth, St Andrews or Stirling.

Open all year except Christmas Day, 1 + 2 Jan
Rooms: 5 with private facilities
Bar Lunch 12 – 1.45 pm except Mon (a)
Dining Room/Restaurant Lunch 12 – 1.45 pm except Mon (b)
Supper 6.30 – 9 pm except Mon (b)
Dinner 6.30 – 9 pm except Mon (c-d)
Closed Mon
No smoking in restaurant
Bed & Breakfast £25 – £28
Dinner B & B £45 – £50
Room Rate £25 – £28
• A warm salad of seared west coast scallops and langoustines with toasted pine nuts and a fresh herb dressing. Breast of woodland pigeon cooked pink and served with braised brown lentils and a port wine jus-lie. Biscuit basket with Drambuie ice-cream and a compote of warm fresh summer fruits.
STB Commended 2 Crowns
Credit cards: 1, 3
Proprietors: Bill & Diane Kerr

THE GROUSE & CLARET RESTAURANT

Heatheryford
Kinross KY13 7NQ
Tel: 01577 864212
Fax: 01577 864920

Junction 6, M90, opposite the Granada Services.
This most charming and unusual restaurant with rooms is within sight of – but not sound of – the motorway, its

entrance drive exactly opposite the motorway service area yet a world apart in style and standard. Taking its unusual name from a fishing fly this really is a special place with a peaceful atmosphere, serving delightful food and wine. The decor is charming and the old sandstone buildings are filled with unusual antique furniture, old rugs and lovely pictures. The dining room overlooks the fishing lochans. There are many examples of fine local craftwork for sale in the art gallery, which also caters for special parties of up to 70 guests and is popular for birthdays, anniversaries and business meetings. Meriel Cairns takes pride in floral table decorations and garlands the beams with flowers and ivy for special occasions. The delicious home-made food is beautifully presented with lots of fresh herbs and garnished with tiny wild flowers. It is a bit like dining with a good friend and one who is an exceptional cook. The accommodation is in a modern annexe with comfortable ground floor rooms overlooking the water. Good fly-fishing for trout is available for the enthusiastic fisherman. French, Italian and German spoken.

Open all year except New Year's Day
Note: Oct to Mar closed pm Sun Mon
Rooms: 3 with private facilities
Bar Lunch 12 – 2 pm (a)
Dining Room/Restaurant Lunch 12 – 2 pm (a-b)
Dinner 7 – 9 pm (b-c)
Table Licence
Facilities for disabled visitors
No smoking in restaurant
Bed & Breakfast from £19.50
• Salmon and chervil fish cakes. Lamb cutlets in breadcrumbs and grainy mustard with rosemary and claret sauce. Fresh seafood daily. Pan-fried fillet of roe deer on a tomato and courgette provençale sauce.
STB Approved 3 Crowns
Credit cards: 1, 3, 6
Proprietors: John & Meriel Cairns

THE MUIRS INN KINROSS

49 Muirs, Kinross
Perthshire KY13 7AU
Tel: 01577 862270

M90 exit Junction 6 and follow A922 Milnathort for a short distance. At 'T' junction, Inn is diagonally opposite to right.
This delightful Scottish country Inn is situated close to the shores of Loch Leven which has historical connections

with Mary, Queen of Scots, who was imprisoned on an island in the loch in 1567. The Inn itself is a Listed building which dates back to the 1800s and was originally a small farmhouse. There is marked attention to detail and to the comfort of guests in the attractively furnished en suite bedrooms, and the 'old world' atmosphere of the Inn proper is well carried through in the Maltings Restaurant with its interesting historical pictures and prints, and dark beams overhead. The Muirs Inn aims to offer good wholesome food at sensible prices and succeeds in doing so, while for the connoisseur there are over 130 malt whiskies and a choice of eight predominantly Scottish Real Ales in addition to the Inn's own branded beers and lagers.

Open all year
Rooms: 5 with private facilities
Bar Lunch 12 – 2 pm (a)
Dining Room/Restaurant Lunch 12 – 2 pm (b)
Traditional High Tea 5 – 6 pm (a)
Bar Supper 5 – 9 pm (a)
Dinner 7 – 9 pm (b)
No dogs
Smoking discouraged
Bed & Breakfast £27.50 – £35
Dinner B & B £40 – £47.50
Special Rates available
• Canapé Carsgore – creamed smoked haddock with cheese, glazed and served on toast. Muirs fish brose. Prime Scottish venison with a bitter-sweet honey and hazelnut sauce. Tripe Threapmuir – cooked in traditional way, served with a creamed onion sauce. Smoked trout served with a Mull whisky dressing. Prime Scottish steaks.
STB Commended 3 Crowns
Credit cards: 1, 3, 6
Proprietors: Gordon Westwood & Graham Philip

Kippen

Location 137

CROSS KEYS HOTEL
Main Street, Kippen
by Stirling FK8 3DN
Tel: 01786 870293

On B822 Callander-Fintry and just off A811 Stirling-Erskine Bridge, only 8 miles west of Stirling.
An attractive old 18th century village inn, now a small family run hotel, set in the peaceful and picturesque village of Kippen, near Stirling. The hotel has

retained its old world character which is enhanced by log fires in the bars during winter. In addition to informal meals in the bar and family room, there is a small restaurant where the interesting menu offers a good selection of freshly prepared dishes.

Open all year except Christmas Night + 1 Jan
Rooms: 3
Bar Lunch 12 – 2 pm Mon to Sat: 12.30 – 2 pm Sun (a)
Dining Room/Restaurant Lunch 12 – 2 pm Mon to Sat: 12.30 – 2 pm Sun (a)
Bar Supper 5.30 – 9.30 pm (a)
Dinner 7 – 8.45 pm (c)
Bed & Breakfast from £19.50
• Home-made soup. Bramble and port liver pâté. Breast of chicken with a lemon and tarragon sauce. Seafood en croûte. Medallions of fillet of beef with a peppered brandy and cream sauce.
Credit cards: 1, 3
Proprietors: Angus & Sandra Watt

Kirkcudbright

Location 138

AULD ALLIANCE RESTAURANT
5 Castle Street
Kirkcudbright DG6 4JA
Tel: 01557 330569

Kirkcudbright town, opposite the castle.
A Listed building constructed of old castle stones and formerly a tradesman's cottage. There are very few airs and graces about the decoration of this little restaurant but the food says it all. Alistair Crawford's cooking is of a very high order combining the best of French and Scottish cuisine in menus of unusual scope for such a relatively small

county town and featuring prominently the excellent local seafood and Galloway beef.

Open Easter to 31 Oct + Christmas wk
Dining Room/Restaurant Lunch 12.30 – 2 pm Sun only (a)
Dinner 6.30 – 9.30 pm (c)
• Home-made chicken, garlic and brandy pâté, baked in pastry with redcurrant and port wine sauce. Pan-fried Scotch sirloin steak with heather honey mustard and Drambuie liqueur. Kirkcudbright Bay queen scallops in garlic butter with smoked Ayrshire bacon in Galloway cream.
No credit cards
Proprietors: Alistair & Anne Crawford

SELKIRK ARMS HOTEL
High Street, Kirkcudbright
Kirkcudbrightshire DG6 4JG
Tel: 01557 330402
Fax: 01557 331639

Off A75, 27 miles west of Dumfries, between Castle Douglas and Gatehouse-of-Fleet.
The Selkirk Arms is an historic 18th century hotel situated in in its own secluded garden in the picturesque harbour town of Kirkcudbright. It has old associations with the poet Robert Burns. Over recent years the hotel has been refurbished to the best modern standards, yet retained the original character of the place. There are extensive à la carte and daily changing table d'hôte menus. Marvellous walking, fishing, bird-watching and beaches nearby.

Open all year
Rooms: 15 with private facilities
Bar Lunch 12 – 2 pm (a)
Dining Room/Restaurant Lunch 12 – 2 pm (a) – booking essential
Bar Supper 6 – 9.30 pm (a)
Dinner 7 – 9.30 pm (c)
Bed & Breakfast £35 – £45
Dinner B & B £52.50 – £62.50
• Poached salmon with white wine, orange and grapefruit segments and dill. Chicken sautéed with juniper berries and gin. Local lamb cutlets with rosemary and mint sauce. Fillet steak coated in crushed black pepper with red wine, brandy, red and green peppers and cream.
STB Highly Commended 4 Crowns
Credit cards: 1, 2, 3, 5
Proprietor: John Morris

Kirkintilloch

THE LADY MARGARET CANALBOAT
Scotland in View Ltd
c/o 22/26 Main Street, The Village
Cumbernauld G67 2RS
Tel: 0836 607755/01236 723523

> Canalboat based at Glasgow
> Road Bridge Jetty, on A803
> between Bishopbriggs and
> Kirkintilloch, near The Stables
> and at the old basin/Speirs
> Wharf, Glasgow city centre, off
> M8.

Calm water canal cruises on the northern
outskirts of Glasgow, in country scenery,
with floodlights and central heating for all
year round operation. The purpose-built
canalboat is tastefully appointed. Crystal
glasses and Wedgwood crockery
enhance attractive table settings, with
pink linen and fresh flowers. A relaxing
experience, unrivalled in Scotland.
Available for group bookings at any time,
any day. The boat provides a quality
venue which is especially suitable for
business entertainment, family
gatherings and weddings any day – as
well as for individual table bookings on
weekend cruises for that special
occasion.
*Operates all year except Christmas Day
+ 1 Jan*
*Note: group bookings only Christmas Day
+ 1 Jan*
Sunday Lunch 1 – 3 pm (c)
Executive Lunch 1 – 3 pm (d)
*Dinner 7.30 – 10.30 pm (e) 4 course
menu*
Advance booking essential
• *Imaginative set menus incorporating
the best in fresh Scottish produce and
dishes with an emphasis on quality and
presentation. Dinner menus incorporate
an exceptional range of Scottish
cheeses.*
Credit cards: 1, 2, 3, 5
Proprietor: Norman Egan

Kirkmichael

THE LOG CABIN HOTEL
Kirkmichael, by Blairgowrie
Perthshire PH10 7NB
Tel: 01250 881288
Fax: 01250 881402
Signposted off A924 in Kirkmichael.
Uniquely built of whole Norwegian pine
logs, the Log Cabin Hotel nestles high in
Glen Derby with some wonderful
panoramic views. The hotel is centrally
heated and double glazed so guests are
assured of a warm welcome. Lovely
views from the restaurant where the
menus change each evening to reflect
the availability of local produce. An ideal
centre for touring Perthshire. Also
popular with hill-walkers and convenient
for skiing in Glenshee.
*Open all year except Christmas +
Boxing Days*
Rooms: 13 with private facilities
*Tea/coffee, homemade cakes etc served
all day*
Bar Lunch 12 – 1.45 pm (a)
Bar Supper 6 – 8.45 pm (a-b)
Dinner 7.30 – 8.45 pm (c) 4 course menu
Bed & Breakfast £25 – £35
Dinner B & B £43 – £51
• *Smoked Drumore rainbow trout on a
passion fruit coulis with salad garnish.
Chicken breast poached in flavoured
stock served on a bed of fresh leeks.
Medallions of pork fillet sautéed in butter
and served with a Madeira sauce. Angus
sirloin steak flamed in brandy with a pink
and peppercorn cream sauce.*
STB Commended 3 Crowns
Credit cards: 1, 2, 3, 5
Proprietor: A F Finch

Kyle of Lochalsh

THE SEAFOOD RESTAURANT
(BIADH MATH)
Railway Platform, Kyle of Lochalsh
Ross-shire IV40 8XX
Tel: 01599 4813
*At Kyle of Lochalsh railway station on
platform 1. Parking on slipway to station.*
You have to know exactly where you are
going to find The Seafood Restaurant
which is right on the railway platform, but
do not be deterred by that. It overlooks
the Cuillin Hills of Skye and the harbour
where much of the fresh seafood and
fish for the restaurant is landed. For

lovers of good food – and seafood in
particular – this is a great find. The
menus feature langoustines, monkfish,
scallops, mussels, oysters, squid – to
name but a few – but for those who
prefer there are also some interesting
venison, steak and chicken dishes. Nor
are children or vegetarians forgotten.
Chutneys, cakes and desserts are all
home-made as is the fudge with your
coffee. On cold nights a coal fire burns
bright and creates a snug little haven. In
the high season, the restaurant is open
every night for dinner and also for
breakfast, home-baking and lunches.
Open Easter to Oct
Breakfast served 10 – 11.30 am
*Dining Room/Restaurant Lunch 12 –
2.45 pm Fri only: Easter Jul + Aug open
Mon to Fri (a)*
Dinner 6.30 – 9 pm (c)
Table Licence
• *Langoustines in garlic butter. Seafood
and tarragon pancakes. Smoked seafood
platter with raspberry and poppyseed
dressing. Monkfish and prawn kebabs in
mango sauce. Queen scallops in white
wine. Flambéd whisky steaks. Venison
and juniper kebabs. Spinach and cream
cheese pancakes. Cranachan. Bread and
butter pudding. Brown sugar and
hazelnut meringues.*
Credit cards: 1, 3
*Proprietors: Andrea Matheson &
Jann Macrae*

SEAGREEN RESTAURANT
& BOOKSHOP
Plockton Road
Kyle of Lochalsh IV40 8DA
Tel: 01599 4388
*North of Kyle of Lochalsh, on road to
Plockton.*
There is an inviting range of home-baking
and unusual salads on display in this
popular cafe situated in what was the old
village school which is on the outskirts of
Kyle of Lochalsh facing the sea. Fiona
Begg's food is varied, good, interesting –
and healthy. It is all prepared and
cooked on the premises from prime
products. You are equally welcome
whether you drop in for a coffee or for
the full meals which are available all day.
There is an outside terrace and garden.
Open 26 Mar to 10 Oct
*Lunch 12 – 5.30 pm except Sat
Spring/Autumn: open 7 days Summer (a)*
*Dinner 6.30 – 8.30 pm except Sat
Spring/Autumn: 6.30 – 9 pm 7 days
Summer (b)*
Reservations essential for dinner

No smoking in restaurant
• Smoked seafood platter of salmon, mussels and mackerel with home-made granary bread. Fresh spinach and crowdie cheese lasagne. Oat pancakes filled with smoked haddock and fennel, with fresh tarragon sauce. Wild Loch Duich salmon. Organic salad vegetables with a spicey peanut dip. Leek, cream cheese and sweetcorn roulade with yoghurt and dill sauce. Meringues filled with Atholl brose and local raspberries. Local cheeses and oatcakes. Rhubarb and banana pie.
Credit cards: 1, 3
Proprietor: Fiona Begg

Kylesku

Location 142

LINNE MHUIRICH
Unapool Croft Road, Kylesku
by Lairg, Sutherland
IV27 4HW
Tel: 01971 502227

½ mile south of the new Kylesku Bridge on A894, last house in a cul-de-sac road.
Fiona and Diarmid MacAulay welcome non-smokers to their modern family home which is peacefully situated overlooking Loch Glencoul with panoramic views of hills and lochs. The Handa Island Nature/Bird Reserve and lovely, lonely sandy beaches are nearby. Directions and maps for many local walks are provided. The dinner menus change daily and are discussed with guests after breakfast. Vegetarian dishes are enthusiastically prepared. Guests are welcome to take their own

wine as the premises are not licensed to provide alcoholic beverages. In the evening at 10 pm guests are offered a choice of hot drink and something tasty to eat. French and German spoken.
Open 7 May to 30 Oct
Rooms: 2 , 1 with private facilities
Dinner at 7.30 pm except Sun Sat (b)
Residents only
No smoking throughout
Bed & Breakfast £17.50 – £20.50
Dinner B & B £27.50 – £30.50
• Local fish and seafood – Kylesku prawn vol au vents; smoked haddock au gratin; fisherman's pie. Celtic salmon medallions with lime and almonds. Loch Beag mussels and Ullapool prawns in garlic butter. Pork, pepper and apple casserole. Home-made quiches and pâtés. Vegetarian dishes. Unusual salads. Tempting desserts and home-baking. Filter coffee. Scottish honey and cheeses.
STB Commended 2 Crowns
No credit cards
Proprietors: Fiona & Diarmid MacAulay

Laide

Location 143

THE OLD SMIDDY
Laide
Ross-shire IV22 2NB
Tel: 01445 731425
Fax: 01445 731425

A835 Inverness-Ullapool. At Braemore junction (44 miles north-west of Inverness) take A832 via Dundonnell to Laide (29 miles).
If you follow this main coastal route to Poolewe, you will discover the village of Laide, just eight miles from the famous Inverewe Gardens. Opposite the church sits The Old Smiddy, a lovely white-washed cottage, which is now a guest house and restaurant. The bedrooms (one double and one family room) are tastefully decorated and comfortably furnished, with Indian pure cotton sheets on the beds. Elsewhere the house is crammed with family treasures and fascinating pieces Steve Macdonald has brought home from his travels abroad – Indian marquetry tables in the comfortable sitting room, hard wood elephants on the mantlepiece. Family photographs are everywhere including an impressive study of ancestor, Long John Macdonald, the whisky distiller. There are views towards An Teallach, the highest mountain on the peninsula, from

the attractive quarry-tiled dining room where guests sit at tables laid with pure linen tablecloths, crystal glasses and Indian embroidered napkins. The menus are compiled taking careful consideration of guests' preferences and the dishes are beautifully presented. Kate Macdonald takes great pride in utilising the best of local produce with specialities such as local seafood and venison complemented by lots of fresh vegetables, and freshly baked bread. The Tea Room is run in the traditional manner with table service, offering freshly prepared home-baking, soups and sandwiches. Both Steve and Kate were born and brought up in the Highlands and are a useful source of information regarding local culture and the many historical places of interest.
Open all year
Rooms: 2 with private facilities
Tea Room 10.30 am – 4.30 pm Mon to Fri May to Sep; 12 – 4.30 pm Apr + Oct (a)
Restaurant Lunch 12 – 2 pm Mon to Fri (a)
Dinner at 7.30 pm (c)
Dinner for non-residents – booking essential
Unlicensed – guests welcome to take own wine
Facilities for disabled visitors
No smoking throughout
Bed & Breakfast £19 – £21.50
Dinner B & B £32.50 – £37
• Cream of wild salmon soup. Torridon scallops sautéed with garlic and fresh herbs. Gairloch monkfish roasted with lcmon, toppcd with a crunchy garlic coating and crisp courgettes and tomatoes. Prime fillet of Scottish pork stuffed with pistachios, apples and herbs. Home-made ice-creams made with Highland cream. Whisky parfait with toffee bark. Apple and almond torte.
STB Highly Commended 3 Crowns
No credit cards
Proprietor: Kate Macdonald

Langbank

GLEDDOCH HOUSE HOTEL & COUNTRY ESTATE

Langbank
Renfrewshire PA14 6YE
Tel: 01475 540711
Fax: 01475 540201

Off M8 Glasgow-Greenock at Langbank (B789).

Gleddoch is a delightful country house which was built originally by Sir James Lithgow as a wedding gift for his wife. It sits high on a hill looking across the River Clyde to the Loch Lomond hills and is surrounded by 360 acres of grounds devoted to the activities of the country club. There is an 18 hole golf course, horse-riding, clay pigeon shooting and off-road driving. 1995 will see the addition of several indoor leisure activities. The house itself has been tastefully extended yet still epitomises the gracious living style of the private family home it once was. Indeed the finest characteristics of the house have been retained and there are still many original pieces of furniture and fine paintings in the beautifully spacious public rooms. Bedrooms and suites are exceedingly comfortable and very tastefully furnished. The standard and presentation of food has always been of the highest calibre with imaginative and well balanced menus.

Open all year
Rooms: 39 with private facilities
Bar Lunch (Clubhouse) 12 – 2 pm (a)
Dining Room/Restaurant Lunch 12.30 – 2 pm (c)
Bar Supper (Clubhouse) 6.30 – 9.15 pm (b)
Dinner 7 – 9 pm (e)
Bed & Breakfast £67.50 – £92.50
Dinner B & B £80 – £105
Special Rates available
• Fillet of Shetland salmon with cumin and black pepper on spinach leaves with vermouth, passion fruit and chive cream sauce. Roast medallions of prime beef fillet with hollandaise sauce on a tomato, courgette and aubergine ragoût. Heart shaped shortbread layers with a white chocolate mousse on a strawberry coulis.
STB Highly Commended 4 Crowns
Credit cards: 1, 2, 3, 5

Letham

FERNIE CASTLE HOTEL

Letham, Cupar
Fife KY7 7RU
Tel: 01337 810381
Fax: 01337 810422

Off A914 Glenrothes-Tay Bridge/Dundee, 1 mile north of A91/A914 Melville roundabout.

The origins of Fernie Castle go back to the 14th century when it was a fortified hunting tower and, with the estate, went the titles of Constable of Cupar and Forester of Falkland. It has seen many changes since but retains an impressive appearance and has been comfortably converted internally. There is an excellently preserved Ice House to the rear of the hotel, one of the finest of the few that still remain in the country and in which blocks of ice were stored from the frozen lochan and used throughout the summer as refrigeration. Menus show a commendable reliance on local produce, and a degree of original thinking and professional skill by the chef.

Open all year
Rooms: 15 with private facilities
Bar Lunch 12 – 3 pm (a)
Dining Room/Restaurant Lunch 12 – 2.30 pm (b)
Bar Supper 6 – 10 pm (a)
Dinner 7 – 9.45 pm (c)
Bed & Breakfast £30 – £55
Dinner B & B £45 – £70
Special Rates available
• Local seafood served cold with an aniseed sauce. Baked Tay salmon with dill and shallot butter. Spring lamb with a chicken and mushroom mousse on a rosemary jus-lie. Guinea fowl stuffed with pigeon. Game pie. Berry cranachan.
STB Commended 3 Crowns
Credit cards: 1, 2, 3 + SWITCH, DELTA
Proprietor: Norman Smith

Isle of Lewis

CORRAN VIEW GUEST HOUSE

22A Breasclete
Callanish
Isle of Lewis PA86 9EF
Tel: 01851 621 300

Located ½ mile off main A858 on west side of Lewis. 18 miles from Stornoway and 40 miles from Tarbert ferry terminals.

Corran View is a modern family run guest house in an elevated position overlooking east Loch Roag, Uig and Harris Hills and the village of Callanish which is famous for its standing stones. It is also close to the Carloway Broch and the black house village at Garenin. There is a friendly and welcoming atmosphere at Corran View. Christine Heslop aims to ensure that her guests have a memorable stay and enjoy the carefully prepared dinner menu she creates from the abundance of local fresh seafood, game and meat. All three en suite bedrooms are comfortably appointed and have tea-making facilities, colour TV and central heating. Corran View is an ideal situation for touring, hill-walking, fishing and bird-watching or just right for a relaxing peaceful holiday. Gaelic spoken.

Open all year except Christmas Day + 1 Jan
Rooms: 3 with private facilities
Dinner 6.30 – 7 pm (c)
Residents only
Unlicensed – guests welcome to take own wine
Dogs – by arrangement only
No smoking in restaurant
Bed & Breakfast from £23
Dinner B & B from £36.50
Special Rate for 7+ nights
• Home-made soups e.g. Scotch broth, Cullen skink, spicy lentil. Seafood specials. Local venison and roast Scotch lamb with a variety of sauces. Hebridean salmon in cucumber sauce. Trout and caper sauce. Traditional puddings with Scottish cream.
STB Highly Commended 3 Crowns
Credit cards: 1, 3
Proprietor: Christine Heslop

ESHCOL GUEST HOUSE
Breasclete, Callanish
Isle of Lewis PA86 9ED
Tel: 01851 621 357

*On A858, 17 miles from Stornoway, 40
miles from Tarbert.*

Isobel and Neil Macarthur run this
modern little guest house on a small
croft in Breasclete, a weaving village on
the west coast of Lewis within walking
distance of the famous Callanish
Stones. There are wonderful views
across Loch Roag to the island of Great
Bernera and beyond, with the hills of Uig
and Harris in the distance. Bedrooms are
en suite with tea-making facilities etc
and are attractively furnished. A small
establishment where you will be made
welcome and comfortable, and from
which you can go walking, fishing,
sightseeing and exploring the splendid
shoreline of West Lewis. Gaelic spoken.

*Open mid Mar to mid Oct
Rooms: 3 with private facilities
Dinner 6.30 – 7 pm Mon to Sat: 6.30 –
8 pm Sun (b)
Residents only
Unlicensed – guests welcome to take
own wine
No smoking in dining room
Bed & Breakfast £20 – £22
Dinner B & B £34 – £36
• Home-made soups. Local smoked
salmon. Lamb with rosemary. Cranachan
(Eshcol-style). Fresh vegetables from
garden.
STB Highly Commended 3 Crowns
No credit cards
Proprietors: Neil & Isobel Macarthur*

HANDA
18 Keose Glebe (Ceos), Lochs
Isle of Lewis PA86 9JX
Tel: 01851 83334

*1½ miles off A859, 12 miles south of
Stornoway: last house in village of
'Ceos'.*

This is a delightful modern home on a
hilltop which seems hundreds of miles
from anywhere but of course is not. It is
a convenient spot for exploring Lewis
and Harris but much nearer at hand –
virtually on the doorstep – there is hill-
walking, bird-watching, fishing, and otter
sighting if you are lucky. In this small
comfortable haven, island hospitality and
personal attention are very much to the
fore. Alongside traditional recipes there
is innovative home-cooking using fresh
herbs and vegetables from the kitchen
garden. Vegetarian and individual dietary
requirements are catered for. There is

brown trout fishing on the private loch
100 yards from the house and a boat
and equipment can be hired.

*Open 1 May to 6 Oct
Rooms: 3, 1 with private facilities
Dinner 6.30 – 7.30 pm Thu to Sat (b)
Unlicensed – guests welcome to take
own wine
No smoking in dining room
Bed & Breakfast £16 – £22
Dinner B & B £29 – £35
Special Rates for 3+ nights
• Home-made breads, soups. Scallops in
brandy. Baked turbot. Edwardian lovage
syllabub.
STB Highly Commended 2 Crowns
No credit cards
Proprietors: Murdo & Christine Morrison*

PARK GUEST HOUSE
& RESTAURANT
30 James Street, Stornoway
Isle of Lewis PA87 2QN
Tel: 01851 70 2485

*½ mile from ferry terminal. At junction of
Matheson Road, James Street and A866
to airport and Eye peninsula.*

This substantial stone-built house dates
back to around 1883 and is situated in
the centre of the town of Stornoway. The
old wood of the interior has been
refurbished and the public rooms and
bedrooms are tastefully decorated,
spacious and comfortable. There is a
warm homely atmosphere in the
restaurant which features a Glasgow
style fireplace. The considerable skills of
chef/proprietor Roddy Afrin are displayed
in his carefully prepared and presented
menus for which he sources the best of
fresh local produce such as shellfish,
game, venison and Lewis lamb. Park
Guest House makes an ideal base for
touring, golf, bird-watching, fishing etc, or
just exploring some of the lunar-like
landscapes of Lewis and Harris.

*Open all year except 24 Dec to 5 Jan +
16 Oct to 11 Nov
Rooms: 5
Packed Lunches available (a)
Dinner 5.30 – 6.30 pm (table d'hôte)
Tue to Sat: Sun Mon residents only (b)
Dinner 7 – 8.30 pm (à la carte) except
Sun Mon (c-d)
Note: Dinner Sun Mon – residents only
No dogs
Bed & Breakfast £21 – £27
Dinner B & B £35 – £41
• Lewis langoustines in garlic butter.
Local lobster. Loin of lamb with apple
and rosemary. Sole and smoked salmon
in a lobster sauce. Apple flan with*

*raspberry and cinnamon sauce. Home-
made tablet.
STB Commended 1 Crown
No credit cards
Proprietors: Catherine & Roddy Afrin*

Loch Earn
St Fillans

Location 147

ACHRAY HOUSE HOTEL
St Fillans, Loch Earn
Perthshire PH6 2NF
Tel: 01764 685 231
Fax: 01764 685 320

A85 in St Fillans, 12 miles west of Crieff.

This popular and well established family
run hotel has a stunning lochside
position in this area of outstanding
natural beauty. The proprietors set
themselves impressively high standards
and it is little wonder that their guests
keep coming back for more. The food, for
which the hotel has been awarded an AA
Rosette, is particularly good and
remarkably inexpensive for the quality
and variety offered. Mrs Ross's puddings
are renowned. The dining room was
recently extended and is very tastefully
appointed. A good base for the many
outdoor activities of the area.

*Open 1 Mar to 1 Nov
Rooms: 10, 7 with private facilities
Bar Lunch 12 – 2 pm Mon to Sat: 12.30
– 2 pm Sun (a)
Bar Supper 6.15 – 9.30 pm (a)
Dinner 7 – 9 pm (c)
Bed & Breakfast £22 – £29.50
Dinner B & B £37 – £44.50
Special Rates available
• Wide choice of Scottish produce –
pheasant, grouse, steaks, salmon,
venison, trout, lamb, pork and seafood.
Good choice of vegetarian dishes always
available. Large selection of freshly
made desserts (the house speciality).
STB Highly Commended 3 Crowns
Credit cards: 1, 3 + SWITCH
Proprietors: Tony & Jane Ross*

THE FOUR SEASONS HOTEL
St Fillans, Loch Earn
Perthshire PH6 2NF
Tel: 01764 685 333
Fax: 01764 685 333

On A85, 12 miles west of Crieff, at west end of St Fillans overlooking Loch Earn.
There are few lovelier locations than that of the Four Seasons at the east end of Loch Earn in the charming little village of St Fillans. Huge picture windows in all the public rooms and most of the bedrooms offer stunning views across and down the loch, and there are six chalets on the wooded hillside behind the hotel. The Scott family are anxious to ensure the comfort of their guests and Chef Andrew Scott has some really interesting and imaginative dishes on his menu. There are not too many places where the bar lunch menu runs to large bowls of Skye mussels cooked in white wine, or Guinea fowl terrine, or Arbroath smokies and poached eggs. That, however, should whet the appetite for a leisurely dinner in the attractive dining room where regularly changing menus emphasise the abundance of game and seafood, but the chef is willing to prepare any special requests, given appropriate notice.
Open 1 Mar to mid Dec
Rooms: 18 with private facilities
Bar Lunch 12.15 – 2.15 pm (a)
Dining Room/Restaurant Lunch 12.30 – 2 pm Sun only (b)
Bar Supper 6.30 – 9.30 pm (b)
Dinner 7 – 9.30 pm (d)
Facilities for disabled visitors
No smoking in dining room
Bed & Breakfast £28 – £45
Dinner B & B £49 – £66
• *Loch Sween oysters. Steamed fillet of lemon sole, with halibut mousse and tomato and lemon butter. Skye scallops and mussels with basil and tomato. Fillet of beef. Saddle of lamb with rosemary and mushrooms.*
STB Commended 4 Crowns
Credit cards: 1, 2, 3, 6
Proprietors: Allan & Barbara Scott

Loch Lomond
Location 148
CAMERON HOUSE HOTEL
Loch Lomond, Alexandria
Dunbartonshire G83 8QZ
Tel: 01389 55565
Fax: 01389 59522

Prestige Award Winner 1991

On A82 near Balloch, on the banks of Loch Lomond.
This most impressive location has been developed carefully and skilfully with due regard to the aesthetics of the site and is now a superb luxury resort hotel set in 108 wooded acres on the south west shore of Loch Lomond. There are excellent leisure facilities and a choice of restaurants. You can choose the elegance of the Georgian Room or the Grill Room with its emphasis on local produce and you can enjoy afternoon tea overlooking the loch in the tranquillity of the Drawing Room. The hotel restaurants are open to non-residents but leisure facilities are for members and residents only.
Open all year
Rooms: 68 with private facilities
Bar Lunch (Marina Clubhouse) 12.30 – 3 pm (a)
Lunch (Brasserie) 12 – 3 pm (b)
Dining Room/Restaurant Lunch (Georgian Room) 12 – 2 pm (c)
Lunch (Grill Room) 12 – 2 pm Sun only (c)
Dinner (Brasserie) 6 – 10 pm (c)
Dinner (Georgian Room) 7 – 10 pm (f)
No dogs
Facilities for disabled visitors
No smoking area in Brasserie
No smoking in Georgian Room – jacket + tie requested
Bed & Breakfast £75 – £125
Dinner B & B £94.50 – £157.50
• *Warm timbale of salmon mousse with grilled scallops on a silver birch and herb sauce. Grilled suprême of halibut resting on lemon noodles with glazed vegetables and crispy fried celeriac. Loin of lamb on a potato, apple and mint filo parcel served with a honey and raspberry jus. Hot pear soufflé infused with dark chocolate served with eau de vie ice-cream.*
STB Deluxe 5 Crowns
Credit cards: 1, 2, 3, 5 + SWITCH

Lochcarron
Location 149
LOCHCARRON HOTEL
Lochcarron
Ross-shire IV54 8YS
Tel: 015202 226
Fax: 015202 612

At east end of village, facing the loch.
This 19th century Highland hostelry sits on the shores of Lochcarron amidst the rugged grandeur of Wester Ross. It is family run and has been modernised to provide the facilities expected of an AA two star hotel. The majority of the accommodation, which includes two suites with their own small sitting rooms, overlooks the sea loch. This view is also shared by the lounge bar and restaurant, where fish and shellfish from local boats and game from nearby sporting estates feature highly on both à la carte and table d'hôte menus which cater for every taste.
Open all year
Rooms: 10 with private facilities
Bar Lunch 12 – 2 pm (a-b)
Note: Bar Meals available all day summer
Dining Room/Restaurant Lunch 12 – 2 pm (a-b)
Bar Supper 5.30 – 9 pm (a-b)
Dinner 6.30 – 9 pm (b-c)
Bed & Breakfast £30 – £40
Dinner B & B £45 – £55
• *King scallops pan-fried in lemon butter. Poached fillet of local salmon with hollandaise sauce. Lobster platter. Marinated venison with a rich gravy and redcurrant jelly. New season lamb slowly casseroled with season vegetables.*
STB Commended 4 Crowns
Credit cards: 1, 3
Proprietors: Pam & Tony Wilkinson

ROCKVILLA HOTEL & RESTAURANT
Main Street, Lochcarron
Ross-shire IV54 8YB
Tel: 01520 722379

Situated in centre of village, c. 20 miles north of Kyle of Lochalsh.
A small family run hotel in the main street of this lochside village with a cheerful air of informality which should appeal to guests. The restaurant has a relaxing bistro feel and marvellous views of the loch. A substantial breakfast is a good start to a day of walking, touring around some of the local scenery or visiting Gairloch, the Applecross Peninsula or the Skye Ferry terminal. On return in the evening there is a fairly wide choice menu of local specialities and some traditional favourites. Bedrooms are simply but

adequately furnished and are immaculate.
Open all year except Christmas Day +
1 Jan
Rooms: 4, 2 with private facilities
Bar Lunch 12 – 2 pm (a)
Dining Room/Restaurant Lunch 12 –
2 pm Jun to Sep only (b)
Bar Supper 6 – 9.30 pm (a)
Dinner 6.30 – 9.30 pm (c)
No dogs
No smoking in restaurant
Bed & Breakfast £22 – £27
Special Rates for 3+/7+ nights
• Cullen skink. Smoked venison with
juniper chutney. Poached halibut steak
with hollandaise sauce. Lamb cutlets
with gooseberry and mint jelly. Prime
beef steaks.
STB Commended 3 Crowns
Credit cards: 1, 3
Proprietors: Lorna & Kenneth Wheelan

Lochearnhead

Location 150

CLACHAN COTTAGE RESTAURANT
Clachan Cottage Hotel
Lochside, Lochearnhead
Perthshire FK19 8PU
Tel: 01567 830247
Fax: 01567 830300

Lochearnhead is on A85 Crieff-Crianlarich.
Clachan Cottage Hotel enjoys a
spectacular lochside setting on the east
side of the village of Lochearnhead. It is
well placed for touring central Scotland
including the Trossachs, Glencoe, Oban
and Scone Palace. For the energetic
there are 28 golf courses within an hour,
and a good choice of walking, fishing and
watersports. The restaurant which is
upstairs has good views across the loch.
It offers freshly prepared meals using
Scottish produce. All rooms have private
facilities and tea and coffee-making
equipment. Open fires – range of malts,
and friendly service in a relaxed
atmosphere. Frequent live
entertainment. Special breaks available
throughout year.
Open 1 Apr to 3 Jan
Note: group bookings only Nov
Rooms: 21 with private facilities
Bar Lunch 12 – 2.30 pm (b)
Dining Room/Restaurant Lunch (b-c) –
group bookings only
Bar Supper 6 – 9.30 pm (b)
Dinner 7 – 9 pm (c)
Taste of Scotland applies to restaurant
only
Smoking not encouraged in restaurant

Bed & Breakfast £25 – £35
Dinner B & B £30 – £50
Special Rates for 3+/7+ nights
• Terrine of salmon with Drambuie and
fresh tarragon. Fillets of lemon sole with
a slice of Cree salmon, served with a
light leek and coriander sauce. Aberdeen
Angus steak with vegetable stuffing,
grilled with a grain mustard crust.
Chocolate and coconut cheesecake with
a trio of sauces. Apple and ginger
steamed pudding with clotted cream.
STB Commended 3 Crowns
Credit card: 1
Proprietor: Andrew Low

Lochgilphead

Location 151

THE CAIRN
Kilmartin, Lochgilphead
Argyll PA31 8RQ
Tel: 01546 5254
(01546 510254 from 1/95)

A816 Lochgilphead-Oban, 8 miles from
Lochgilphead.
The Cairn is situated in the historic village
of Kilmartin and was originally built in
1840 as a grocers and drapers shop. Ian
and Marion Thomson converted this
traditional stone building into a restaurant
in 1972. Over the years The Cairn has
become renowned for its high standard of
cooking using local produce in traditional
Scottish and European dishes. The menus
encompass anything from morning coffee
and afternoon teas with home-baking, to
quick snacks and bar meals. But it is the
à la carte at dinner which has earned the
restaurant an AA Rosette for the past four
years. Within the restaurant is the
Templewood Gallery which provides a
changing exhibition of contemporary and
traditional art, featuring recognised and
new Scottish artists.
Open all year except Christmas Day +
1 Jan
Note: Nov to Mar closed Mon to Wed
Bar Lunch 12 – 3 pm (a)
Bar Supper 5 – 8 pm (a)
Dinner 7.30 – 10 pm (c)
Facilities for disabled visitors
• Coronet of smoked salmon and
prawns. Highland mushrooms with a
ginger, whisky and cream sauce.
Smoked salmon fritters with a hot tangy
sauce. Scallops in a light white wine and
cream sauce. Escalope of venison in a
Cumberland sauce with cranberries. Fillet
of lemon sole with banana and prawns.
Duet of Scotch beef and lamb with

burgundy and white onion sauces.
Interesting vegetarian dishes.
No credit cards
Proprietors: Marion & Ian Thomson

Lochinver

Location 152

THE ALBANNACH
Baddidarroch, Lochinver
Sutherland IV27 4LP
Tel: 01571 844407

From Lochinver follow signs for Baddidarroch.
After ½ mile, pass turning for Highland
Stoneware, turn left for the Albannach.
This fine old 19th century house has
spectacular views across Lochinver Bay
towards Suilven and Canisp. There are
four tastefully decorated bedrooms all with
en suite facilities and from 1995 there will
be a conservatory added to the house. A
licence has been granted and there is now
no need for guests to take their own wine.
Good reports have come in from satisfied
guests so it is clear that those factors and
standards which established Albannach's
reputation are being maintained. The
Albannach presents an original style of
cooking, without shortcuts, emphasising
the best of game and seafood. Using
home-grown herbs, vegetables and fruit in
season, meals are served before an open
log fire in the wood-panelled dining room.
There is a daily changing set menu and
vegetarian meals are willingly provided with
prior notification. French spoken. Children
over five years welcome.
Open 1 Mar to 23 Dec
Rooms: 4 with private facilities
Dining Room/Restaurant Lunch 1 – 3 pm
except Mon (a-b)
Dinner at 7.30 pm (c) 4 course menu
Non-residents welcome by prior
arrangement
Table Licence
No dogs
Facilities for disabled visitors
No smoking throughout
Dinner B & B £38 – £44
• Locally oak-smoked salmon with an
avocado and dill dressing. Lochinver Bay
oysters in the half shell. Carrot, lentil and
cardamom soup. Roast leg of hill-fed
Highland lamb with a gravy of its own
juices. Lemon tart with fresh strawberries.
Belgian chocolate Grand Marnier mousse
with caramelised walnuts.
STB Highly Commended 3 Crowns
Credit cards: 1, 3
Proprietors: Colin Craig &
Lesley Crosfield

LOCHINVER LARDER'S RIVERSIDE BISTRO

Main Street, Lochinver
Sutherland IV27 4JY
Tel: 01571 844356

A837 to Lochinver, second property on right as enter village.

Polished wooden tables and chairs, Highland stoneware, good glassware and attractive table settings, give a pleasing appearance to this 44 seat restaurant which you enter through the delicatessen shop. It is situated on the bank of the River Inver as it flows into the sea and a large bay window provides pleasant panoramic views of the bay and its activities. With a plentiful supply of seafood landed directly at the village harbour, the menu majors on this and on really good steaks, but there are sufficient other items to provide adequate choice. At lunchtime the bistro operates on a self-selection basis, whereas in the evening there is waitress service. The presentation of food is good and the atmosphere pleasant and unhurried. Very popular and very busy in the season.

Open 1 Apr to 31 Oct
Food service 9 am – 9 pm Mon to Sat:
10.30 am – 9 pm Sun
Dining Room/Restaurant Lunch 12 –
2 pm (a)
Dinner 6.30 – 8.30 pm (c-d)
Facilities for disabled visitors
No smoking in restaurant
• Locally cured smoked salmon.
Noisettes of minted lamb with bacon and tomatoes in red wine. Halibut in lime and ginger butter with chopped chives. Cauliflower, broccoli and cheese bake served with puff pastry crowns.
Credit cards: 1, 3, 6 + DELTA
Proprietors: Ian & Debra Stewart

Lockerbie

Location 153

SOMERTON HOUSE HOTEL

Carlisle Road, Lockerbie
Dumfriesshire DG11 2DR
Tel: 01576 202583
Fax: 01576 202583

Outskirts of Lockerbie about ½ mile from M74.

Somerton House is a robust red sandstone Victorian mansion, reputedly designed by Alexander (Greek) Thomson, which stands in its own well kept gardens on the edge of the town. It retains the distinctive features of Kauri

timber panelling, period fireplaces and attractive corniced ceilings. All bedrooms are en suite with TV, central heating, trouser press and direct dial telephone. The Arthurs began a programme of upgrading when they took over the hotel two years ago and refurbishment of some of the accommodation as well as the lounge bar has already taken place. The restaurant is very popular locally and offers varied and interesting menus. Golf and fishing for salmon and trout can be arranged for guests.

Open all year
Rooms: 7 with private facilities
Bar Lunch 12 – 2 pm (b)
Dining Room/Restaurant Lunch 12 –
2 pm (c)
Bar Supper 6 – 9 pm (b)
Dinner 7 – 9 pm (c)
No smoking in restaurant
Bed & Breakfast £25.75 – £46
Dinner B & B £60 – £80
Room Rate £41 – £56.50
• Prawn terrine with avocado. Fresh Solway salmon sautéed in butter, cream and cheese and lightly toasted. Lobster Newburg. Rainbow trout en papillote with white wine and toasted almonds. Fillet steak flamed with brandy and Madeira and a touch of cream. Venison medallions in a juniper berry sauce. Lamb noisettes sautéed in butter with Stilton and pears.
STB Commended 4 Crowns
Credit cards: 1, 2, 3
Proprietors: Alex & Jean Arthur

Lundin Links

Location 154

OLD MANOR HOTEL

Lundin Links, nr St Andrews
Fife KY8 6AJ
Tel: 01333 320368
Fax: 01333 320911

On A915 Kirkcaldy–St Andrews, 1 mile east of Leven, on right overlooking Largo Bay.

The area of course is a golfers' paradise and golfers would especially appreciate staying at the Old Manor Hotel where the proprietors, the Clark family, are a mine of information, advice and assistance on the game of golf. But there is much more to the hotel than that: the food is of a high order and the Prince Charlie Restaurant presents excellent fare of originality and imagination, complemented by an extensive wine list. As an alternative

there is informal eating in the Coachman's Grill and Ale House – in the old coachman's cottage in the grounds – specialising in grilled steaks and seafood. Refurbishment of the restaurant, lounge and bar areas was completed during 1994 and additional bedrooms are planned.

Open all year except New Year's Day
Rooms: 19 with private facilities
Bar Lunch 12 – 2.30 pm (a)
Dining Room/Restaurant Lunch 12 –
2 pm except Sun Sat (b)
Bar Supper 5 – 9.30 pm (a)
Dinner 7 – 9.30 pm except Sun (d)
Facilities for disabled visitors
No smoking in restaurant
Bed & Breakfast £30 – £60
Dinner B & B £51 – £82
Room Rate £60 – £90
Special Weekend Rates available
• Talisker Bay scallops with crispy leeks on a saffron sauce. Rosettes of Border lamb on a rosemary jus with cloves of roasted garlic. Fillet of Aberdeen Angus beef with a burgundy sauce. Selection of Scottish cheeses.
STB Commended 4 Crowns
Credit cards: 1, 2, 3
Proprietors: The Clark Family

Lybster

Location 155

PORTLAND ARMS HOTEL

Lybster
Caithness KW3 6BS
Tel: 01593 721208
Fax: 01593 721446

On A9, 12 miles south of Wick.

The Portland was built to serve as a staging post early last century. There have been many changes since, but the quality of personal service established then has been maintained. The hotel is fully central heated and double glazed. All rooms have private facilities including colour TV, telephone, tea-making facilities, and some have four-poster beds. Executive rooms with jacuzzi baths are also available. There is a lovely lounge in which to relax and the dining room menus have an excellent choice of local food representing very good value.

Open all year
Rooms: 20 with private facilities
Bar Lunch 12 – 2.30 pm (a)
Dining Room/Restaurant Lunch 12 –
2.30 pm Sun only (a)
Bar Supper 5 – 10 pm (a)

Dinner 7 – 10 pm (c)
Bed & Breakfast £29 – £48.50
Dinner B & B £45 – £65
Special Weekend Breaks available
• Oak-smoked salmon with dill sauce.
Fillet of beef Wellington with Madeira
sauce. Baked fillet of lemon sole with
cream and grapes.
STB Commended 4 Crowns
Credit cards: 1, 2, 3, 5, 6 + SWITCH
Proprietors: Gerald & Helen Henderson

Mallaig

MARINE HOTEL
Station Road, Mallaig
Inverness-shire PH41 4PY
Tel: 01687 462217
Fax: 01687 462821

Adjacent to railway station. First hotel on
right off A82, and a 5 minute walk from
ferry terminal.
Mallaig marks the end of the famous
West Highland Line and the equally
famous Road to the Isles. It is also a
busy fishing port and a ferry terminal.
The Marine Hotel is perched overlooking
the harbour where you can see most of
the action. It is family run and friendly,
and most of the bedrooms are en suite
and are well appointed with colour TVs
and the usual facilities. In the attractive
newly refurbished dining room the menu
takes full advantage of the freshly
landed fish and shellfish and
specialises in it, but there is a also a
selection of non-fish items. Meals are
also available in the more informal
atmosphere of the bar.
Open all year except Christmas +
Boxing Days, 1 + 2 Jan
Note: restricted service Nov to Apr
Rooms: 21, 16 with private facilities
Bar Lunch 12 – 2 pm (a)
Dining Room/Restaurant Lunch on
request (b)
Bar Supper 6 – 9.30 pm (b)
Dinner 6 – 8.30 pm winter: 7 – 9 pm rest
of year (c)
Bed & Breakfast £22 – £30
Dinner B & B £35 – £48
Special Rates available
• Coronets of smoked salmon and
prawn. Chicken in Drambuie cream
sauce. Loch Nevis salmon with
Hollandaise sauce. Home-made
desserts.
STB Commended 3 Crowns
Credit cards: 1, 3
Proprietors: Elliot & Dalla Ironside

by Maybole

LADYBURN
by Maybole
Ayrshire KA19 7SG
Tel: 016554 585
Fax: 016554 580

A77 (Glasgow-Stranraer) to Maybole then
B7023 to Crosshill. Turn right at War
Memorial (Dailly-Girvan). After exactly
2 miles, turn left and follow signs. 5
miles south of Maybole.
A superb away-from-it-all retreat
contiguous to the magnificent Kilkerran
Estate, the grounds of which are made
available for guests of Ladyburn to
enjoy. Jane and David Hepburn's
gracious house exemplifies life as it
used to be lived and ought to be lived.
Jane Hepburn is a charming hostess
and the moment you arrive, you are
made to feel welcome and somewhat
special. The accommodation is superb
and there are fresh flowers from the
garden everywhere. Food is delicious –
honest traditional cooking at its best
with none of the pretentious frills that
are sometimes adopted to disguise
inferior cuisine. Jane uses only fresh
local produce, garden vegetables and
herbs, and old family recipes. The
whole experience here will send you
home with a warm glow of satisfaction.
Italian, French, German and Russian
spoken. Children over 14 years
welcome.
Open all year except 2 wks Nov + 4 wks
during Jan to Mar
Rooms: 8 with private facilities
Dining Room/Restaurant Lunch 12.30 –
1.30 pm except Mon (b)
Dinner 7.30 – 8.30 pm except Sun
Mon (d)
Reservations essential for non-residents
Restricted Licence
No dogs
No smoking in dining room + bedrooms
Bed & Breakfast £70 – £80
Dinner B & B £95 – £105
Special Rates for 3+ nights
• Home-made soups. Roast gigot of
Ayrshire lamb served with home-made
mint jelly and mint sauce. Vicarage fish
pie. Roast sirloin and Yorkshire pudding.
Aunt Ella's traditional chicken and
mushroom pie. Strawberry pavlova.
'Boozy' chocolate mousse.
STB Deluxe 3 Crowns
Credit cards: 1, 2, 3
Proprietors: Jane & David Hepburn

Melrose

BURTS HOTEL
Market Square, Melrose
Roxburghshire TD6 9PN
Tel: 01896 822285
Fax: 01896 822870

A6091, 2 miles from A68, 38 miles
south of Edinburgh.
This distinguished family run townhouse
hotel, built in 1722, sits in the main
square of Melrose. Its situation in the
heart of the Borders makes it an ideal
centre for touring this beautiful area of
the country. The hotel is tastefully
furnished and the en suite bedrooms are
all modernly equipped with colour TVs,
direct dial telephones, tea/coffee-making
facilities. The elegant restaurant offers
both à la carte and table d'hôte menus
where the emphasis is on the abundance
of local game and fresh fish, prepared
and presented with flair by Chef Gary
Moore whose cooking has earned the
hotel much recognition in national
guides. The lounge bar menu offers light
lunches and suppers. The hotel has its
own private car park and extensive
gardens. There are several golf courses
within easy reach. Salmon and trout
fishing can be arranged, so too can
game shooting on local estates with prior
notice.
Open all year except 24 to 27 Dec
Rooms: 21 with private facilities
Bar Lunch 12 – 2 pm (a)
Dining Room/Restaurant Lunch 12.30 –
2 pm (b)
Bar Supper 6 – 9.30 pm (b)
Dinner 7 – 9 pm (d)
Bed & Breakfast £36 – £46
Dinner B & B £53 – £58
Special Rates for 2+ nights
• Roulade of venison and Guinea fowl.
Home-smoked duck breast panache.
Cornucopia of rabbit in fresh herbs.
Baked fillet of salmon. Rosettes of
venison. Collops of monkfish in a
wholegrain mustard and tarragon sauce.
Noisette of lamb in a whisky sauce.
STB Highly Commended 4 Crowns
Credit cards: 1, 2, 3, 5, 6
Proprietors: Graham & Anne Henderson

MELROSE STATION RESTAURANT

Palma Place, Melrose
Roxburghshire TD6 9PR
Tel: 01896 822546

*Close to Market Square. Follow
signposts to Melrose Station, which is
up hill to right of dairy.*

A friendly and unpretentious restaurant
within the historic Melrose Railway
Station building which has been restored
and converted to include comfortable
and attractive surroundings for diners in
a peaceful situation. Simple but
imaginative blackboard menus offer a
choice of light or more substantial
lunches and a more formal table d'hôte
dinner at weekends, all at very
reasonable prices. The proprietors, Claire
and Ian Paris, have gained a good
reputation for their personal attention
and home-style cooking, using only the
best of local produce.

*Open all year
Morning coffee 10 am – 12 noon except
Mon
Dining Room/Restaurant Lunch 12 –
2 pm except Mon (b)
Dinner 6.45 to 9 pm Thu to Sat only (c)
Closed Mon*
• *Fillet of lemon sole poached with
mussels in a lemon and tarragon cream
sauce. Lamb noisettes in a mint and
redcurrant sauce. Beef stew stuffed with
wild rice, orange and pecan nuts in a
creamy orange sauce. Gratin of fresh
asparagus and mushrooms topped with
an almond and garlic crust.
Credit cards: 1, 3 + DELTA
Proprietors: Ian & Claire Paris*

Melvich

by Thurso

Location 159

THE SHEILING GUEST HOUSE

Melvich, by Thurso
Caithness KW14 7YJ
Tel: 016413 256
Fax: 016413 356

*Melvich on A836, 18 miles west of
Thurso.*

The Sheiling stands on the outskirts of
the village with superb views over the
Halladale River and Melvich Bay. It
makes an ideal stop for those touring
the wild enchanting expanse of
Caithness and Sutherland, being midway
between Wick and Cape Wrath and within
reach of trips to Orkney. Joan Campbell's
warm hospitality endears itself to her

guests, many of whom return year after
year to enjoy her imaginative home
cooked meals. The menus change daily
and the breakfast really does set you up
for the day. There are two spacious
lounges and the bedrooms have
tea/coffee making facilities and electric
blankets. The Sheiling is one of only four
B & B establishments in Scotland in the
top 20 of the Which? Good B & B Guide.

*Open 1 Apr to 30 Sep
Rooms: 3 with private facilities
Dinner 6 – 7.30 pm except Sat (b)
Residents only
Unlicensed – guests welcome to take
own wine
No smoking in dining room
Bed & Breakfast £21 – £22
Dinner B & B £33 – £35
Special Rates for 7+ nights*
• *Baked Atlantic salmon with garlic
seafood sauce. Local smoked haddock.
Caithness beef and Sutherland lamb.
Steamed sponge with whisky marmalade
sauce. Gooseberry and rhubarb meringue
pie.
STB Highly Commended 3 Crowns
No credit cards
Proprietor: Joan Campbell*

Moffat

Location 160

AUCHEN CASTLE HOTEL
& RESTAURANT

Beattock, Moffat
Dumfriesshire DG10 9SH
Tel: 016833 407
Fax: 016833 667

*Direct access from A74, 1 mile north of
Beattock village, 55 miles south of
Edinburgh and Glasgow.*

Located just off the ever-changing
A74/M74 and almost midway between
Carlisle and Edinburgh or Glasgow, this
fine old country mansion has long been a
popular place at which to break a journey
for an accommodation stay or a meal
time break. It stands in 50 acres of fine
shrubs and trees well sheltered and well
isolated from the traffic on the main
route. The house was built by General
Johnston in 1849 and became the home
of the William Younger family – the well
known Scottish brewers. It is comfortably
furnished throughout and decorated in
keeping with its original features, which
include elegant wood panelling, parquet
floors and a gilt staircase. Ten of the 25
bedrooms are in a modern wing and all
have private facilities. The trees and

walks around the hotel are being
mapped and off-road driving in ex-army 4
X 4 and 6 X 6 vehicles is also available.
The hotel has formed "The Auchen
Castle Hotel Herd of Pedigree
Galloways", the distinctive local breed of
cattle. Children welcome. A little French,
German and Italian spoken.

*Open all year except 3 wks
Christmas/New Year
Rooms: 25 with private facilities
Bar Lunch 12 – 2 pm (a)
Dinner 7 – 9 pm (c)
Bed & Breakfast £27 – £36
Dinner B & B from £37 (min 2 nights
stay)
Special Rates available*
• *Sliced Guinea fowl and duck breast
with apricot glaze. Lamb cutlets with
rosemary, served with minted pear
purée. Solway salmon steak with
tarragon and cucumber. Medallions of
fillet steak with black peppercorns.
STB Commended 4 Crowns
Credit cards: 1, 2, 3, 5, 6
Proprietor: Hazel Beckh*

WELL VIEW HOTEL

Ballplay Road, Moffat
Dumfriesshire DG10 9JU
Tel: 01683 20184

*At south end of Moffat take A708
(Selkirk). At crossroads, left into Ballplay
Road – hotel on right.*

This traditional town mansion house
dates back to the 19th century and
enjoys a quiet and peaceful setting in its
own half acre of garden, yet is within
easy walking distance of the centre of
Moffat. The rooms are comfortably
furnished and have those thoughtful little
extra touches like a welcoming glass of
sherry, fresh fruit and home-made
biscuits, that indicate caring hosts. Janet
Schuckardt shows much flair and skill in
the kitchen and the food is of a high
standard more often associated with
large hotels. John Schuckardt takes care
of front of house activities and the
smooth running of the dining room. He is
particularly knowledgeable on wines and
this is demonstrated in a well balanced
but not over expensive wine list. Well
View is popular so advance booking is
advised. German and a little French

spoken. Children are welcome.
Open all year except 14 Jan to 6 Feb
Rooms: 6 with private facilities
Dining Room/Restaurant Lunch 12.30 –
1.15 pm except Sat (b)
Dinner 7 – 8.30 pm (d)
Prior reservation essential for both lunch
+ dinner
Facilities for disabled visitors
No smoking in dining room
Bed & Breakfast £25 – £42
Dinner B & B £47 – £65
Room Rate £50 – £76
Special Rates for 3+ nights
• Fennel soup with Pernod. Gigot lamb
steak with pear and rosemary sauce.
Roast breast of duck with mango sauce
and ginger. Fillet of baby sea bass with
caper sauce. Medallions of venison with
rowanberry and thyme sauce.
STB Deluxe 3 Crowns
Credit cards: 1, 2, 3
Proprietors: Janet & John Schuckardt

Moniaive
nr Thornhill

Location 161
MAXWELTON HOUSE
Moniaive, nr Thornhill
Dumfriesshire DG3 4DX
Tel: 0184 82 385
Entrance on B729, off A76 Dumfries-
Thornhill, or A702 New Galloway-
Thornhill.
The very name is evocative, and anyone
with the slightest claim to Scottish
ancestry together with many millions
more who have heard the well loved
ballad will be drawn to Maxwelton House,
the birthplace of Annie Laurie. The house
has been magnificently restored by Mr
and Mrs Hugh Stenhouse and – together
with the chapel and an interesting
museum of agricultural and domestic
tools – is well worth a diversion on a
journey and a few hours of anyone's
time. The tearoom is in the Pavilion
attached to the house and it serves
morning coffee, light and inexpensive
lunches, and that rarity now – delicious
traditional afternoon teas with freshly
made home-baking.
Open daily Easter to end Sep
Tearoom 10.30 am – 5.30 pm (a)
Unlicensed
• Variety of home-made items. Afternoon
teas.
Credit cards: 1, 3
Proprietors: Maxwelton House Trust

Muir of Ord

Location 162
ORD HOUSE HOTEL
Muir of Ord
Ross-shire IV6 7UH
Tel: 01463 870492
Fax: 01463 870492
On A832 Ullapool-Marybank, ½ mile west
of Muir of Ord.
Ord House is a fine old 17th century
laird's house which stands in 50 acres
of woodlands and beautiful formal
gardens. It is now a most comfortable
country house hotel where John and Eliza
Allen offer guests a relaxed and
enjoyable stay. The bedrooms are
decorated and furnished to a high
standard and each is individual in style.
Log fires add to the atmosphere in the
elegant drawing rooms as well as in the
bar where lunches are served. In the
dining room interesting dinner menus are
presented utilising the best of local
meat, game and fish, complemented
with vegetables, herbs and fruit from the
house's own gardens. There are lovely
walks within the grounds as well as
croquet and clay pigeon shooting. Fluent
French is spoken. Children and dogs are
welcome.
Open 5 May to 25 Oct
Rooms: 12 with private facilities
Bar Lunch 12 – 2 pm (b)
Dinner 7 – 9 pm (c) 4 course menu
Bed & Breakfast £33 – £39
Dinner B & B £53 – £59
Special Rates for 7+ nights
• Scottish prawn mousse. Home-made
soups e.g. courgette and Brie, Highland
smoked chicken. Poached wild salmon
with hollandaise sauce. Roast breast of
duck with a peppercorn sauce. Chicken

with sherry vinegar and tarragon sauce.
Pan-fried quail with grapes in Madeira.
STB Commended 3 Crowns
Credit cards: 1, 2, 3
Proprietors: John & Eliza Allen

Isle of
Mull

Location 163
ARDFENAIG HOUSE
by Bunessan, Isle of Mull
Argyll PA67 6DX
Tel: 01681 700210
Fax: 01681 700210
2 miles west of Bunessan on A849, turn
right on private road to Ardfenaig House,
½ mile.
Once occupied by the notorious Factor
Mor, chamberlain to the Duke of Argyll,
and latterly a private shooting lodge,
Ardfenaig House stands in a glorious
position on the shore of Loch Caol on
the Ross of Mull. Surrounded by open
moorland and quiet secluded beaches
Ardfenaig is perfect for walking, sailing,
painting, exploring or simply relaxing.
The Island of Iona is a short ferry ride
away and Fingals Cave on Staffa is
easily reached. The house is set
amongst 15 acres of woodland and
gardens. It is the home of Malcolm and
Jane Davidson who offer warm
hospitality, good food and fine wine in a
country house setting.
Open 1 Apr to 31 Oct – or by
arrangement
Rooms: 5 with private facilities
Dinner 8 – 9 pm (d) 4 course menu
Restricted Licence
No smoking in dining room + bedrooms
Dinner B & B from £85
Special Rates for 2+/6+ nights
• Home-made bread, soups and ice-
creams. Collops of venison pan-fried with
lemon juice and port. Fresh home-grown
vegetables. Fillet of salmon with lemon
butter sauce. Iced Grand Marnier nougat
with apricot coulis. Bread and butter
pudding. Scottish cheeses.
STB Highly Commended 3 Crowns
Credit cards: 1, 3
Proprietors: Malcolm & Jane Davidson

ARDRIOCH

Ardrioch Farm, Dervaig
Isle of Mull PA75 6QR
Tel: 01688 400264

1 mile from Dervaig on Calgary road.
Ardrioch is a traditionally furnished comfortable cedar wood farmhouse. Guests may relax in the mellow wood-panelled sitting room with its peat fire and extensively filled bookshelves, and enjoy the view of the sea-loch and surrounding hills. All bedrooms have tea-making facilities, wash-basins and room heaters; en suite facilities available. The house is a short stroll to the loch side and two miles from the harbour, where Ardrioch's inter-island day-sailing cruises are available. Ideal for walking, bird-watching and fishing. Multi-activity holidays also available. Working farm – sheep, cows, friendly collies, lambs and calves, enjoyed by children.

Open 1 Apr to 31 Oct
Rooms: 4, 1 with private facilities
Dinner 6.30 – 7.30 pm (b)
Unlicensed – guests welcome to take own wine
No dogs
No smoking throughout
Bed & Breakfast £17 – £19.50
Dinner B & B £27.50 – £30
Special Rates available
• Avocado with smoked trout pâté. Freshly caught mackerel stuffed with gooseberries. Fillets of chicken with a whisky and ginger sauce. Crunchy coffee and chocolate ice-cream.
STB Commended 2 Crowns
No credit cards
Proprietors: Jenny & Jeremy Matthew

CALGARY FARMHOUSE HOTEL

Calgary, nr Dervaig
Isle of Mull PA75 6QW
Tel: 01688 400256

B8073 just up hill from Calgary beach.
There are few more delightful places along the beautiful west coast of Mull than the white sands beach at Calgary, and just up the hill the Calgary Farmhouse Hotel has been created from some farm steadings. The rustic charm of the place has been retained as has the comfortable homely atmosphere. The Dovecote Restaurant in what was once a barn with an original dovecote serves a goodly range of the best of Mull's prime produce, particularly local fish and shellfish, and there is an emphasis on genuine home-cooking. Additionally, a stone arched carthouse has been converted to form the Carthouse Gallery

and Function Room where you can have teas and delicious home-baking throughout the day, light lunches at weekends, or just browse and enjoy the exhibition of paintings by local artists many of which are for sale.
Open 28 Mar to 28 Oct
Rooms: 9 with private facilities
Light Lunch 12 – 2.30 pm Sun Sat only (a)
Dinner 6.30 – 9 pm (b)
No smoking in restaurant
Bed & Breakfast £31 – £34
Dinner B & B from £45.80
Special Rates for 3+ nights
• Smoked Mull mussels in a lemon and herb cream. Locally caught crab. Chicken with a port and blackcurrant sauce. Home-made berry crumble. Selection of Isle of Mull cheeses.
STB Commended 3 Crowns
Credit cards: 1, 3
Proprietors: Matthew & Julia Reade

DRUIMARD COUNTRY HOUSE

Dervaig, by Tobermory
Isle of Mull PA75 6QW
Tel: 01688 400345/400291

Situated adjacent to Mull Little Theatre, well signposted from Dervaig village.
Druimard Country House stands in an elevated position just on the outskirts of the pretty little village of Dervaig and only eight miles from Tobermory, the island's capital. A carefully restored and well maintained Victorian country house, it has extremely comfortable en suite bedrooms, including a two bedroomed suite. Under the ownership of Haydn and Wendy Hubbard, the restaurant has established a reputation for good food and has been recognised by the award of an AA Rosette. The thoughtfully planned and well presented menus take full advantage of the excellent raw materials for which Mull is renowned.
Open 1 Apr to 30 Oct
Rooms: 6, 4 with private facilities
Dinner 6 – 8.45 pm Mon to Sat: residents only Sun (c)
Restaurant Licence only
No smoking in restaurant
Bed & Breakfast £38.25 – £49.50
Dinner B & B £53.75 – £65
• Duck breast roasted with marmalade and butter, served with an orange and brandy sauce. Argyll lamb on a creamy onion sauce with melting mint and lemon butter. Fillet of wild Mull salmon on a Noilly Prat sauce. Home-made desserts.
STB Highly Commended 3 Crowns
Credit cards: 1, 3
Proprietors: Haydn & Wendy Hubbard

DRUIMNACROISH

Dervaig, Isle of Mull
Argyll PA75 6QW
Tel: 01688 400274
Fax: 01688 400311

Via ferry from Oban to Craignure. On Salen-Dervaig road, 1½ miles south of Dervaig.
Druimnacroish is an interesting place to stay and is the home of Donald and Wendy McLean. Donald virtually converted the ruins of the old buildings himself to create this unusual country house hotel in this delightful part of Mull. His wife, Wendy, presides in the kitchen where she creates excellent meals utilising the abundance and variety of game etc on the island, complemented by vegetables and fruit culled from the hotel's own six acre garden. There is a carefully selected wine cellar. A holiday in this peaceful and comfortable setting can have a wonderfully relaxing effect.
Open mid Apr to mid Oct
Rooms: 6 with private facilities
Packed Lunches to order
Dinner at 8 pm (e) set 4 course menu
No smoking in restaurant
Bed & Breakfast from £59
Dinner B & B from £78
Special Rates for 4+/7+ nights
• Specialities include roast pheasant; lamb; rib of Aberdeen Angus beef carved at table off the bone. Wild salmon. Chocolate mousse. Fresh fruit meringue.
STB Commended 4 Crowns
Credit cards: 1, 2, 3, 5
Proprietors: Donald & Wendy McLean

THE OLD BYRE HERITAGE CENTRE

by Dervaig
Isle of Mull PA75 6QR
Tel: 01688 400229

1½ miles from Dervaig. Take Calgary road for ¾ mile, turn left along Torloisk road for ¼ mile, then left down private road following signs.
This old stone farm byre with its outside staircase is now one of those fascinating small heritage centres that you love to discover on holiday when there is all the time in the world to drift round and enjoy the interesting aspects of it. There is an audio-visual presentation upstairs and a variety of animals to see which children particularly enjoy. The tearoom is unpretentious but wholesome, with genuine home-baking and fresh Mull produce in season as daily specials. By prior arrangement special meals will be prepared for groups and there are always vegetarian dishes available.

Open 9 Apr to 27 Oct
Light Meals served throughout day
10.30 am – 6 pm (a)
• *Crofter's soup served with warm rolls.*
Ploughman's lunch with Mull cheese.
Cloutie dumpling. Selection of home-
baking.
No credit cards
Proprietors: Michael & Ursula Bradley

THE PUFFER AGROUND
Main Road
Salen, Aros
Isle of Mull PA72 6JB
Tel: 01680 300389

On A849 Craignure–Tobermory, at
junction of road signed to the pier.
The main road from the Craignure ferry
terminal to Tobermory passes through
Salen where The Puffer Aground often
provides a convenient stopping place for
a meal or snack. Its unusual name
derives from the old days when the
"puffer" – the local steamboat – ran right
on to the shore to unload its cargo and
floated off again on the next high tide.
There is a maritime theme about the
restaurant and the menus are primarily
popular demand items with a little extra
touch. Lunchtime food is simple and can
be soup and sandwiches or something
more substantial. In the evenings two
menus offer a wide variety of choice,
including a vegetarian option.
Open 1 May to 30 Sep
Light Lunch 12 – 2.30 pm except Sun
Mon (a-b)
Dinner 7 – 8.30 pm except Sun: 7 –
9 pm Jul Aug except Sun (b-d)
Closed Sun
• *Scottish and Mull produce used*
whenever possible to create 'home-type'
cooking in a friendly atmosphere.
Credit cards: 1, 3
Proprietors: Graham & Elizabeth Ellis

WESTERN ISLES HOTEL
Tobermory
Isle of Mull PA75 6PR
Tel: 01688 302012
Fax: 01688 302297

Tobermory is a 40 minute drive from
Oban/Craignure ferry.
This magnificent Gothic style building
enjoys a truly remarkable situation high
on the cliff overlooking Tobermory Bay.
The views from the dining room, terrace
lounge and many of the bedrooms are
breathtaking and must surely be
regarded as some of the best in
Scotland. Sue and Michael Fink over the
past few years have undertaken a major
programme of upgrading throughout this
112 year old building, adding to the
comfort and facilities of the hotel. A
suite and some of the other master
bedrooms have been lavishly and
luxuriously equipped and all other
bedrooms are furnished to a very high
standard with private bathrooms, colour
TV, tea/coffee-making equipment etc.
Michael Fink creates interesting four
course dinner menus featuring a
selection of local game and seafood, as
well as a vegetarian option. From the
elegant and spacious high ceilinged
Victorian dining room, guests can enjoy
the wonderful views looking out over the
bay. Dogs accepted by prior
arrangement, at a small charge.
Open 21 Jan to 3 Jan except 20 to
27 Dec
Rooms: 28 with private facilities
Bar Lunch 12 – 1.45 pm (a)
Bar Supper 7 – 8 pm except Sun (a)
Dinner 7 – 8.30 pm: 7 – 8 pm winter (d)
No smoking in dining room
Bed & Breakfast £35 – £71.50
Dinner B & B £56 – £92.50
Special Rates for 3+ nights
• *Lightly poached local scallops on*
saffron sauce with rice pilaff. Pan-fried
slices of venison in a plum and walnut
sauce. Grilled Aberdeen Angus steak
with mushrooms and a light garlic cream
sauce. Home-made rhubarb and apple
strudel with a cinnamon egg custard.
Strawberry and green peppercorn parfait
with an orange coulis.
STB Highly Commended 4 Crowns
Credit cards: 1, 3 + SWITCH
Proprietors: Sue & Michael Fink

Nairn

Location 164
THE GOLF VIEW HOTEL
Seabank Road
Nairn IV12 4HD
Tel: 01667 52301 • Telex: 75134
Fax: 01667 55267

At west end of Nairn. Seaward side of
A96. Turn off at large Parish Church.
The Golf View is a grand old Victorian
building in a commanding position
overlooking the Moray Firth to Easter
Ross. It is well known to the many
thousands of golfers for whom the
nearby championship golf course
presents a special challenge. This
comfortable well run hotel has recently
been refurbished but still retains an air
of Victorian grandeur in many of the
public rooms, such as the large dining
room with its wood-panelled walls.
Dinner is a four course menu offering
some very interesting dishes with a
good selection of fresh local produce.
The lunch and bar menu is good value
and small portions are available for the
not so hungry! From October 1994 there
is a new Leisure Club with swimming
pool, sauna, spa, solarium and fitness
centre.
Open all year
Rooms: 48 with private facilities
Bar Lunch 12 – 2 pm (a)
Dining Room/Restaurant Lunch 12 –
2 pm (a)
Bar Supper 6.30 – 9 pm (a)
Dinner 7 – 9.30 pm (d) 4 course menu
Bed & Breakfast £38 – £75
Dinner B & B £48 – £72 (min 2 nights
stay)
• *Grilled fillet of Scotch salmon on a*
bed of Pernod with creamed leeks and
prawns topped with dill. Timbale of
smoked trout, prawn and brandy
mousse wrapped in thinly sliced cured
halibut. Pan-fried escalope of beef
sirloin on a smoked bacon and shallot
potato cake with tomato and tarragon
sauce.
STB Commended 5 Crowns
Credit cards: 1, 2, 3, 5, 6 + SWITCH

Newbigging

Location 165

NESTLERS HOTEL

Dunsyre Road, Newbigging
Lanark ML11 8NA
Tel: 01555 840 680

On A721 midway between Carnwath and Elsrickle, 18 miles north of Peebles.

This traditional stone-built house has all the character of the old village inn and has a happy and welcoming atmosphere provided by the friendly and attentive staff. It is now an intimate and unpretentious family hotel with lots of character and a bird's nest theme befitting its name. Nestlers is well situated in rural Clydesdale, almost equidistant from Edinburgh and Glasgow. The cosy bar doubles as a tourist information bureau. Elaine and Nick Anderson go to great trouble to ensure their guests enjoy good hospitality as well as good food. The menu is sensibly planned with good home-cooking the order of the day and the desserts in particular are renowned locally.

Open all year except 1 Jan
Rooms: 3 with private facilities
Bar Lunch 12 – 5 pm (a)
Dining Room/Restaurant Lunch 12 – 2.30 pm (b)
Bar Supper 5 – 9.30 pm (b)
Dinner 6 – 9.30 pm (c)
No smoking in restaurant
Bed & Breakfast £22.50 – £27.50
Dinner B & B £37.50 – £39.50
Special Rates for 2+ nights
• Venison steak slowly braised and served with a port and lemon sauce. Ham oven-baked with local Pentland honey and cloves, served with fresh parsley sauce. Scottish salmon coated in oatmeal with a Drambuie sauce.
STB Commended 3 Crowns
Credit cards: 1, 3, 5
Proprietors: Elaine & Nick Anderson

Newburgh

Aberdeenshire

Location 166

UDNY ARMS HOTEL

Main Street, Newburgh
Aberdeenshire AB41 0BL
Tel: 01358 789444
Fax: 01358 789012

On A975, 2½ miles off A92 Aberdeen-Peterhead, 15 minutes from Aberdeen.

A solid Victorian country hotel owned and run by the Craig family who take pains to ensure the comfort of their guests. Bedrooms are furnished with period furniture which blends in well with the building. During 1994 some significant changes were made at the hotel with the conversion of the former Victorian dining room to a comfortable residents lounge. The Forvie Room is now the fine dining room, a split-level room with windows on the upper level overlooking the golf course and the Sands of Forvie. A well composed à la carte menu features a good selection of fish and shellfish, as well as meat and game dishes. In the informal surroundings of the new brasserie – The Parlour – there is an interesting and reasonably priced menu, supplemented by daily specials highlighted on a blackboard. The recently revamped Cafe Bar offers food to appeal to the whole family. Service is cheerful, friendly and unobtrusively attentive.

Open all year
Rooms: 26 with private facilities
Bar Meals 12 – 9 pm Sun (a)
Bar Lunch (Bar + Parlour) 12 – 2 pm (a)
Dining Room Lunch (Forvie Room) 12 – 2 pm (d)
Bar Supper (Cafe Bar) 5 – 9 pm (a)
Dinner (Parlour) 6.30 – 9.30 pm Mon to Sat: 6 – 9 pm Sun (a-b)
Dinner (Forvie Room) 6.30 – 9.30 pm Mon to Sat: 6 – 9 pm Sun (d)
Bed & Breakfast £31 – £58
Dinner B & B £48 – £58 (min 2 nights stay)
• Forvie Room: Shetland salmon fillet on basil sauce. Rack of new season lamb, tomato provençal and rosemary sauce.

Fillet steaks. Pear tart served with caramel sauce with a hint of orange. The Parlour: a bowl of Orkney mussels in wine sauce. Cod baked with avocado, bacon and cheese. Chargrilled rib eye steaks.
STB Commended 4 Crowns
Credit cards: 1, 2, 3, 5 + SWITCH
Proprietors: Denis & Jennifer Craig

Newton Stewart

Location 167

CREEBRIDGE HOUSE HOTEL

Minnigaff, Newton Stewart
Wigtownshire DG8 6NP
Tel: 01671 402121
Fax: 01671 403258

From roundabout signposted Newton Stewart on A75, through the town, cross bridge over river to Minnigaff. 250 yards – hotel on left.

At one time home of the Earl of Galloway, this fine old country house sits in peaceful well kept gardens, sheltered by mature trees. Yet it is only a few minutes walk from the small bustling market town of Newton Stewart. There is a lovely feeling of unhurried elegance and comfort in the gracious public rooms. Fishing memorabilia feature in the bar which has been recently refurbished and features beamed ceilings in keeping with the old world style of Creebridge. An interesting light menu is served in the bar at lunchtime. There is a comfortable drawing room, with baby grand piano and a fine mahogany fireplace, where guests may enjoy pre-dinner drinks. Dinner is served in the main restaurant which overlooks the lovely gardens to the front of the house. Award winning Chef/Proprietor Chris Walker has created menus with good emphasis on quality local produce and has rightly earned a fine reputation for his high standard of food.

Open all year
Note: accommodation closed over Christmas
Rooms: 18 with private facilities
Bar Lunch 12 – 2 pm: 12.30 – 2 pm
Carvery Sun (a)
Bar Supper 6 – 9 pm (b)
Dinner 7 – 8.30 pm (c)
No smoking in restaurant
Bed & Breakfast £27.50 – £35
Dinner B & B £45 – £55
Special Rates for 3+ nights
• Fillet of lemon sole stuffed with scallops and lobster wrapped in filo

Credit Card Code		Meal Price Range	
1.	Access/Mastercard/Eurocard	(a)	under £10
2.	American Express	(b)	£10 – £15
3.	Visa	(c)	£15 – £20
4.	Carte Bleu	(d)	£20 – £25
5.	Diners Club	(e)	£25 – £30
6.	Mastercharge	(f)	over £30

pastry topped with a light crayfish sauce.
Oven-roast breast of duckling coated in a
tangy orange and Cointreau sauce.
Medallions of prime fillet of beef with
Dunsyre cheese and Glayva liqueur.
STB Commended 4 Crowns
Credit cards: 1, 3
Proprietors: Chris & Sue Walker

THE KIRROUGHTREE HOTEL
Newton Stewart
Wigtownshire DG8 6AN
Tel: 01671 402141
Fax: 01671 402425

Prestige Award Winner 1993

*Signposted 1 mile outside Newton
Stewart on A75.*
This splendid 18th century mansion is
set in its own beautifully kept grounds at
the end of a long private drive through
pasture and mature woodland. It has all
the attributes of a grand hotel with
opulently furnished public rooms,
spacious comfortable bedrooms and
suites, and a staff who take obvious
great pride in ensuring a high standard of
service. The mansion has historical
associations with the poet Robert Burns
who visited the Heron family for whom
the house was built. In these elegant and
comfortable surroundings a relaxed and
peaceful atmosphere prevails. Some of
the best food in the region is carefully
prepared and presented by Roux-trained
Head Chef Ian Bennett and his team. Two
sumptuously appointed dining rooms lead
from the wood-panelled lounge where a
pianist plays gentle background music
during dinner. In the grounds are a
croquet lawn, pitch and putt, and tennis
courts. Guests also have access to the
leisure facilities at sister hotels (Cally
Palace, Gatehouse-of-Fleet, and North
West Castle, Stranraer – listed in this
Guide), including free golf on the 18 hole
course at the Cally Palace. In addition
there are concessionary rates on five
local golf courses. Children over 12 years
are welcome at the hotel. The overall
experience is one of quality, service and
value.
Open mid Feb to 3 Jan
Rooms: 17 with private facilities
Snack Lunch 12 – 1.30 pm (a)
*Dining Room/Restaurant Lunch 12 –
1.30 pm (c)*
Dinner 7 – 9.30 pm (d)
No smoking dining room available
Bed & Breakfast £42.50 – £73.50
Dinner B & B £58 – £93
Special Rates for 7+ nights + over 60s

• Griddled tranche of Cree salmon set
on an infusion of olive oil, basil, garlic
and tomato. Roast Guinea fowl with
cranberries and limes. Steamed turbot
on a bed of fennel with a grain mustard
sauce. Saddle of Kirroughtree venison
garnished with braised red cabbage and
wild mushrooms. A selection of local
seafood on a langoustine sauce. Iced
nougat glace garnished with grilled
hazelnuts, set on a melba sauce.
STB Highly Commended 5 Crowns
Credit cards: 1, 3 + SWITCH
Proprietors: The McMillan Family

North Berwick

Location 168
MACFARLANE'S RESTAURANT
2 Station Road, North Berwick
East Lothian EH39 4AU
Tel: 01620 894737
Next to North Berwick railway station.
This quaint little white building with the
slate roof and astragalled windows was
originally an Edwardian tea room. It is
situated by the railway station, looking
towards North Berwick Law. The simple
interior is light and airy with light oak
chairs and colourful tablecloths and on
the walls there is a display of framed
local art. Michael and Kate French took
over the restaurant in 1994 and their
aim is to provide a welcoming and
informal atmosphere so diners can relax
and enjoy the food whether it be a light
lunch or a candlelit dinner. Interesting
menus display good combinations of
tastes and textures. The regular wine list
is cleverly displayed on old wine bottles
and there is a blackboard which
highlights bin ends available.
*Open 18 Jan to 22 Dec except 9 to
19 Oct*
*Dining Room/Restaurant Lunch 12.15 –
2 pm except Mon Tue (a)*
*Dinner 6.30 – 9.30 pm except Mon
Tue (c)*
Closed Mon Tue
*Smoking is discouraged until after
2.15 pm (lunchtime), after 9 pm (dinner)*
Facilities for disabled visitors
• Wild salmon pan-fried served with basil
vinaigrette and roasted pinenuts. Pan-
fried pigeon breast and Madeira sauce.
Grilled Scotch lamb cutlets brushed with
a redcurrant and geranium jelly. Pan-fried
fillet of trout with a toasted hazelnut
pâté. Chocolate and orange terrine.
Credit cards: 1, 3
Proprietors: Michael & Kate French

North Middleton

Location 169
BORTHWICK CASTLE HOTEL
& RESTAURANT
North Middleton, nr Edinburgh
Midlothian EH23 4QY
Tel: 01875 820514
Fax: 01875 821702
*A7 to North Middleton, 12 miles south of
Edinburgh, then follow signs for
Borthwick. A private road leads to the
Castle.*
Built in 1430 by the Borthwick family,
the ancient stronghold of Borthwick
Castle has witnessed at first hand many
of the great events of Scotland's
history. The most notable of these were
the safe-keeping of Mary Queen of
Scots following her wedding to the Earl
of Bothwell, and a forceful visitation by
Oliver Cromwell in 1650. The castle sits
in idyllic surroundings in the Midlothian
countryside. The guest bedchambers
are in keeping with the character of the
building and four have four poster beds.
The en suite facilities have been added
with great care so as not to detract
from the layout of these historic rooms.
In the evening guests dine in the
magnificent setting of the Great Hall
where a four course set menu is
prepared by Chef Martin Russell, who
describes his cuisine as modern British
with a strong bias for Scotland's natural
larder. The atmosphere of the Great
Hall, with suits of armour on display,
makes an unforgettable dining
experience – whether on the grand
scale of a banquet or an intimate dinner
for two.
Open 15 Mar to 2 Jan
Rooms: 10 with private facilities
*Restaurant/Dining Room Lunch (c) – by
arrangement*
*Dinner at 8 pm (e) 4 course set menu –
reservations essential*
Table Licence
Bed & Breakfast £47.50 – £82.50
• Pan-fried skate wings with red wine,
baby fennel and star anise. Braised
monkfish with rocket leaves, saffron and
shallots. Casserole of Scotch lamb with
leeks, roast shallots and pesto potatoes.
Grilled halibut, scallops and mussels
with saffron and courgettes. William pear
poached in red wine and cinnamon with
vanilla ice-cream.
*Credit cards: 1, 2, 3, 5, 6 + SWITCH,
DELTA*

North Queensferry

Location 170
SMUGGLERS RESTAURANT
17 Main Street, North Queensferry
Fife KY11 1JT
Tel: 01383 412567

Take Junction 1 M90, follow B981 into North Queensferry.

Set in a spectacular location beneath the Forth Rail Bridge is Smugglers, a small intimate bistro style restaurant which has established an excellent reputation for its food. Skilfully created dishes with innovative sauces and liberal use of fresh herbs make for a particularly interesting menu. Ernest Kallus excels particularly in his treatment of seafood but game, beef and lamb dishes are also handled with skill and imagination. There is a relaxed informal atmosphere in the candlelit restaurant where Judi Short provides the attention to detail that ensures all guests are well looked after.

Open all year
Dinner 7 – 10.30 pm Thu Fri Sat only (d)
Closed Sun to Wed
No smoking in restaurant
• Grilled squid with chilli and coriander. Breast of wood pigeon and wild mushrooms. West coast langoustines with dill mayonnaise. New season Scotch lamb gigot steak, with mint salsa and roast garlic. Pan-fried duck breast served with green lentils and rowanberry sauce. Market selection of fresh fish.
Credit cards: 1, 2, 3
Proprietors: Ernest Kallus & Judi Short

Oban

Location 171
ARDS HOUSE
Connel, by Oban
Argyll PA37 1PT
Tel: 01631 71 255

On main A85 Oban–Tyndrum, 4 miles north of Oban.

Ards House is a Victorian villa which sits near the shores of Loch Etive, with views over the Firth of Lorn and the Morvern Hills. This is a comfortable family run guest house. John and Jean Bowman are caring hosts who strive to make their guests feel relaxed and at home. All the bedrooms have private facilities, with either baths or showers, and are equipped for making tea and coffee. The small set menu for dinner is displayed each afternoon and changes daily to reflect the best of fresh food available.

Dinner is served in the intimate atmosphere of the quaint little cottage-style dining room which benefits from beautiful views over the loch.

Open 1 Mar to 30 Nov
Rooms: 6 with private facilities
Dinner at 7.30 pm – later by arrangement (b)
Dinner for non-residents by arrangement
Restricted Licence
No children
No dogs
No smoking throughout
Bed & Breakfast £21 – £35
Dinner B & B £36 – £50
Special Rates available
• Salmon and vegetable terrine. Cream of mushroom and hazelnut soup with home-baked bread. Mull wild salmon. Breast of chicken with sun-dried tomatoes and a port cream sauce. Medallions of pork fillet in a cream and brandy sauce. Lemon and almond tart.
STB Commended 3 Crowns
Credit cards: 1, 3
Proprietors: John & Jean Bowman

DUNGALLAN COUNTRY HOUSE
Gallanach Road, Oban
Argyll PA34 4PD
Tel: 01631 63799
Fax: 01631 66711

On left, ½ mile past entrance to ferry terminal.

This fine old Victorian house is set in five acres of natural woodland and from the site high above Oban Bay there are splendid views of the Isle of Mull and the Morvern Hills. The atmosphere is homely and the surroundings comfortable and relaxing. Appropriately at this prime port on the west coast, the menus take full advantage of the excellent range of fresh fish and shellfish so readily available and there is a well balanced wine list and a good selection of Scottish malt whiskies.

Open all year except Nov Feb + Christmas Day
Rooms: 10 with private facilities
Dinner 6.30 – 9 pm except Mon (d)
No smoking in restaurant
Bed & Breakfast £30 – £50
Dinner B & B £48.50 – £69

Special Rates for 2+ nights
• Smoked salmon filled with asparagus mousse garnished with petals of endive. Fillet en croûte with mushrooms, onions, spinach and beetroot garnished with parisienne potatoes. Medallions of venison, quail and pheasant presented on a croûton napped with juniper sauce. Fillet of Scottish trout pan-fried in oatmeal garnished with prawn capers.
STB Commended 3 Crowns
Credit cards: 1, 3
Proprietor: Elspeth Allan

THE GATHERING SCOTTISH RESTAURANT & CEILIDH BAR
Breadalbane Street, Oban
Argyll PA34 5NZ
Tel: 01631 65421/64849/66159

Entering Oban from A85 (Glasgow) into Dunollie Road and one-way system, then first left. On foot from town centre – just past cinema leads to Breadalbane Street.

There is a wealth of character in this unique restaurant built over 100 years ago to cater for guests attending the annual Gathering in the adjacent Gathering Hall, and the historical association and atmosphere have been well maintained. In late August at the time of the annual Highland Games in Oban, The Gathering is taken over completely for The Gathering Ball (usually the last Thursday of the month). Now considered one of Oban's premier restaurants, visitors flock to it to absorb the ambience and enjoy the food. While the menu specialises in seafood and steaks, it has lots of imaginative starters, some game dishes and some "lighter bites". Portions are generous, prices are modest and the service is cheerful.

Open Easter to 1 Jan: weekends only Oct to Jan
Note: closed to public last Thu in Aug
Bar Lunch (Jul to Sep) 12 – 3 pm except Sun (a)
Bar Supper 5 – 11 pm (a)
Dinner 5 – 11 pm (d)
Facilities for disabled visitors
No smoking area in restaurant
• Crofters chowder – seafood soup with scallops and mussels. Inverawe trout with pan-fried prawns, capers and parsley. Chargrilled prime steaks. Oban Bay seafood platter. Roast Scottish lamb. Poached scallops in Islay cheese sauce.
Credit cards: 1, 3
Proprietor: Elaine Cameron

ISLE OF ERISKA HOTEL
Ledaig, by Oban
Argyll PA37 1SD
Tel: 01631 72 371
Fax: 01631 72 531

*A85 towards Oban. At Connel proceed by
bridge on A828 for 4 miles to north of
Benderloch village, then follow signposts.*

This is an exceptional place by whatever
standards you care to measure it, and
not only the imposing late 19th century
Baronial home but the whole island of
over 300 acres becomes an integral
part of your stay and your enjoyment.
You will find an executive golf facility
has now been introduced creating a
short but challenging par 27 course and
by early 1995 a new indoor leisure
facility is due to be completed within the
stables area providing a swimming pool,
spa, sauna, steamroom and gymnasium.
The Buchanan-Smiths have long had an
outstanding reputation for their warmth
of welcome to guests and the
remarkable way in which they make
everyone feel very special. The house is
dignified and elegant yet in no way
austere; public rooms are impressive
and bedrooms are very comfortable,
provided with all sorts of thoughtful little
extras. Dinner – indeed more of a
banquet – is an occasion to remember,
beautifully prepared and presented. The
Isle of Eriska is somewhere to which you
will surely want to return.

*Open Mar to Jan
Rooms: 17 with private facilities
Bar Lunch – residents only
Dinner 8 – 9 pm (f) 6 course menu
Open to non-residents for dinner only
Children over 10 years welcome
No dogs in public rooms
Facilities for disabled visitors
Bed & Breakfast £82.50 – £135
Dinner B & B £117.50 – £170
Special Rates for 3+ nights*
• *Slices of marinated duck breast with a
hazelnut salad and dressing. Seafood
chowder. Panache of west coast seafish
on a chive butter sauce. Baked fillet of
cod with a herb crust and served with a
Mull cheddar sauce. Scottish rib of beef
carved at table. Hazelnut shortcake filled
with fresh strawberries. Warm chocolate
pithivier served with minted anglaise.*
*STB Deluxe 5 Crowns
Credit cards: 1, 3 + SWITCH
Proprietors: The Buchanan-Smith Family*

MANOR HOUSE HOTEL
Gallanach Road, Oban
Argyll PA34 4LS
Tel: 01631 62087
Fax: 01631 63053

*From south side of Oban follow signs to
car ferry. At ferry entrance continue along
main road for further ½ mile.*

Perched on a commanding promontory
above the bay, the Manor House offers a
panorama of harbour, town and islands,
yet you can walk into the town centre in
just five minutes. There is a comforting
feel of chintzy, cosy country cottage
about it. Some bedrooms are small but
all have en suite facilities, television,
direct dial telephone and central heating.
The dining room is well appointed and
the food is of remarkably high standard
with lots of interesting and unusual
presentations of the wide range of fish
and shellfish so readily available in this
west coast port.

*Open 1 Feb to 25 Dec
Rooms: 11 with private facilities
Bar Lunch 12.30 – 2 pm (a)
Dining Room/Restaurant Lunch 12.30 –
2 pm (c) – booking essential
Dinner 7 – 9 pm (d) 5 course menu
No smoking in dining room
Bed & Breakfast £32 – £55
Dinner B & B £46 – £75
Special Rates for 2+ nights*
• *Seafood vol au vent. Grilled goats
cheese on summer salad. West coast
scallops Noilly Prat. Lamb cutlets with
rosemary. Lobster Hebridean. Loin of
veal with chanterelles. Blackcurrant
meringue tart.*
*STB Highly Commended 4 Crowns
Credit cards: 3, 6 + SWITCH, DELTA
Proprietor: J L Leroy*

SEA LIFE CENTRE – SHORELINE RESTAURANT
Barcaldine, Oban
Argyll PA37 1SE
Tel: 0163 172 386

*On A828 Oban-Fort William, 10 miles
north of Oban.*

The Shoreline Restaurant is within the
Sea Life Centre. In this self-service
restaurant a full range of meals and
snacks is available including a salad
table and a smaller oyster bar. You'll also
be enjoying your meal in comfortable
surroundings which give you the best
possible vantage point to appreciate fully
the majestic splendour of the glorious
views over Loch Creran to the mountains
beyond.

Open mid Feb to end Nov + weekends

*only Dec to mid Feb
Note: closed Christmas Day + 1 Jan
Coffee Shop open 10 am – 5.30 pm
Meals available 12 – 5.30 pm:
10 am – 6.30 pm Jul Aug (a)
Table Licence only
No smoking area in restaurant*
• *Fisherman's pie. Chicken, ham and
mushroom pie. Vegetarian special –
'harvester's pie'. Local oysters with
Scottish wine. Coffee shop has fresh
ground coffee.*
Credit cards: 1, 3

SOROBA HOUSE HOTEL
Soroba Road, Oban
Argyll PA34 4SB
Tel: 01631 62628

A816 to Oban.

Soroba House is an old Georgian house
that has been well maintained over the
years. It stands in a dominant and
beautiful site of nine acres on the
outskirts of Oban, yet close enough to
take advantage of the town's facilities
and be convenient for the ferry terminal
etc. The accommodation is in the form of
suites and flatlets, some within the
gardens around the hotel, so guests
have the option of catering for
themselves or experiencing the
specialities of the hotel's dining room. A
selection of local produce features on
the menus ranging from seafood and fish
to venison, lamb, Scotch beef etc.

*Open all year except 23 Dec to 5 Jan
Rooms: 25 with private facilities
Bar Lunch 12 – 2.30 pm (a)
Dining Room/Restaurant Lunch 12 –
2.30 pm (b)
Bar Supper 7 – 9.30 pm (a)
Dinner 7 – 9.30 pm (c)
Bed & Breakfast £28 – £48
Dinner B & B £40 – £62
Room Rate £35 – £60*
• *Cullen skink. Local salmon served with
a sauce of white wine, leeks, orange and
cream. Pan-fried Rannoch venison steak
flamed with port, served with cranberry
jelly. Grilled Appin lamb cutlets served
with onions, mushrooms and mint sauce.
Local scallops pan-fried in butter and
garlic.*
*Credit cards: 1, 2, 3 + DELTA
Proprietor: David Hutchison*

THE WATERFRONT RESTAURANT

No 1 The Waterfront
The Pier, Oban
Argyll PA34
Tel: 01631 63110

The waterfront, Oban.
It would be difficult to get closer to the main source of supply than this. The Waterfront Restaurant has built up its reputation by concentrating on the local seafood arriving at the pier at Oban and likes to boast that it gets it "from the pier to the pan as fast as we can". Lovers of fish and shellfish go here to savour the daily catch at remarkably moderate prices. Part of the same complex but on the ground floor is Creel's Coffee Shop which specialises in home-baking and in a range of sandwiches, including some superb seafood fillings – a very popular rendezvous for a quick and satisfying snack.
Open all year
Creel's Coffee Shop 8.30 am – 6 pm (a)
Dining Room/Restaurant Lunch 12 – 3 pm (a)
Dinner 6 – 10 pm (b)
• *Home-made soup. Balvicar Bay oysters. Tobermory scallops and prawns in a cream sauce. Loch Feochan salmon with hollandaise sauce. Fresh seafood platter of the day. Fillet steaks.*
Credit cards: 1, 3
Proprietor: Stuart Walker

WILLOWBURN HOTEL

Clachan Seil, Isle of Seil
by Oban PA34 4TJ
Tel: 01852 300276

11 miles south of Oban, via A816 and B844, signposted Easdale, over Atlantic Bridge.
The lovely little Isle of Seil is noted for the wide range of its natural wildlife and if you are lucky you may spot badgers, buzzards, seals, heron and kestrels amongst others. It attracts bird-watchers, photographers, walkers, artists, naturalists and fishermen, almost all of whom get there by crossing the 'only single span bridge to cross the Atlantic' – or a bit of it anyway! Willowburn is a small modern family run hotel in two acres of ground with the dining room especially having lovely views out over Seil Sound. Both table d'hôte and à la carte menus are available with good use being made of the west coast's excellent seafood in some intriguing combinations of flavours.
Open 1 Apr to 3 Jan + Nov/Dec by

arrangement
Rooms: 6 with private facilities
Bar Lunch 12.30 – 2 pm (a)
Bar Supper 6 – 8.30 pm (a)
Dinner 7 – 8 pm (c)
Dinner B & B £41 – £48
Special Rates for 3+ nights
• *Queenie clams in wine and shallot butter. Baked crab with lemon. Chicken breast stuffed with leek sauté finished with a smoked cheese and whisky sauce. Spicy lamb casserole with fresh vegetables in a golden pastry case. Venison steak with citrus and red wine juices. Grilled megrin sole with lime and fennel butter. Chocolate meringues with rum whipped cream.*
STB Commended 3 Crowns
Credit cards: 1, 3
Proprietors: Archie & Maureen Todd

Onich
by Fort William

Location 172
ALLT-NAN-ROS HOTEL

Onich, by Fort William
Inverness-shire PH33 6RY
Tel: 0185 582 1210
Fax: 0185 582 1462

On A82, 10 miles south of Fort William.
A Highland country house in a magnificent location on a garden knoll on the shores of Loch Linnhe. From its elevated position this former Victorian shooting lodge gives spectacular uninterrupted views over the loch and the surrounding mountains. The Macleod family have done much over recent years to improve standards providing bedrooms that are comfortable and well equipped with all the facilities expected of a well run hotel. The cuisine is an interesting blend of French and Scottish taking full advantage of the wealth of Highland game, salmon and seafood for which the west coast is noted.
Open 10 Feb to 10 Nov, 10 to 22 Dec, 29 Dec to 4 Jan
Rooms: 21 with private facilities
Bar Lunch 12.30 – 2.30 pm (b)
Dining Room/Restaurant Lunch 12.30 – 2.30 pm (b)
Dinner 7 – 8.30 pm (d) 5 course menu
No dogs
No smoking in dining room
Bed & Breakfast £35 – £49.50
Dinner B & B £50 – £69.50
Special Rates for 3+/5+/7+ nights
• *Ravioli of monkfish flavoured with*

chives and a cream sauce infused with coriander. Pan-fried breast of duck glazed with honey and served on an orange sauce. Fillet of salmon grilled with garlic butter on a bed of spinach. Prune and Armagnac ice-cream. Baked apple strudel with crème anglaise. Selection of cheeses with walnut and rosemary bread.
STB Highly Commended 4 Crowns
Credit cards: 1, 2, 3, 5 + SWITCH
Proprietor: James Macleod

THE LODGE ON THE LOCH HOTEL

Onich, by Fort William
Inverness-shire PH33 6RY
Tel: 0185 582 1237
Fax: 0185 582 1463

On A82, 1 mile north of the Ballachulish Bridge.
Everything about The Lodge on The Loch Hotel spells good taste and good standards. There is a refined elegance about this acclaimed family run hotel which is immediately apparent and promises to apply to every aspect of it – as indeed it does. The public rooms, the dining room and many of the bedrooms have superb views out over Loch Linnhe to the Morvern mountains beyond. The menus are compiled with the same care and attention that is devoted to the rest of the hotel and meals are of unusually high standard. Guests enjoy complimentary membership of the leisure facilities of a sister hotel nearby, where there is an indoor heated pool, sauna, steam room and turbo pool.
Open Feb to Nov + Christmas/New Year
Rooms: 20, 18 with private facilities
Bar Lunch 12.30 – 2.30 pm (a)
Dining Room/Restaurant Lunch 12.30 – 2.30 pm (a)

Dinner 7 – 9.30 pm (d) 4 course menu
Facilities for disabled visitors
No smoking in dining room
Bed & Breakfast £40.50 – £60.50
Dinner B & B £58.50 – £78.50
Special Rates for 3+/7+ nights
• Sauté wild mushrooms with fine herbs served on a puff pastry case, set on a Moniack Castle wine and cream sauce. Baked suprême of Loch Linnhe salmon on a cucumber and ginger butter. Grilled Glencoe lamb cutlets coated with a gooseberry and mint glaze. Blackcurrant and whisky charlotte set on a lime crème anglaise.
STB Highly Commended 4 Crowns
Credit cards: 1, 3
Proprietors: The Young Family

Isles of
Orkney

Location 173
CREEL RESTAURANT & ROOMS
Front Road, St Margaret's Hope
Orkney KW17 2SL
Tel: 01856 831 311

13 miles south of Kirkwall over Churchill Barriers, at seafront.

A scenic drive which takes you over the famous Churchill Barriers, relics of World War II, brings you to St Margaret's Hope and the Creel Restaurant. This delightful restaurant overlooks the seafront and enjoys a reputation to rival the best. It has won many accolades over the years including the Taste of Britain Award in 1986 and being listed in the AA's Top 500 Restaurants in Britain. Chef/Proprietor Alan Craigie excels in his treatment of fish and shellfish. The short carefully compiled menus change daily and there is much focus on Orkney specialities. The spacious bedrooms are furnished to an extremely high standard, are very comfortable and have sea views. The Creel's reputation for good food has made it very popular with Orcadians and visitors from all over the world, so it is advisable to book.

Open Feb to Dec except Christmas Day
Rooms: 3 with private facilities
Dining Room/Restaurant Lunch 12.30 – 2 pm Sun only (b)
Dinner 7 – 9.15 pm (d)
Note: open daily Jun to Aug; advisable to book, especially in low season
Bed & Breakfast £25 – £30
• Traditional salt ling, lightly grilled, set on a bed of buttered cabbage. Topside of

beef cured in chef's special marinade, served with home-made rhubarb chutney. Selection of local seafoods lightly poached with a fresh dill sauce. Chump of lamb with an oatmeal crust, garnished with a baby haggis, on creamed leeks. Roast pears arranged around a honey basket, with luxury dairy ice-cream and traditional Orcadian brides cog.
STB Commended 3 Crowns
Credit cards: 1, 3
Proprietors: Alan & Joyce Craigie

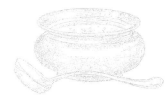

FOVERAN HOTEL
nr Kirkwall, St Ola
Orkney KW15 1SF
Tel: 01856 872389

On A964 Orphir road, 2½ miles from Kirkwall.

One of the few purpose built hotels on Orkney, the Foveran is all on one level with a location that provides sweeping views over Scapa Flow to the South Isles. The Scandinavian style dining room is light and airy with beautiful views. Polished pine tables set with crystal and fresh flowers add to the welcoming atmosphere of this tastefully decorated room. The Foveran's menu is well compiled and makes great use of local Orkney produce, in particular the abundance of seafood. The hotel has earned a very good reputation for the quality and presentation of its food.

Open Feb to Dec except Christmas Day
Rooms: 8 with private facilities
Dinner 7 – 9 pm Mon to Sat: Sun residents only (c)
Bed & Breakfast £34 – £43.50
• Arbroath smokies served hot with butter. Orkney salmon steak poached gently and served with a light champagne sauce. King of scallops served with a cheese and garlic sauce. Orkney bouillabaisse. Pan-fried noisette of lamb served with a marinated minted pear and a light sauce. Breast of chicken in a light lemon and sage sauce.
STB Commended 4 Crowns
Credit cards: 1, 3 + SWITCH, DELTA
Proprietors: Ivy & Bobby Corsie

Peat Inn

Location 174
THE PEAT INN
Peat Inn
Fife KY15 5LH
Tel: 01334 840 206

In A Class of Its Own 1989

At junction of B940/941, 6 miles south-west of St Andrews.

The Peat Inn has not just a national, but an international reputation. David Wilson and his wife Patricia have achieved wonders since they acquired this modest looking 18th century village inn situated in the village which bears its name. The Peat Inn is synonymous with good food, bold imaginative cooking of style and distinction. David Wilson was one of the early pioneers who set out to demonstrate to the world at large that not only did Scotland have the prime produce but it also had skilled chefs who could transform it into memorable meals. Recognition and success have followed. Awards and accolades line the walls of the comfortable sitting room where guests enjoy an aperitif before sampling the culinary delights. This is somewhere not to be missed if visiting Fife – booking is advised.

Open all year except Christmas Day + 1 Jan
Rooms: 8 with private facilities
Dining Room/Restaurant Lunch 12.30 for 1 pm except Sun Mon (c) 4 course menu
Dinner 7 – 9.30 pm except Sun Mon (e) 4 course menu
Closed Sun Mon
No smoking in dining rooms
Bed & Breakfast £65 – £95
Dinner B & B £93 – £123
Room Rate £135 – £140
• Sauté of scallops, monkfish and pork with spiced apple. Grilled fillet of beef with roasted shallots and a meat juice. Whole local lobster poached in a vegetable and herb broth. Selection of fish from the market. Caramelised apple pastry with a caramel sauce. Little pot of chocolate and rosemary.
Credit cards: 1, 2, 3, 5 + SWITCH
Proprietors: David & Patricia Wilson

Peebles

Location 175

CRINGLETIE HOUSE HOTEL
nr Peebles EH45 8PL
Tel: 01721 730 233

Off A703 Edinburgh-Peebles, 2½ miles north of Peebles.
Cringletie is a fine old turreted red sandstone baronial mansion set in peaceful and serene surroundings within 28 acres of gardens. This is a perennial favourite of its many enthusiastic patrons and continues to demonstrate high standards in all aspects of hotel-keeping. Bedrooms are furnished to a very high standard and have fine views onto the grounds. Aileen Maguire exercises a close personal supervision of food preparation and presentation, and the meals are imaginative and exemplify home-cooking at its best. Many of the herbs and vegetables for the kitchen come from Cringletie's own garden.
Open 11 Mar to 1 Jan
Rooms: 13 with private facilities
Light Lunch except Sun (a)
Dining Room/Restaurant Lunch 1 – 1.45 pm Mon to Sat (a): Sun (b)
Afternoon Tea 3.30 – 4.30 pm
Dinner 7.30 – 8.30 pm (d) 4 course menu
No smoking in restaurant
Bed & Breakfast £49 – £62.50
• *Avocado, Inverloch and smoked Cumberland ham with fresh basil dressing. Baked rock turbot with lentil and mustard sauce. Cranachan ice-cream with Drambuie served in an oatmeal basket.*
STB Highly Commended 4 Crowns
Credit cards: 1, 3
Proprietors: Stanley & Aileen Maguire

PARK HOTEL
Innerleithen Road, Peebles
Tweeddale EH45 8BA
Tel: 01721 720451
Fax: 01721 723510

At eastern end of High Street (A72).
The Park Hotel is an attractive example of Scottish architecture, sitting in its own superb gardens with beautiful views over the River Tweed. The atmosphere is warm and welcoming, befitting the family hotel that it is, and the service is caring and attentive. As the Park is owned by the Peebles Hotel Hydro, there is the added bonus that all the leisure facilities of that larger establishment are available to resident guests. From the oak-panelled restaurant there are wonderful views over well tended gardens to the hills beyond. The restaurant menus offer a good choice of items ranging from the traditional to more innovative dishes, the accent being on quality Scottish produce. At lunchtime, good value light meals are available both in the bar and the restaurant.
Open all year
Rooms: 24 with private facilities
Bar Lunch 12 – 2 pm (a)
Dining Room/Restaurant Lunch 12 – 2 pm (a)
Bar Supper 6.30 – 9.30 pm (a)
Dinner 7 – 9 pm (c) 4 course menu
Bed & Breakfast £34.50 – £60
Dinner B & B £44.50 – £70
• *Leg of Border lamb roasted with rosemary, served with redcurrant jelly. Grilled halibut served over sweet green pepper sauce with orange segments. Prime cut of Aberdeen salmon, lightly poached with lemon sauce. Suprême of chicken stuffed with haggis, tomato and garlic sauce. Prime Scottish sirloin steak cooked with mushroom and Traquair ale sauce.*
STB Commended 4 Crowns
Credit cards: 1, 2, 3, 5, 6 + SWITCH

PEEBLES HOTEL HYDRO
Innerleithen Road
Peebles EH45 8LX
Tel: 01721 720602
Fax: 01721 722999

On A72, eastern outskirts of Peebles on Innerleithen Road.
A large imposing chateau style hotel which opened in 1907 as a hydropathic spa. It sits in 30 acres of gardens and grounds overlooking the valley of the River Tweed and the Border hills and is now an all year round resort hotel. An air of Edwardian graciousness still remains, notably in the grand public rooms with their lofty ceilings. There is a wide range of accommodation from family rooms to suites, all tastefully appointed and with all the facilities expected in a resort hotel of this class. Tennis, squash and horse-riding are available and there is an excellent leisure centre with swimming pool, jacuzzi, gymnasium etc. The food is traditional and caters well for the great variety of demand occasioned by a large number of guests. The hotel is much in demand as a conference venue, but is also a popular location for family holidays.
Open all year
Rooms: 137 with private facilities
Bar Lunch 12.30 – 3.30 pm (a)
Dining Room/Restaurant Lunch 12.45 – 2 pm (b)
Dinner 7.30 – 9 pm (c)
Bed & Breakfast £38.50 – £61.50
Dinner B & B £55 – £80
• *Smoked sea trout with lemon. Grilled halibut steak with parsley butter and king prawns. Fillet of beef cooked in brandy.*

Escalope of pork fillet dressed in a sage and onion crumb served with apple sauce and prunes. Cold poached salmon with salad. Hazelnut profiteroles filled with Scottish berries and Drambuie cream.
STB Commended 5 Crowns
Credit cards: 1, 2, 3, 5, 6

Perth

Location 176

Country House Hotel of the Year 1994

BALLATHIE HOUSE HOTEL
Kinclaven, by Stanley
Perthshire PH1 4QN
Tel: 01250 883268
Fax: 01250 883396

Off A9 north of Perth through Stanley or off A93 south of Blairgowrie to Kinclaven.
Ballathie is a magnificent country house sitting in its own estate on the banks of the River Tay. Rolling lawns stretch from the house down to the river famous for its salmon fishing. Graciously proportioned public rooms and splendidly comfortable bedrooms, each with its own character and style, enhance the elegant country house atmosphere. The pace is unhurried and restful. In the tastefully appointed dining room overlooking the river, the interesting menus change daily to reflect the best of available produce. The food is skilfully prepared and presented to a very high standard.
Open all year
Rooms: 27 with private facilities
Bar Lunch 12 – 2 pm except Sun (a)
Dining Room/Restaurant Lunch 12 – 2 pm Easter to Oct: 12 – 2 pm Sun Fri Sat only Nov to Easter (b)
Dinner 7 – 9 pm (d)
No smoking in dining rooms
Bed & Breakfast £55 – £90
Dinner B & B £70 – £105
Special Rates for 2+/3+ nights
• *Warm queen scallop salad with a chive cream sauce. Ballathie's home-cured salmon served with an Arran mustard sauce. Escalope of salmon, pan-fried on a bed of spinach with a tomato coulis. Grilled fillet steak with fresh herbs, shallot puree and Madeira sauce. Fillet of turbot steamed on a bed of samphire with a red pepper sauce.*
STB Deluxe 4 Crowns
Credit cards: 1, 2, 3, 5, 6 + DELTA

HUNTINGTOWER HOTEL
Crieff Road
Perth PH1 3JT
Tel: 01738 83771
Fax: 01738 83777

Signposted off A85, 1 mile west of Perth, towards Crieff.

This splendid old country house sits in four acres of beautifully landscaped gardens through which runs a little stream frequented by a selection of ducks. Over the last few years the hotel has been extended to provide a range of meeting rooms and more recently the addition of a conservatory leading from the cocktail bar has created a popular venue for bar meals. Overlooking the garden is the elegant dining room with its wood panelling, chandeliers and intricate cornices, and a beautiful old inglenook fireplace. The standard of food measures up to the quality ambience in which it is served. This is a peaceful and quiet rural retreat just outside the city of Perth and makes a splendid base from which to explore the many attractions of Perthshire.

Open all year
Rooms: 25 with private facilities
Bar Lunch 12 – 2.30 pm except Sun (a)
Bar Meals available all day Sun (a)
Dining Room/Restaurant Lunch 12 – 2.30 pm (b)
Bar Supper 6 – 10 pm (a)
Dinner 7 – 9.30 pm (c)
Bed & Breakfast from £41
Dinner B & B from £62
Special Rates for 2+ nights
• *Peppered roast sirloin of beef with a red wine sauce. Collops of venison with spring onion cream sauce. Seafood casserole bound in a saffron sauce served in a puff pastry case. Oven-baked salmon with creamed leeks and a herb crust.*
STB Commended 4 Crowns
Credit cards: 1, 2, 3, 5, 6 + SWITCH

THE LANG BAR & RESTAURANT
Perth Theatre, 185 High Street
Perth PH1 5UW
Tel: 01738 39136
Fax: 01738 24576

Perth city centre in pedestrian zone at middle section of High Street.

The Lang Bar and Restaurant forms an integral part of Perth Theatre and is imbued with the vibrant atmosphere of live entertainment. Built in 1900, the Theatre has been beautifully restored giving a wonderful rich setting for the Restaurant, Coffee Bar and Bar. Enter the front door of the Theatre and pass through the Box Office, and you come to the Coffee Bar where home-baking and light meals are available at lunchtime and in the evening. The Coffee Bar often plays host to art exhibitions by local artists. A short flight of stairs leads to the Restaurant and bar area. Dinner in the Restaurant is dependent on theatre productions and consequently there are occasions when it is not available, so booking or enquiry in advance is recommended.

Open all year except Christmas + New Year
Bar Lunch 11.45 am – 2.15 pm except Sun (a)
Dining Room/Restaurant Lunch 11.45 am – 2.15 pm except Sun (a)
Bar Supper 6 – 7 pm except Sun (a)
Dinner 6 – 10 pm except Sun (b) – booking advised
Closed Sun
Facilities for disabled visitors
• *Home-made soup. Roast loin of lamb with spinach and hazelnut stuffing. Mushroom stroganoff. Salmon in filo pastry. Crusty bread, ham and prawns.*
Credit cards: 1, 2, 3 + SWITCH

MURRAYSHALL COUNTRY HOUSE HOTEL
Scone, nr Perth
Perthshire PH2 7PH
Tel: 01738 51171
Telex: 76197
Fax: 01738 52595

Prestige Award Winner 1988

4 miles out of Perth, 1 mile off A94.
A grey stone mansion house with corner turret, and the quiet grace and dignity of a bygone age. It is set in its own extensive gardens and parklands and has a golf course with its own club house and facilities for conferences and functions. The Old Masters Restaurant is an elegant room, furnished with good taste and with high quality place settings. The chef bases his menus on the best of seasonally available produce and with interesting combinations of texture and flavour creates imaginative dishes of a high standard. Many of the vegetables and herbs are grown in the hotel's own four acre kitchen garden. French spoken. Dogs welcome.

Open all year
Rooms: 19 with private facilities
Bar Lunch (Club House) 12 – 2.30 pm (a)
Dining Room/Restaurant Lunch (Club House) 12 – 2.30 pm (a)
Dinner 7 – 9.30 pm (c)
Bed & Breakfast £55 – £65
Dinner B & B £52.50 – £85
Special Rates available
• *Fillet of Scotch beef topped with a tarragon and mushroom duxelle accompanied with a whisky and pickled walnut sauce. Fillet of North Sea turbot and scallops topped with a creamed leek sauce. Rack of new season lamb carved and presented with a mint and rosemary jus.*
STB Highly Commended 4 Crowns
Credit cards: 1, 2, 3, 5 + SWITCH

Credit Card Code	Meal Price Range
1. Access/Mastercard/Eurocard	(a) under £10
2. American Express	(b) £10 – £15
3. Visa	(c) £15 – £20
4. Carte Bleu	(d) £20 – £25
5. Diners Club	(e) £25 – £30
6. Mastercharge	(f) over £30

NEWTON HOUSE HOTEL

Glencarse
nr Perth PH2 7LX
Tel: 01738 860250
Fax: 01738 860717

*Set back from A90 (formerly A85)
between Perth (4 miles) and Dundee
(13 miles).*

Newton House was originally built as a
Dower House and dates from around
1840. It is now a three star hotel
situated right in the heart of Scotland so
making it an ideal location from which to
explore the beautiful countryside and
visit the numerous places of interest –
Glamis Castle, Scone Palace, Discovery
Point, the nearby Carse of Gowrie
Antique Centre, to name but a few. The
area is also a golfer's paradise – 40
courses within easy travelling distance,
including the world famous St Andrews
and Gleneagles courses – and fishermen
can obtain permits locally for beats on
the Rivers Tay and Earn. The 10
individually decorated en suite bedrooms
overlook the gardens and there are two
comfortable lounges where guests may
relax and enjoy the tranquillity. The hotel
offers a range of eating from snacks and
informal meals in Cawley's Bar to
dinners in the Country House Restaurant
where the menus, which focus on fresh
local produce prepared with a Scottish/
French flavour, have earned the hotel an
AA Rosette. French, German and Spanish
spoken.

Open all year
Rooms: 10 with private facilities
Food available all day (a)
Bar Lunch 12 – 2 pm (a)
Restaurant Lunch 12 – 2 pm (b)
Bar Supper 5 – 9 pm (a)
Dinner 5 – 9 pm (c) + à la carte
No smoking in restaurant
Bed & Breakfast £37 – £43
Dinner B & B £48 – £60
*Special Rates for 2+ nights/Oct to
Apr/Hogmanay Breaks*
• *Game pâté on a bed of fruit
Cumberland sauce. Scottish rainbow
trout oven-baked with thyme and served
with a sherry and lemon sauce. Prime
Scotch sirloin steak with smooth mild
green peppercorn sauce. Escalope of
pork fillet sautéed with apples and cider.
Hot sticky toffee pudding.*
STB Highly Commended 4 Crowns
Credit cards: 1, 2, 3, 5, 6
Proprietors: Christopher & Carol Tallis

NUMBER THIRTY THREE SEAFOOD RESTAURANT

33 George Street
Perth PH1 5LA
Tel: 01738 33771

Perth city centre.

Number Thirty Three is a specialist fish
and shellfish restaurant in the heart of
the city of Perth. It has established a
sound reputation for the quality of its
food and is therefore a very popular
place. The pink and grey art deco theme
is stylish and restful. Tasteful wooden
screens create an intimate atmosphere
within the main restaurant and subtly
separate it from the Oyster Bar and
informal dining area to the front. The
principal emphasis of the menu is on fish
and shellfish and there are some good
speciality soups and sweets. You can
enjoy light meals in the Oyster Bar – even
just mussels and a coffee – or indulge in
a more leisurely and more serious meal
in the restaurant. The attractive ambience
of the place combined with this excellent
balance of eating styles and the
undoubted quality of the food has
ensured Number Thirty Three's place as
one of Perth's premier restaurants.

*Open all year except 10 days
Christmas/New Year*
*Light Lunch 12.30 – 2.30 pm except Sun
Mon (b)*
*Dining Room/Restaurant Lunch 12.30 –
2.30 pm except Sun Mon (c)*
*Light Supper 6.30 – 9.30 pm except Sun
Mon (b)*
Dinner 7 – 9.30 pm except Sun Mon (c)
Closed Sun Mon
• *Fillet of salmon in a parcel with thyme
butter. Poached Loch Sween king
scallops in a vermouth sauce. Cold
platter of smoked and marinaded fish
and shellfish. Grilled fillet steak Auld
Alliance.*
Credit cards: 1, 2, 3
Proprietors: Gavin & Mary Billinghurst

PARKLANDS HOTEL & RESTAURANT

St Leonards Bank
Perth PH2 8EB
Tel: 01738 622451
Fax: 01738 622046

*Junction of St Leonards Bank and
Marshall Place in centre of Perth
adjoining South Inch Park.*

Originally the home of the Lord Provost of
Perth, this classical town house has a
commanding site overlooking open
parkland making it difficult to believe you
are in the centre of this historic old city
and ancient capital of Scotland. The
restoration of the property has been well
done, retaining some of the fine old
features such as the cornices and wood
panelling, and providing bedrooms that
are spacious and comfortably equipped.
Parklands has a good reputation locally
and is much used by the local business
community but it is equally popular with
visitors as a base from which to explore
some of the many attractions and
historic places in Perthshire and beyond.
In the restaurant there is an interesting
range of choice in the menus both at
lunchtime and in the evening when an
ample à la carte is offered as well as the
daily changing table d'hôte. The quality
and presentation of food has been
recognised with the award of two AA
Rosettes.

Open all year except Christmas to 6 Jan
Rooms: 14 with private facilities
Bar Lunch 12 – 2 pm (a-b)
*Dining Room/Restaurant Lunch 12 –
2 pm (c)*
Dinner 7 – 9 pm (d-e)
Bed & Breakfast £40 – £65
Dinner B & B £58 – £70
Room Rate £70 – £130
Special Rates available
• *Roulade of halibut lined with smoked
salmon presented on a light tomato
sauce. Choux pastry cups filled with
smoked chicken and lime cream with a
hazelnut dressing. Grilled fillet of cod
with a fresh herb butter. Roast rack of
lamb studded with orange and garlic with
a sherry sauce.*
STB Highly Commended 4 Crowns
*Credit cards: 1, 2, 3, 5, 6 + SWITCH,
DELTA*
Proprietors: Pat & Allan Deeson

SCONE PALACE

Perth PH2 6BD
Tel: 01738 552300

*On A93 Braemar road, 2 miles out of
Perth.*

Scone Palace was the ancient crowning
place of Scotland's kings. It is also the
historic home of the Earl and Countess
of Mansfield. Visitors can view the
antique treasures in the Palace and
explore the grounds, then enjoy lunch

beside the range in the 'Old Kitchen' restaurant or perhaps a snack in the coffee shop. There is also a shop where you may buy some speciality food items to take home. Although not open to the public all year round, it is possible to arrange special off-season visits by arrangement with the Administrator.

Open 14 Apr to 9 Oct
Food Service 9.30 am – 5 pm Mon to Sat: 1.30 – 5 pm Sun (a)
Dining Room/Restaurant Lunch 11.30 am – 2 pm except Sun (a)
Note: open Sun for Lunch Jul + Aug only (a)
Dinner 7 – 8 pm (f) – by arrangement only
• *Fresh Tay salmon, home-made soup always available on the lunch menu. Home-baking, chutney and marmalade a speciality.*
Credit cards: 1, 2, 3

Peterhead

Location 177
WATERSIDE INN
Fraserburgh Road, Peterhead
Aberdeenshire AB42 7BN
Tel: 01779 471121
Fax: 01779 470670

30 miles north of Aberdeen on A952. 1 mile north of Peterhead.

It comes as a surprise to most people to learn that Peterhead is the most easterly town in mainland Scotland. Another surprise is in store at the Waterside Inn, Peterhead's leading hotel on the northern side of the town but just sufficiently out of it to give a quiet rural setting. The name may suggest a riverside pub but nothing could be further from the truth. The concept is nearer that of a good international chain, with splendid executive and family facilities and extensive conference suites. There is also a leisure complex offering swimming pool, jacuzzi, Turkish steam room, saunas and gymnasium. Ogilvies Restaurant is a sophisticated elegant dining room with a menu to match. Food is imaginative, very well presented and served by courteous well trained staff who seem to take genuine pleasure and pride in their work.

Open all year
Rooms: 110 with private facilities
Bar Lunch 12 – 2 pm (a)
Dining Room/Restaurant Lunch 12 – 2 pm (a)
Bar Supper 6 – 9 pm (a)

Dinner (Ogilvies) 6.30 – 10 pm except Sun Mon (b)
Dinner (Grill Room) 6.30 – 10 pm (b)
Taste of Scotland applies to Ogilvies Restaurant
Bed & Breakfast £27 – £45
Dinner B & B £37 – £39
• *Creamy smoked salmon soup with croûtons. Salmon dressed with grapes and fresh ginger sauce. Strips of fillet of beef and mushrooms flambéd with cognac and finished with cream. Medallions of lamb encrusted in crumbs and garlicky herbs, with a dark sherry sauce.*
STB Commended 5 Crowns
Credit cards: 1, 2, 3, 5

Pitlochry

Location 178
AUCHNAHYLE FARM
Tomcroy, Pitlochry
Perthshire PH16 5JA
Tel: 01796 472318
Fax: 01796 473657

Off East Moulin Road, at end of Tomcroy Terrace.

A delightful little 18th century farmhouse with neat gardens shared by the family's peacocks. It is the home of Penny and Alastair Howman who make their guests feel genuinely welcome and offer them every home comfort and memorable meals. Penny Howman is a cook of distinction and creativity who uses the best of fresh farm and local produce and enhances it with herbs from the herb garden. Dinner is served by candlelight round the family dining table with other guests and conversation flows freely. The four course dinner menu changes daily and is invariably something special. This is a place that is much in demand and not one that you can just expect to drop in to so do telephone and book in advance. Well behaved dogs and children over 12 years welcome.

Open 6 Jan to 20 Dec
Rooms: 3 with private facilities
Picnic Lunches on request
Pre-Theatre Supper at 6.45 pm (b) 2 course menu
Dinner 6.45 – 8 pm (c) 4 course menu
Unlicensed – guests welcome to take own wine
No children under 12 years
No smoking in dining room
Bed & Breakfast £28 – £38
Dinner B & B £42 – £56.50
• *Smoked trout mousse. Wild duck*

paprika. Scallops with a white wine and cheese sauce. Pan-fried fillet of venison with plums and ginger. Rhubarb and orange meringue pie. Chocolate Drambuie marquise. Scottish cheeseboard with home-made oatcakes.*
Credit cards: 1, 3
Proprietors: Penny & Alastair Howman

BIRCHWOOD HOTEL
East Moulin Road, Pitlochry
Perthshire PH16 5DW
Tel: 01796 472477
Fax: 01796 473951

200 yards off Atholl Road on Perth side of Pitlochry.

A lovely warm and homely hotel where the proprietors, Brian and Ovidia Harmon, maintain a family atmosphere and are committed to making their guests feel welcome and to providing every comfort for them. It is a fine old stone Victorian mansion on a wooded knoll with four acres of attractive grounds, and hospitality is the keynote allied to good food. There is a choice of table d'hôte or à la carte menus with the option to interchange if you prefer and there is sufficient choice available to satisfy most tastes, together with an extensive wine list. All bedrooms have private bathroom, colour TV, telephone and courtesy trays. Dogs are accepted by arrangement.

Open mid Mar to end Oct
Rooms: 16 with private facilities
Dining Room/Restaurant Lunch 12 – 1.30 pm (a)
Dinner 6.30 – 8.15 pm (c-d)
No smoking in restaurant
Bed & Breakfast £30 – £38
Dinner B & B £48 – £51
Special Rates for 2+ nights
• *Seafood with horseradish cream. Baked wild salmon with cucumber and yoghurt sauce. Sirloin steak with Drambuie haggis stuffing. Noisettes of lamb with local berries. Chicken suprême stuffed with skirlie in leek sauce.*
STB Highly Commended 3 Crowns
Credit cards: 1, 3
Proprietors: Brian & Ovidia Harmon

CASTLEBEIGH HOUSE

Knockard Road, Pitlochry
Perthshire PH16 5HJ
Tel: 01796 472925
Fax: 01796 474068

Just off Pitlochry-West Moulin road.
A fine 19th century house originally built by an English boys' school as a retreat. It sits high on the hillside above Pitlochry with magnificent views of the green hillside across the valley, and is well situated and convenient for the many attractions and places of interest that make the town and the county so popular. All rooms are en suite, and there is a putting green in the garden which is much used. Menus change regularly, concentrate on good Scottish products, are imaginative and excellent value for money.
Open all year
Rooms: 21, 20 with private facilities
Dinner 6 – 7.45 pm (b)
No smoking in restaurant
Bed & Breakfast £20 – £35
Dinner B & B £30 – £45
• *Roast haunch of Scottish venison with a blackberry, cream and tarragon sauce. Deep-fried ice-cream in Drambuie batter served with butterscotch sauce.*
STB Commended 3 Crowns
Credit cards: 1, 3
Proprietors: Alistair & Diane McMenemie

CRAIGMHOR LODGE, HOTEL & RESTAURANT

27 West Moulin Road, Pitlochry
Perthshire PH16 5EF
Tel: 01796 472123
Fax: 01796 472123

Take A924 Moulin/Braemar road in Pitlochry – 800 yards up hill.
Craigmhor is a delightful Victorian lodge set in two acres of secluded grounds overlooking the Tummel Valley. The entrance to the hotel is over a small bridge under which flows the Moulin Burn. Much of the appeal of this hotel is that right balance of personal attention and genuine warmth of welcome. The accommodation is of a high standard and each of the bedrooms has its own individual character. From the restaurant there are wonderful views over the gardens and hills beyond. The creative à la carte and supper menus focus on the finest of fresh Scottish produce, complemented by a carefully selected wine list. After dinner guests can relax in the cosy atmosphere of the lounge with its Adam style fireplace. In addition there is an attractive mahogany-panelled

cocktail bar which boasts over 60 single malt whiskies.
Open all year
Rooms: 9 with private facilities
Light Lunch 12 – 2.30 pm (a)
Restaurant Lunch 12 – 2.30 pm (b) – reservations only
Supper 6 – 10 pm (a)
Dinner 7 – 9.30 pm: 6.30 – 9.30 pm during Theatre season (c)
Facilities for disabled visitors
No smoking in restaurant
Bed & Breakfast £20 – £35
Dinner B & B £30 – £52
Special Rates for 2+/5+ nights
• *Scallops and king prawns interleaved with filo pastry, served with a light tomato sauce. Medallions of Aberdeen Angus beef set on fresh spinach leaves, accompanied with bernaise sauce. A rich chocolate and amaretto mousse layered with sable biscuits, served on a white chocolate sauce. Home-baked bread. Hand-made Scottish cheeses. Vegetarian dishes.*
STB Highly Commended 3 Crowns
Credit cards: 1, 2, 3
Proprietor: Sandra Wallace Hutton

DUNFALLANDY HOUSE

Logierait Road, Pitlochry
Perthshire PH16 5NA
Tel: 01796 472648
Fax: 01796 472017

On south side of Pitlochry, signposted off road leading to Festival Theatre.
The present house is built on foundations which date back to the 13th century and was originally built for General Archibald Fergusson in 1790. This Georgian mansion house is now a beautifully refurbished country house hotel. It is magnificently situated within the Dunfallandy Estate and has unrivalled views of the glorious Tummel Valley, with the popular Highland town of Pitlochry nestling below. This characterful house retains its historical features including marble fireplaces, log fires and the 'General's Bath' – the original Georgian ceramic bath of rather alarming depth! The elegant dining room offers imaginative food expertly prepared and presented, enhanced by fresh flowers, silver cutlery, crystal glasses and candlelight. Jane and Michael Bardsley are dedicated to the service of all the good things in Scottish cuisine, complemented with fresh herbs from their garden. An extensive wine list features traditional and New World wines.

Open 10 Feb to 3 Jan
Rooms: 9 with private facilities
Dinner 6 – 8 pm (c)
No children
No dogs
No smoking in dining room
Bed & Breakfast £25 – £30
Dinner B & B £40 – £45
• *Wild duck breast poached with local chanterelles, fresh garden herbs and claret. Varied selection of vegetarian dishes always available.*
STB Highly Commended 3 Crowns
Credit cards: 1, 2, 3
Proprietors: Jane & Michael Bardsley

EAST HAUGH COUNTRY HOUSE HOTEL & RESTAURANT

East Haugh, by Pitlochry
Perthshire PH16 5JS
Tel: 01796 473121
Fax: 01796 472473

On old A9 road, 1 mile south of Pitlochry.
East Haugh House is a beautiful 17th century turreted stone Clan house, set in two acres of lawned gardens, which has been sympathetically refurbished to offer a high standard of accommodation. The bedrooms are individually designed and furnished, one of which features an antique pine four poster bed and an open fire. All rooms have direct dial telephone, colour TV and tea/coffee-making facilities. Dinner is served in the Game Keeper's Restaurant with its open fire and windows overlooking the garden. Neil McGown, the proprietor/chef, takes the greatest pride in preparing his dishes which are becoming renowned and display a mix of traditional Scottish and classic French cooking. He may even shoot or catch the ingredients for you himself as he specialises in arranging fishing and shooting parties. Lunches are offered in the informal atmosphere of the conservatory bar. There is also a children's menu. A new games room facility – with pool table – is now available.
Open all year
Rooms: 8 with private facilities
Bar Lunch 12 – 2 pm (b)
Dining Room/Restaurant Lunch 12 – 2.30 pm Sun only (a)
Bar Supper 6 – 10.30 pm (b)

*Dinner (Game Keeper's Restaurant) 7 –
10.30 pm (d)
No smoking in restaurant
Bed & Breakfast £20 – £46
Dinner B & B £39 – £65
Special Rates for 2+ nights*
• *Terrine of pheasant, duck and rabbit
studded with pistachio nuts, served with
wild rowan jelly and toasted fruit bread.
Prawn and mushroom parcels on a lobster
and brandy sauce. Roast rack of
Perthshire lamb served on a potato mat,
with a sauce of fresh rosemary, shallots,
tomato and fresh cream. Escalope of fresh
salmon served with hollandaise sauce.*
*STB Commended 3 Crowns
Credit cards: 1, 3
Proprietors: Neil & Lesley McGown*

KNOCKENDARROCH HOUSE HOTEL
Higher Oakfield, Pitlochry
Perthshire PH16 5HT
Tel: 01796 473473
Fax: 01796 474068
*High on a hill overlooking village – just
off main road in the centre of town, up
Bonnethill Road and take first right turn.*
Very much a large family home,
Knockendarroch is a splendidly confident
Victorian house standing squarely on its
hill overlooking the Tummel Valley and
Pitlochry. The prevailing atmosphere is
one of informality and welcome and
guests feel very much at ease from the
moment they arrive. John and Mary
McMenemie are warm and enthusiastic
hosts, attentive to the comfort of their
guests, and this is evident in the
standard of accommodation. There is a
total 'no smoking' policy throughout the
house which meets a very popular
requirement nowadays. Overlooking the
garden is the dining room which is set
with fine china and silver. The food is
described as home-cooking to the
highest standard and has earned a red
Rosette from the Automobile
Association. Bookings are advisable and
essential for non-residents.
*Open 1 May to 30 Nov
Rooms: 12 with private facilities
Dinner 6.15 – 7.45 pm (b)
Bed & Breakfast £32 – £37
Dinner B & B £42 – £52*
• *Cream of courgette and rosemary
soup. Smoked salmon quiche. Roast leg
of Perthshire lamb with minted pears.
Sole, salmon, trout and prawn in a parcel
of puff pastry. Hazelnut and carrot burger
in tomato and orange sauce. Collops of
venison with cranberry and port sauce.
Strawberry shortcake. Summer pudding.*

*STB Highly Commended 3 Crowns
Credit cards: 1, 2, 3, 5
Proprietors: John & Mary McMenemie*

MILL POND COFFEE SHOP
Burnside Apartment Hotel
19 West Moulin Road
Pitlochry PH16 5EA
Tel: 01796 472203
Fax: 01796 473586
*Around 300 yards north of junction of
A924 Pitlochry-Braemar (West Moulin
Road) and Atholl Road, Pitlochry.*
A delightful little coffee shop within an
apartment hotel, with 10 serviced
studios/apartments, situated in a
convenient quiet location. An imaginative
menu is served throughout the day, with
home-made soups and hot dishes, tasty
snacks and sandwiches, vegetarian
dishes, home-baking and speciality ices.
Selection of teas, coffees and health
drinks. Children welcome. There is also a
gallery featuring mixed exhibitions of
paintings by local/area artists.
*Open 1 Apr to 31 Oct
All Food Service 10 am – 6.30 pm Mon
to Sat: 10 am – 5 pm Sun (a)
No smoking in coffee shop
Bed & Breakfast from £24
Room Rate from £20*
• *Home-made soup. Savoury nut loaf.
Open sandwiches – e.g. Tay salmon.
Toasted sandwiches. Baked potato with
creamed Arbroath smokie and egg. Warm
salad of chicken, diced smoked bacon
and onions on a bed of mixed salad.
Smoked trout salad. Salmon
mayonnaise. Ginger cream meringues.
Carrot, parsnip, banana and apple
cakes.*
*Credit cards: 1, 2, 3
Proprietors: Bill & Jessie Falconer*

PITLOCHRY FESTIVAL THEATRE RESTAURANT
Port-na-Craig, Pitlochry
Perthshire PH16 5DR
Tel: 01796 473054
Fax: 01796 473054
*On south bank of the River Tummel,
approx ¼ mile from centre of town.
Clearly signposted.*
Scotland's 'Theatre in the Hills' is
beautifully situated on the banks of the
River Tummel and its glass frontage
allows wonderful views from the Brown
Trout Restaurant and Coffee Bar. Home-
baking is a feature of the coffee bar in the
foyer, and there is a lunchtime buffet with
hot and cold dishes and an extensive
salad bar. There is always plenty of food

but seating can become scarce on a
matinee day! Table d'hôte dinners in the
evening are served in the spacious
modern dining room in one sitting before
theatre, normally at 6.30 pm, and booking
is essential. French spoken.
*Open 28 Apr to 7 Oct
Note: open early Apr for Coffee + Lunch
only
Dining Room/Restaurant Lunch 12 –
2 pm except Sun (a)
Dinner 6.30 pm except Sun * (c) –
booking essential
* If theatre performance Sun, buffet
served – booking essential
Facilities for disabled visitors
No smoking in restaurant
Smoking area in Coffee Bar*
• *Scampi, scallops, salmon and prawns
in a cream and dill sauce. Poached fillet
of Scottish salmon with spinach and leek
sauces. Loin of lamb filled with apricots,
herbs and walnuts. Mincemeat roulade
filled with a Glayva flavoured cream.*
Credit cards: 1, 2, 3, 5, 6 + SWITCH

TORRDARACH HOTEL
Golf Course Road, Pitlochry
Perthshire PH16 5AU
Tel: 01796 472136
*On road signposted to golf course at
north end of town.*
Torrdarach is a traditional old Scottish
house offering a high standard of personal
service and traditional home-cooking. The
hotel is in a quiet and peaceful woodland
setting overlooking Pitlochry, and is
maintained in immaculate condition with
recently refurbished bedrooms. Good
value unpretentious home-cooking is
complemented by an improved wine list,
and menus change regularly. There are
few better locations than Pitlochry from
which to set out and explore the myriad
attractions of Scotland.
*Open 1 Apr to mid Oct
Rooms: 7 with private facilities
Dinner 6.30 – 7 pm (b) 4 course menu
Residents only
No dogs
No smoking throughout
Bed & Breakfast £20 – £28
Dinner B & B £35 – £42
Special Rates for 3+ nights*
• *Home-made soups. Smoked salmon
pâté. Poached salmon steak served with
Drambuie sauce. Home-roast Perthshire
turkey with cranberry sauce. Aberdeen
Angus beef.*
*STB Highly Commended 3 Crowns
No credit cards
Proprietors: Richard & Vivienne Cale*

WESTLANDS OF PITLOCHRY
160 Atholl Road, Pitlochry
Perthshire PH16 5AR
Tel: 01796 472266
Fax: 01796 473994
On old A9 north of town centre.
Westlands is a pleasant stone-built house set back from the road in its own well kept grounds, close to the centre of the town. It enjoys fine views of the surrounding mountains and the Vale of Atholl. The original building was sympathetically extended using traditional grey and pink Scottish stone. Bedrooms in this part of the hotel are particularly spacious and all the rooms are furnished to the highest standards of comfort. In the tasteful surroundings of the restaurant, guests can sample a selection of interesting dishes – ranging from traditional Taste of Scotland fare to international favourites – utilising the best of Scottish produce, in particular seafood, meat and game.
Open all year except Christmas + Boxing Days
Rooms: 15 with private facilities
Bar Lunch 12 – 2 pm (a)
Bar Supper 6.15 – 9.30 pm (b)
Dinner 6.15 – 9 pm (c)
Bed & Breakfast £29 – £48
Dinner B & B £38.50 – £63
Special Rates available
• Orkney herring and cucumber terrine with crisp salad leaves. Roast gigot of Scottish lamb cooked with fresh herbs and garlic, served with a mint and redcurrant jelly. Poached fillets of sole with tomato, shallots, cream and white wine sauce. Tender beef in puff pastry set on a smooth tomato sauce.
STB Commended 4 Crowns
Credit cards: 1, 3
Proprietors: Andrew & Sue Mathieson

Plockton

Location 179

THE HAVEN HOTEL
Innes Street, Plockton
Ross-shire IV52 8TW
Tel: 01599 554223
Fax: 01599 554467

Prestige Award Winner 1993

In the village of Plockton.
No one should ever be in this part of Scotland without seeing Plockton. With its palm trees along the waterfront and stunning views out over the sea it really is one of the country's loveliest villages. The aptly named Haven Hotel lives up to

its name and makes a delightful retreat. It has been carefully converted from a 19th century merchant's house but it is much larger internally than it appears from the outside. This is, in every way, an excellent little hotel which has been furnished and equipped to high standards. The same care goes into the food. Chef Ian James creates menus which are imaginative and skilful, with an admirable reliance on prime local produce.
Open 1 Feb to 18 Dec
Rooms: 13 with private facilities
Bar Lunch except Sun Sat (a) – reservations only
Dining Room/Restaurant Lunch 12.30 – 1.45 pm except Sun Sat (b) – reservations only
Dinner 7 – 8.15 pm (c) 5 course menu
No smoking in restaurant
Bed & Breakfast £32 – £35
Dinner B & B £44 – £54
Special Rates for 3+ nights
• A platter of smoked fish served with a light salad and soured cream. Roast sirloin of Scottish beef flavoured with syrup and spices, served with a port wine sauce. Pheasant suprêmes filled with basil and garlic, wrapped in bacon and served with a creamy cognac sauce. King scallops sautéed in a ginger and lemon butter, topped with spring onions.
STB Highly Commended 4 Crowns
Credit cards: 1, 3, 6
Proprietors: Marjorie Nichols & John Graham

OFF THE RAILS
The Station, Plockton
Ross-shire IV52 8TN
Tel: 01599 554423/554306
On platform of Plockton railway station – ½ mile from centre of village and lochside.
Plockton Station is on the famous "Kyle Line" and trains still pass through it regularly. It was built in 1897 and has not changed much since, with the original timber panelling and black iron grates still in position in the converted waiting rooms. This provided an unusual and interesting location, therefore, for Calum and Jane Mackenzie to have set up their characterful little restaurant. You can enjoy everything from a morning coffee – perhaps, weather permitting, at tables on the platform amid the flower filled tubs – to a relaxed candlelit dinner in the evening. Jenny Moulds' menu takes full advantage of the west coast's bountiful harvest of seafood and there

are some very interesting and subtle recipes, flavoured with herbs from the garden created by Calum Mackenzie. There is also an interesting gift shop in the old ticket office, full of specially selected items hand-crafted in Scotland.
Open Easter to Oct
Food service 10.30 am – 9.30 pm over Easter + from late May
Dining Room/Restaurant Lunch 11.30 am – 5 pm (a)
Dinner 6.30 – 9.30 pm (b-c)
Note: Easter to late May open Thu Fri Sat Sun evenings only
No smoking in restaurant
Smoking at outside tables only
• Local prawns in garlic butter. Skate wing with mustard and lime sauce. Roast leg of lamb with rosemary and anchovy. Haunch of venison with juniper berries and red wine. Sirloin steak with garlic whisky cream. Sticky toffee pudding. Oatcakes with a selection of local cheese.
Credit card: 1
Proprietor: Jane Mackenzie

Port Appin

Location 180

THE PIERHOUSE HOTEL
Port Appin
Argyll PA38 4DA
Tel: 0163 173 302
Fax: 0163 173 521
Fort William-Oban on Argyll tourist route. Enter village of Appin, take road signed for Lismore ferry. Situated at pier.
The Pierhouse is primarily a seafood restaurant to which guest bedrooms were added in 1993. It sits at the pier on the edge of Loch Linnhe, with outlooks across to Lismore and the Morvern Hills. The property is traditional and of unique design, with two semi-rotunda buildings forming the front of the hotel. It was originally the village post office and latterly the waiting room for the ferry. The MacLeod family have been at The Pierhouse some seven years and their

restaurant and reputation has been built around the local shellfish catches. Quality of produce is such that the oysters and lobsters remain in holding creels at the end of the jetty clearly visible from the restaurant and sea facing windows. Occasionally when stocks are low and the tide is high Callum can be seen wading waist deep to the end of the pier to retrieve oysters – but only when there is an audience! The preparation of most of the shellfish dishes is extremely simple and they are served unadorned with a few sauces purely as an accompaniment. There is a spectacular arrangement of shellfish which is called the Giant Platter prepared for two and consisting of a half lobster, scallops, langoustine prawns, Pacific oysters and mussels. The hotel's purpose-built extension provides delightful accommodation, five of the rooms facing the sea and the surrounding islets, the rest to the rear looking on to the large tree covered land mass. Within a six mile radius there is a selection of recreational facilities including boating, horse-riding, fishing and some delightful walks on the island of Lismore. The area around Port Appin is steeped in history and there is much architectural evidence of this to be seen, especially Castle Stalker.

Open all year except Christmas Day
Rooms: 11 with private facilities
Bar Lunch 12 – 3.30 pm (a)
Dining Room/Restaurant Lunch 12 – 3.30 pm (a)
Dinner 6.30 – 9.30 pm (d)
No dogs
Bed & Breakfast from £35
Room Rate £70 – £85
• The Pierhouse Giant Platter: ½ lobster, mussels, prawns, oysters, scallops (2 persons). Loch Linnhe scallops cooked on a ribbed grill dry heat served with lemon butter. Fillet of salmon and langoustine Mornay served with fresh potatoes and vegetables. Lunch speciality: fresh salmon and potatoes bound together and covered in breadcrumbs.
Credit cards: 1, 3
Proprietors: Sheila & Alan MacLeod

Port of Menteith

Location 181
LAKE HOTEL
Port of Menteith
Perthshire FK8 3RA
Tel: 01877 385 258
Fax: 01877 385 671

On A81 – at Port of Menteith – 200 yards on road south to Arnprior.
This former 19th century manse became a hotel over 50 years ago but in the last few years it has been carefully extended and completely refurbished to become the very comfortably appointed hotel it is today. It stands on the shore of the Lake of Menteith – Scotland's only lake, others being lochs – in the Trossachs, an area renowned for its outstanding scenic beauty. From the Conservatory Restaurant there are the most delightful views across the lake to Inchmahome Priory which at different points in history was a haven for both Robert the Bruce and Mary Queen of Scots. The dishes on the menu have simple descriptions but the quality and presentation of the food is extremely good.

Open all year
Rooms: 14 with private facilities
Bistro Lunch 12 – 2 pm (b)
Dining Room/Restaurant Lunch 12 – 2 pm Sun only (c) – booking essential
Bistro Supper 6.30 – 9 pm (b)
Dinner 7 – 8.30 pm (d) 4 course menu
No smoking in hotel
Bed & Breakfast £32 – £65
Dinner B & B £42 – £80
• Fresh fillet of plaice grilled with butter and chives. Breast of pheasant pan-fried with bacon, fresh basil and Madeira. Fresh monkfish tail poached with Pernod and cream. Noisettes of lamb charcoaled and coated in a fresh rosemary and garlic sauce.
STB Highly Commended 4 Crowns
Credit cards: 1, 3 + SWITCH, DELTA
Proprietor: J L Leroy

Portpatrick

Location 182
THE FERNHILL HOTEL
Heugh Road, Portpatrick
nr Stranraer DG9 8TD
Tel: 01776 810220
Fax: 01776 810596

Just off main road into Portpatrick.
Set high above this beautiful unspoilt fishing village and harbour, is the Fernhill Hotel. The main building dates back to 1872 but over the past 30 years while it has been in the Harvie family it has been extensively enlarged and equipped to the highest modern standards, achieving three star status. Anne and Hugh Harvie have a policy of ongoing improvement and updating to maintain these standards throughout. From the delightful conservatory restaurant there are spectacular views over Portpatrick to the sea. Chef John Henry presents menus which offer a fine selection of dishes, making good use of local produce, and the style of food is modern Scottish with a French influence. This is a popular hotel with a good reputation for the quality of its cuisine, both for restaurant and bar meals. Ample overnight parking is available within the walled grounds.

Open all year
Rooms: 20 with private facilities
Bar Lunch 12 – 2 pm (a-b)
Dining Room/Restaurant Lunch 12 – 2 pm (b-c)
Bar Restaurant Meals 6 – 10 pm (b)
Dinner 6.30 – 9.30 pm (c)
No dogs in public rooms
No smoking in restaurant + conservatory
Bed & Breakfast £37.50 – £75
Dinner B & B £55 – £92.50
Special Rates available
• Steamed slices of salmon and king scallops layered with spinach in thin pastry served with saffron sauce. Queenie scallops lightly cooked in a vermouth cream sauce with sliced mushrooms. Medallions of venison marinated with juniper berries, pan-fried and served with a gin and redcurrant sauce. Galloway fillet steak with scampi tails in hot garlic butter.
STB Highly Commended 4 Crowns
Credit cards: 1, 2, 3, 5 + SWITCH
Proprietors: Anne & Hugh Harvie

Powmill
by Dollar

GARTWHINZEAN HOTEL & RESTAURANTS

Powmill, by Dollar
Clackmannanshire FK14 7NW
Tel: 01577 840595
Fax: 01577 840595

On A977 Kincardine Bridge-Kinross.
Paul and Diane Brown have been steadily refurbishing and upgrading the Gartwhinzean over the past couple of years since they came to the hotel. During the summer of 1994 part of the process came to fruition with the opening of the new restaurant and lounge and future plans include extending the bedroom accommodation. The Browns are welcoming hosts and offer guests a relaxed and informal style of dining. Food is available throughout the day and the menus have been carefully planned utilising the best of Scottish produce to cater for a wide variety of tastes.
Open all year
Rooms: 3 with private facilities
Meals available 11 am – 10 pm (b)
Facilities for disabled visitors
No smoking area in restaurant
Bed & Breakfast £22.50 – £40
Dinner B & B £32.50 – £50
Room Rate £45 – £60
• Scallop shell of puff pastry filled with langoustines served with a chive and beurre blanc sauce. Darne of poached Tay salmon with a light orange and ginger sauce. Noisettes of new season lamb with celeriac and rosemary crust on a Madeira and plum purée. Pan-fried sirloin steak glazed with oyster mushrooms, shallots and red wine. Honey, apple and raspberry charlotte with brandy and cinnamon crème fraîche.
Credit cards: 1, 2, 3
Proprietor: Paul M Brown

Rogart

SCIBERSCROSS LODGE

Strath Brora, Rogart
Sutherland IV28 3YQ
Tel: 01408 641 246
Fax: 01408 641 465

A9 over Dornoch Firth Bridge for c. 10 miles, then A839 for 4 miles. In Rogart turn right onto single-track road (Balnacoil) for 7 miles, lodge on left.
A classic Highland sporting lodge built just over a century ago for the Duke of Sutherland and set in spectacular scenery. Peter and Kate Hammond, whose home it is, create a relaxed friendly country house atmosphere, and log fires and the profusion of fresh flowers emphasise that "personal guest" feeling. Bedrooms and public rooms are beautifully furnished and much thought goes into the preparation of interesting five course dinners, drawing on the quality supplies from the locality. The location is such that it appeals to all lovers of outdoor pursuits. A courtesy car service operates to and from Inverness. The Hammonds sum up their philosophy nicely in the phrase – "arrive as strangers, leave as friends."
Open 1 Feb to 30 Nov
Rooms: 5 with private facilities
Dinner at 8 pm (or by arrangement) (f)
5 course menu
Dinners for non-residents by prior booking only
Bed & Breakfast from £40
Dinner B & B from £80
• Home-made soups. Wild venison pâté. Roast leg of Rogart lamb with redcurrant sauce. Fillet of fresh wild salmon with hollandaise sauce. Chocolate truffle torte. Selection of cheeses.
Credit cards: 1, 3
Proprietors: Peter & Kate Hammond

Isle of Rum

KINLOCH CASTLE

Isle of Rum
Inverness-shire PH43 4RR
Tel: 01687 2037

The Isle of Rum National Nature Reserve is on the route taken by the small isles ferry service operated from Mallaig by Caledonian MacBrayne.
Kinloch Castle is one of Scotland's most remarkable hotels. Situated on an island nature reserve of spectacular wildness and beauty, the hotel offers guests a chance to experience living history in the Edwardian castle rooms which have changed little since the turn of the century. Over your pre-dinner drink listen to the extraordinary 'orchestrion' – a mechanical organ reputedly built for Queen Victoria. Enjoy the best of fresh local fare served at the original dining table taken from the owners ocean-going yacht 'Rhouma' during the Boer War. This is a castle with a difference in an island with a difference, and nature lovers will find so much to enjoy.
Open Mar to Oct
Rooms: 9
Dinner at 7.30 pm (d)
Children over 7 years welcome
No dogs
No smoking in dining room
Dinner B & B £68 – £88
• The best of Mallaig fish and seafood. Rum venison in season and freshly caught brown trout from the lochs.
No credit cards
Proprietors: Kathleen & Iain MacArthur

St Andrews

THE GRANGE INN

Grange Road, St Andrews
Fife KY16 8LJ
Tel: 01334 472670

From centre of town follow A917 signs to Crail/Anstruther. At edge of St Andrews take right fork signposted Grange, c. ¾ mile to inn.
This lovely old inn is situated on a hillside just to the south of the town, with a spectacular view of St Andrews Bay. It has long been a favourite rendezvous in St Andrews and offers an informal and relaxed style of eating. There are now three separate dining areas, two of which are for non-smokers. Menus are carefully compiled and augmented by daily dishes displayed on a blackboard. All of the charm of this lovely old world inn has been retained and the two en suite bedrooms are simply furnished in cottage-style. Whether you are looking for a delicious light lunch or a leisurely gourmet dinner, you will find it here.
Open all year
Note: Nov to Mar closed Mon Tue
Rooms: 2 with private facilities
Restaurant Lunch 12.30 – 2.15 pm (a-b)

Dinner 6.30 – 9.15 pm (c)
No smoking dining area available
Bed & Breakfast £30 – £35
• *Home-made soups. Loin of spring lamb wrapped in pastry lattice with Madeira sauce. Escalope of salmon with prawns and herb butter. Fillet steaks. Rhubarb in a pastry case with a vanilla cream. Caramel and pistachio cream served with home-made chocolate shortbread.*
Credit cards: 1, 2, 3, 5, 6 + SWITCH
Proprietors: Ann Russell & Peter Aretz

RUFFLETS COUNTRY HOUSE & GARDEN RESTAURANT
Strathkinness Low Road, St Andrews
Fife KY16 9TX
Tel: 01334 472594
Fax: 01334 478703
On B939, 1½ miles west of St Andrews.
This turreted mansion house is set in beautifully landscaped gardens, 1½ miles west of St Andrews – the mecca of the golfing world – yet only one hour's drive north from Edinburgh. The hotel has been in the same private family ownership since 1952 and is personally managed by proprietor Ann Russell and Peter Aretz, the general manager. Service is friendly and personal within a relaxed ambience. Each of the bedrooms is individually designed and furnished to a very high standard. There are three ground floor rooms available in the delightful Rose Cottage in the grounds. Public rooms are spacious and attractively furnished in contemporary country house style. The award winning Garden Restaurant is noted for the high standard of its cuisine, recognised by the RAC with merit awards over past years and also by the award of an AA Rosette. Cooking is light with an emphasis on fresh Scottish produce. Many of the fresh vegetables, herbs and fruits are supplied by the hotel's own gardens.
Open all year
Rooms: 25 with private facilities
Bar Lunch 12.30 – 2 pm (a)
Dining Room/Restaurant Lunch 12.30 – 2 pm: Nov to Apr Sun Sat only (b)
Dinner 7 – 9.30 pm (d)
Bed & Breakfast £65 – £75
Dinner B & B £70 – £80
Special Rates available Nov to Apr
• *Light mousse of fresh salmon with fan*

of avocado pear and Orkney oatcakes. Fillet of North Sea halibut baked with lemon butter. Collops of Scottish beef fillet grilled with Stilton cheese and chives. Medallions of Rannoch venison on a garden beetroot, port wine and ginger sauce. Warm cloutie dumpling with coddled cream. Bramble shortcake.
STB Highly Commended 4 Crowns
Credit cards: 1, 2, 3, 5, 6 + SWITCH
Proprietor: Ann Russell

ST ANDREWS GOLF HOTEL
40 The Scores, St Andrews
Fife KY16 9AS
Tel: 01334 472611
Telex: 94013267
Fax: 01334 472188
A91 to St Andrews, turn left at Golf Place then follow round to right to The Scores.
This family run hotel is situated on the cliffs with magnificent views over the Links and St Andrews Bay, 200 yards from the world famous "Old Course". The building is Victorian, tastefully modernised with most comfortable bedrooms and elegant public rooms. Quality prints of the best of Scottish artists line the walls. The oak-panelled restaurant offers a fine selection of dishes prepared from the best of local produce and complemented by an extensive and carefully selected wine list. Golf arranging is a speciality, either using one of the hotel's packages or having a holiday tailored to your requirements. Children welcome. Dogs accepted – small charge. Italian and some French spoken.
Open all year
Rooms: 23 with private facilities
Bar Lunch 12 – 3 pm (a)
Dining Room/Restaurant Lunch 12.30 – 2.30 pm (b)
Bar Supper 5 – 8 pm (a)
Dinner 7 – 9.30 pm (d)
No smoking in restaurant
Bed & Breakfast £60 – £75
Dinner B & B £77 – £90
Special Rates available Nov to Mar
• *Roulade of smoked salmon and lemon sole with a light dill sauce. Fresh Tay salmon grilled with julienne of crisp vegetables and lemon butter. Noisettes of Perthshire lamb with garden rosemary served with pan juices. Prime Scottish sirloin with wholegrain Arran mustard. Vegetable strudel with a watercress and red pepper sauce.*
STB Highly Commended 4 Crowns
Credit cards: 1, 2, 3, 5, 6
Proprietors: Maureen & Brian Hughes

ST ANDREWS OLD COURSE HOTEL
St Andrews
Fife KY16 9SP
Tel: 01334 474371
Telex: 76280
Fax: 01334 477668
A91 to St Andrews.
This luxurious modern hotel has an international reputation and is hailed as one of Scotland's leading resort hotels. It is set in a spectacular location overlooking the famous 17th Road Hole and the historic Royal & Ancient Clubhouse, with superb views of the city, St Andrews Bay and the distant mountains of the Highlands. All the bedroom accommodation, including 17 sumptuously appointed suites, share these outlooks. There is an air of quiet elegance throughout the hotel which has been awarded five stars by the AA. A choice of dining styles is available and food is of a high standard which matches the overall excellence of the establishment. Overlooking the golf course is The Road Hole Grill, with its wood panelling and tapestry hangings, which offers the top of the range in dining at the hotel. Light meals are available throughout the day in summer in The Conservatory. In addition there is the Jigger Inn which was originally a 19th century cottage and is now a popular golfing pub serving real ale and wholesome food. A wide range of leisure activities is also available including a health spa and swimming pool.
Open all year
Rooms: 125 with private facilities
Bar Lunch 11 am – 4 pm (a)
Dining Room/Restaurant Lunch 11.30 am – 7 pm (b)
Afternoon tea available
Dinner 7 – 10 pm (e)
Facilities for disabled visitors
Room Rate £150 – £235
Special short break rates available
• *Salad of Comrie goats cheese with green beans and walnut vinaigrette. Woodland mushroom fricassée on toasted brioche. Shellfish cappuccino. Darne of Orkney salmon with fettucine and cherry tomato salsa. Hot-grilled Scotch sirloin with ratatouille of vegetables cooked in a red wine sauce. Pan-fried loin of Ayrshire lamb with a parsley and onion flan, herb potato scone and basil jus. Crème brûlée with minted raspberries.*
STB Deluxe 5 Crowns
Credit cards: 1, 2, 3, 5

St Boswells

Location 187

DRYBURGH ABBEY HOTEL
St Boswells
Roxburghshire TD6 0RQ
Tel: 01835 822261
Fax: 01835 823945

At St Boswells take B6404 signposted Dryburgh Abbey for 2 miles, then B6356 for just over 1½ miles.

In a tranquil setting on the banks of the River Tweed, by the old abbey, is this magnificent old red sandstone baronial building which has been converted into a splendid luxury hotel. It is well placed for fishing, sightseeing in the Borders, and there are 14 golf courses within 30 minutes drive of the hotel. Public rooms, bedrooms and suites are very comfortably appointed and maintained to high standards. Situated on the first floor with views over the lawns to the river is The Tweed Restaurant where Chef Patrick Ruse shows originality and imagination in his daily changing table d'hôte menus. At lunchtime a range of interesting light meals is also available, served in the comfortable lounge and bar on the ground floor. A new indoor heated swimming pool was added to the hotel during 1994.

Open all year
Rooms: 26 with private facilities
Bar Lunch 12.30 – 2.30 pm except Sun (a)
Dining Room/Restaurant Lunch 12.30 – 2.30 pm (b)
Dinner 7.30 – 9.15 pm (c)
Facilities for disabled visitors
No smoking in restaurant
Bed & Breakfast £40 – £75
Dinner B & B £45 – £85
Special Rates for 2+/5+ nights
• *Highland venison terrine studded with pine kernels set on Cumberland sauce. Poached Tweed salmon with watercress sauce. Grilled cutlets of Border lamb served with natural pan juices flavoured with rosemary. Sirloin steaks. Selection of Scottish cheeses.*
STB Highly Commended 5 Crowns
Credit cards: 1, 3, 6 + SWITCH, DELTA
Proprietors: David & Graham Grose

Selkirk

Location 188

PHILIPBURN HOUSE HOTEL
Selkirk TD7 5LS
Tel: 01750 20747
Fax: 01750 21690

Situated on A707 Moffat-Peebles, 1 mile from A7 on outskirts of Selkirk.

Philipburn, built in the mid 18th century, was once the Dowager House to the Philiphaugh Estate and is set in award winning gardens and grounds overlooking the historic town of Selkirk. The Hill Family has enhanced this already delightful Georgian house with their own distinctive style and the hotel has earned increasingly high ratings for all of the last decade as it has increased the range and scope of its facilities. There is a choice of very comfortable accommodation available, from the charming chintzy country house rooms or spacious family suites to cottage apartments close by the hotel or the exclusive poolside suites. Jim Hill is an energetic progressively minded hotelier and is constantly seeking to improve standards. Throughout the hotel there is a distinctly Austrian influence in the pine furniture and mellow pine panelling which contributes to the unique character of the place. Guests have the choice of dining in the Garden and Poolside Restaurants or perhaps in the informal atmosphere of Soutars Bar. The kitchen team led by Jim Hill produces imaginative menus with some distinctive touches and presents food to a very high standard.

Open all year
Rooms: 16 with private facilities
Bar Lunch 12 – 2 pm (b)
Dining Room/Restaurant Lunch 12.30 – 2 pm (b)
Bar Supper 7 – 9.30 pm (b)
Dinner 7.30 – 9.30 pm (d) 5 course menu
No smoking in dining room
Bed & Breakfast £38.50 – £58.50
Dinner B & B £55 – £79.50
Special Rates available
• *Selection of seafood tossed in butter with mushrooms, flared in brandy and glazed with parmesan cheese. Rack of Border lamb with a minted orange sauce. Medallions of pork coated in oatmeal and pan-fried with a light caper and Arran mustard sauce. Raspberries flared in cassis, served with vanilla ice-cream and home-made shortbread.*
STB Highly Commended 4 Crowns
Credit cards: 1, 3, 6 + SWITCH
Proprietors: Jim Hill & Family

Isles of Shetland

Location 189

BUSTA HOUSE HOTEL
Busta, Brae
Shetland ZE2 9QN
Tel: 0180622 506
Fax: 0180622 588

On the Muckle Roe road, 1 mile off A970 Hillswick road.

The impressive but slightly severe external appearance of Busta House gives no hint of the charm and elegance of the interior. This is reputedly the oldest continuously inhabited building in Shetland and it enjoys a commanding site overlooking Busta Voe. The public rooms are impressive and have been furnished with good taste while the bedrooms have every thoughtful facility that one would expect from caring hosts. The food lives up to the standard of the rest of the hotel concentrating on the plentiful harvest of good local produce from both land and sea, and there is a well chosen wine list and a stock of over 100 malt whiskies. Peter and Judith Jones can arrange holidays including flights or ferry from the UK mainland, and organise car hire, with a car to meet you at the airport or ferry terminal.

Open all year except 22 Dec to 3 Jan
Rooms: 20 with private facilities
Bar Lunch 12 – 2 pm Mon to Sat: 12.30 – 2 pm Sun (a-c)
Bar Supper 6.30 – 9.30 pm (a-c)
Dinner 7 – 9 pm (d) 4 course menu
No smoking in dining room
Bed & Breakfast £42 – £63
Dinner B & B £30 – £60 (min 3 nights stay)
• *Poached local turbot fillet with a fresh rosemary and mushroom sauce. Roast sirloin of beef with a wholegrain mustard sauce. Baked Shetland salmon with a honey and sesame glaze. Roast breast of duck with a peach and spring onion sauce. Home-made orange and Cointreau ice-cream.*
STB Commended 4 Crowns
Credit cards: 1, 2, 3, 5 + SWITCH, DELTA
Proprietors: Peter & Judith Jones

ST MAGNUS BAY HOTEL
Hillswick
Shetland ZE2 9RW
Tel: 0180 623 372
Fax: 0180 623 373

36 miles north of Lerwick, on north-west branch of A970.

A timber clad hotel erected at the turn of the century with a most unusual history. It was built in Norway and floated across the North Sea for an international exhibition in Glasgow, then brought again by sea to Shetland. It occupies a splendidly dominating position in the village and must rank as one of the most northerly hotels in the British Isles. The original building has been extended over the years, but retaining the impressive stairway and the pine-lined dining room. In addition there is a separate coffee or supper room and a public bar. The chef relies heavily – and rightly – on a copious supply of fresh fish and local shellfish. Children are welcome.

Open all year
Rooms: 26 with private facilities
Bar Lunch 12.30 – 1.45 pm (a)
Dining Room/Restaurant Carvery Lunch 1 – 2 pm Sun only (a)
Bar Supper 6.30 – 8.45 pm (a)
Dinner 7.30 – 8.45 pm (c)
Bed & Breakfast £35 – £40
• Local smoked salmon. Home-made soups. Local scallops in a white wine and cream sauce. Prime roast Aberdeen Angus beef served with horseradish sauce.
STB Approved 3 Crowns
Credit cards: 1, 3 + SWITCH
Proprietors: Peter & Adrienne Titcomb

Isle of
Skye

Location 190
ARDVASAR HOTEL
Ardvasar, Sleat
Isle of Skye IV45 8AS
Tel: 0147 14 223

At roadside A851, close to Armadale pier (Armadale-Mallaig ferry).

Ardvasar was built as a coaching inn in the early 18th century and is an attractive small white-washed stone building with superb views over the Sound of Sleat to the mountains of Wester Ross. Guests are made very welcome and the atmosphere is cosy and homely with traditional furniture and usually a log fire in the sitting room. Bedrooms are extremely comfortable and attractive. Food is served both in the dining room and bar and a good balance of local produce is highlighted in the small but interesting daily changing menus.

Open Mar to Nov
Note: bar open all year except Christmas + New Year
Rooms: 10 with private facilities
Bar Lunch 12 – 2.15 pm (a)
Dining Room/Restaurant Lunch 12 – 2.15 pm
Bar Supper 5 – 7 pm (b)
Dinner 7 – 8.30 pm (b-c)
Bed & Breakfast £30 – £35
Dinner B & B £50 – £55
• Cullen skink. Ardvasar smoked salmon and seafood platter with horseradish cream. Roast stuffed lamb with plum and cranberry sauce. Saulé salmon steak fillet with leeks and white wine. Pan-fried haddock fillet and local scallops meunière.
STB Commended 3 Crowns
Credit cards: 1, 3 + DELTA
Proprietors: Bill & Gretta Fowler

FLODIGARRY COUNTRY HOUSE HOTEL & THE WATER HORSE RESTAURANT
Staffin, Isle of Skye
Inverness-shire IV51 9HZ
Tel: 01470 552203
Fax: 01470 522301

A855 north from Portree to Staffin, 4 miles from Staffin to Flodigarry.

Set in five acres of gardens and mixed woodland, this fine 19th century mansion house is steeped in history and has strong Jacobite associations. Now this delightful hotel is a warm sheltered haven amidst the dramatic scenery of northern Skye with views across Staffin Bay to the Torridon Mountains, and the towering pinnacles of the Quiraing provide a remarkable skyline to the views inland. In the Water Horse Restaurant, which is open every evening for dinner and lunch on Sunday, residents and non-residents can enjoy four course daily changing table d'hôte menus featuring traditional dishes and other specialities which are prepared using fresh and where possible local produce. The standard of food is first class. In addition there is the Conservatory where excellent bar meals are available throughout the day and evening. Adjacent to the hotel is the little cottage once owned by the legendary Flora MacDonald which now provides seven luxury period-style additional bedrooms.

Open all year
Rooms: 23, 18 with private facilities
Bar Meals (Conservatory) 11 am – 10 pm (a)
Dining Room/Restaurant Lunch 12.30 – 2.30 pm Sun only (b) or by arrangement
Dinner 7 – 10 pm (c) 4 course menu
Bed & Breakfast £23 – £46
Dinner B & B £40 – £63
Special Rates available
• Baked avocado pear with prawns and walnut dressing. Grilled lamb cutlets with an apricot and mint glaze. Prime Scottish steak on a bed of puff pastry with a mushroom and red wine sauce. Mushroom and leek crêpes with elderflower wine sauce. Local king scallops with ginger and spring onions. Hand-made confectionery.
STB Commended 3 Crowns
Credit cards: 1, 3 + SWITCH, DELTA
Proprietors: Andrew & Pamela Butler

Credit Card Code		**Meal Price Range**	
1.	Access/Mastercard/Eurocard	(a)	under £10
2.	American Express	(b)	£10 – £15
3.	Visa	(c)	£15 – £20
4.	Carte Bleu	(d)	£20 – £25
5.	Diners Club	(e)	£25 – £30
6.	Mastercharge	(f)	over £30

HARLOSH HOUSE
by Dunvegan
Isle of Skye IV55 8ZG
Tel: 0147 022 367

Off A863, 4 miles south of Dunvegan.
Harlosh House is situated on the shores of Loch Caroy in the beautiful, remote but easily accessible west of Skye, with fine views of the Cuillins and the small islands of Loch Bracadale. The house dates back to 1750 and has been skilfully and tastefully upgraded by Peter and Lindsey Elford to become one of those cosy friendly small hotels you just love to discover. Lindsey greets guests with great charm and courtesy and throughout there is a very relaxed and homely atmosphere. The six en suite bedrooms are superb, extremely comfortable and very well appointed. Peter has earned a fine reputation for the high standard of food he presents in the restaurant. He makes imaginative use of the excellent fresh produce for which Skye is renowned, specialising in the abundance of fish and shellfish, but also shows his deft touch in a small range of non-fish dishes. Harlosh is popular with many visitors to the island so it is best to book in advance.
Open Easter to mid Oct
Rooms: 6, 5 with private facilities
Dinner 7 – 8.30 pm (d-e)
No dogs
No smoking in restaurant
Bed & Breakfast from £45
• *Local scallops, smoked bacon and mushrooms in a filo parcel with chive sauce. Trio of white fish and mussels in a star anise broth. Braised shoulder of Scottish lamb in its own juices with fine beans and flavoured with tomato. Fillet of wild venison with Puy lentils and Dijon mustard. Redcurrant meringue pie with toasted almond ice-cream.*
STB Highly Commended 3 Crowns
Credit cards: 1, 3 + SWITCH
Proprietors: Peter & Lindsey Elford

HOTEL EILEAN IARMAIN
Sleat, Isle of Skye
Inverness-shire IV43 8QR
Tel: 01471 833332
Fax: 01471 833275

Barely 20 minutes drive on A851 Armadale-Kyleakin.
Hotel Eilean Iarmain (Isle Ornsay Hotel) is a traditional inn dating back to the early 19th century, which sits in an idyllic setting overlooking the harbour. The hotel has that genuine warmth of welcome and level of hospitality for which the Highlands and Islands are so renowned. There is a good standard of en suite accommodation, six of the rooms being in the main hotel and the rest in the Garden House across the drive. In the award winning restaurant you will find menus described in Gaelic with an English translation underneath. The chef prepares well balanced and interesting dishes specialising in the excellent seafood for which local waters are famous as well as game from the hills. It is advisable for non-residents to book in advance to dine in the restaurant. This makes a good centre from which to enjoy stalking, shooting, walking, fishing, riding, golf or just laze and lap up the tranquillity.
Open all year
Rooms: 12 with private facilities
Bar Lunch 12.30 – 2.30 pm (a)
Dining Room/Restaurant Lunch 12.30 – 2 pm (b)
Bar Supper 6.30 – 9.30 pm (a)
Dinner 7.30 – 9 pm (d)
No smoking in restaurant
Bed & Breakfast £39 – £55
Dinner B & B £65 – £70
Special Rates available
• *Eilean Iarmain oysters grilled with parmesan. Roast breast of duck with plum and port gravy. Salmon steaks with asparagus sauce. Herb pancakes with green pea pâté served with a creamy mushroom sauce. Chocolate and mint syllabub flan. Selection of cheeses with home-made oatcakes and biscuits.*
Credit cards: 1, 2, 3, 6
Proprietors: Sir Iain & Lady Noble

LOCHBAY SEAFOOD RESTAURANT
1/2 Macleod's Terrace
Stein, Waternish
Isle of Skye IV55 8GA
Tel: 01470 592235

Situated 5 miles down the Waternish Peninsula, in Stein Village. Last house in the village.
Situated in the old fishing village of Stein and located just 30 yards from the jetty and shore with some lovely unspoilt views of the loch and the Outer Isles. It has been converted from two cottages which were built in 1740 and is now a speciality seafood restaurant with accommodation. There is a lot of atmosphere about this friendly little restaurant where you will be made welcome whether formally or informally dressed and enjoy some of its superb fish and shellfish landed by local fishermen practically at the doorstep.
Open Easter to Nov
Rooms: 3
Dining Room/Restaurant Lunch 12 – 3 pm except Sat (a)
Dinner 6 – 9 pm except Sat (b)
Restaurant closed Sat except Easter Sat
No smoking in restaurant
Bed & Breakfast from £16
• *Starters of squat lobster, princess scallops, oysters, mussels etc. Seafood platter, lobster, king prawns, scallop, various selection of fresh fish. Clootie dumpling etc.*
Credit cards: 1, 2, 3
Proprietors: Peter & Margaret Greenhalgh

ROSEDALE HOTEL
Beaumont Crescent, Portree
Isle of Skye IV51 9DB
Tel: 01478 613131
Fax: 01478 612531

Harbourside location, 100 yards from village square.
The Rosedale sits on the harbourside in the heart of old Portree. From modest beginnings in a row of fishermen's houses which date from the reign of William IV, it has spread its wings in all directions so that it now occupies practically all of one side of the Portree waterfront. Growth was in response to demand and demand was created by satisfied guests returning yet again for another stay. There are many unique and interesting features – not least of which is finding your way to the first floor restaurant! – from which there are splendid views out over the bay. When you get there you will most certainly enjoy Linda Thomson's creative cooking and excellent presentation of food which contribute so materially to the good standards which prevail throughout this hotel.
Open 8 May to 30 Sep
Rooms: 23 with private facilities
Dinner 7 – 8.30 pm (d)
No smoking in restaurant
Bed & Breakfast £30 – £40

Dinner B & B £50 – £60
Special Rates for 3+ nights
• *Roast leg of Skye lamb with coriander served with its own juices. Baked salmon with fennel and cream. Caramelised breast of duck with lime and ginger. Fillet of beef with a layer of pesto and pine nuts accompanied by tomato butter sauce. Hot whisky rice cream with a meringue topping.*
STB Commended 4 Crowns
Credit cards: 1, 3
Proprietor: Hugh Andrew

SKEABOST HOUSE HOTEL
Skeabost Bridge
Isle of Skye IV51 9NP
Tel: 0147 032 202
Fax: 0147 032 454

4 miles north of Portree on Dunvegan road.

Built in 1870 this former hunting lodge is now a family run hotel, and turning into the drive to the house is like entering a new world. In direct contrast to the spectacular but stark countryside around it Skeabost is an oasis of cultivated serenity. It is wonderfully positioned on the shore of Loch Snizort and its woodlands and gardens wander down to the waters edge and incorporate a nine hole golf course. During 1994 a large Victorian style conservatory overlooking the loch was opened which has extended the dining facilities at the hotel. A buffet menu is available at lunchtime and a new style menu has been introduced in the evening. In the more formal surroundings of the splendid wood-panelled dining room Angus McNab presents daily changing table d'hôte menus showing considerable flair and skill, particularly with fish and game. Staff are attentive to every need and make guests feel very welcome.

Open 1 Apr to 24 Oct
Rooms: 26 with private facilities
Bar Lunch/Buffet Table 12 – 2 pm (a)
Bar Supper 6.30 – 9.30 (b)
Dinner 7 – 8.30 pm (c-d)
Room Rate £45 – £95
Special Rates for 3+ nights Apr + Oct
• *Warm brioche with steamed leeks and smoked salmon. Rack of lamb on a cranberry and onion sauce. Chargrilled steak with a mixed peppercorn sauce. Queen scallops poached in garlic and chive butter. Fresh lobsters when available.*
STB Commended 4 Crowns
Credit cards: 1, 3 + SWITCH, DELTA
Proprietors: Stuart/McNab/Stuart

THREE CHIMNEYS RESTAURANT
Colbost, nr Dunvegan
Isle of Skye IV55 8ZT
Tel: 01470 511258 (Glendale)

Prestige Award Winner 1992

4 miles west of Dunvegan on B884 road to Glendale. Look out for Glendale Visitor Route signs.

This is a gem of a place right down by the shore of Loch Dunvegan. It is an old crofter's cottage with beamed ceilings, interior stone walls, and open fires. It exudes atmosphere and a candlelit dinner here could not fail to be memorable. Eddie and Shirley Spear are a charming couple, and Shirley who presides in the kitchen is much acclaimed by food writers and has earned a high reputation for her cooking. Naturally she specialises in the abundance of delicious shell fish and fresh fish so readily available in the island but she is equally adept in the preparation and presentation of beef, lamb and venison dishes. The piece de resistance in the dessert menu is her special marmalade pudding and local legend has it that people go back to Skye just to have another helping! Dinner is a four course meal with a wide choice at each course. Lunch offers a large selection of dishes and there is also a daytime menu which offers coffees, teas, home-baking and light meals. There is excellent accommodation in and around the nearby village of Dunvegan and local B & B. No visit to Skye can be really complete without a meal at the Three Chimneys, Macallan/Decanter Scottish Restaurant of the Year 1990 and winner of the Talisker Quality Award for Finest Food 1993.

Open 31 Mar to 21 Oct
Daytime Menu 10.30 am – 12 noon: 2 – 4.30 pm except Sun (a)
Dining Room/Restaurant Lunch 12.30 – 2 pm except Sun (a-d)
Dinner 7 – 9 pm except Sun (e) 4 course menu
Closed Sun except Easter Sun + Whitsun
No smoking in restaurant
• *Home-baked bread. Home-made soups including fish brees and bisques. Skye seafood platter. Warm salad of scallops and monkfish with prawns and bacon. Hot lobster medley. Seafood treasure trove. Rabbit and hare terrine with walnut oil dressing. Fillet of venison with raspberry and bitter chocolate game sauce. Sirloin steak*

split and filled with peat-smoked salmon. Delicious puddings, hot and cold.
Credit cards: 1, 3 + SWITCH
Proprietors: Eddie & Shirley Spear

UIG HOTEL
Uig, Portree
Isle of Skye IV51 9YE
Tel: 01470 542 205
Fax: 01470 542 308

Entering Uig from Portree on A856, hotel is halfway down hill on right.

On its dominating site on a hillside overlooking Uig Bay and Loch Snizort, this former coaching inn is a well known and popular stopping-over point to or from the Hebridean ferries or, indeed, as a base from which to explore Skye. The tasteful decor and furnishings of the bedrooms and public rooms owe much to the personal touch and influence of Grace Graham who has owned the hotel since 1946 and now operates it with her son, David Taylor, who supervises the day to day operations. The hotel has some self-catering apartments and its own pony-trekking centre. This is a hotel where you can expect to find comfort and good standards all round.

Open 10 Apr to 10 Oct
Rooms: 17 with private facilities
Coffee Shop serves morning coffee + afternoon tea
Buffet Lunch 12 – 1.45 pm (a)
Dinner 7.15 – 8.15 pm (d) 4 course menu
Dogs by arrangement only
No smoking in restaurant
Bed & Breakfast £35 – £45
Dinner B & B £45 – £60
Special Rates available
• *Home-made fishcakes. Roast leg of Dornoch lamb with mint sauce and redcurrant jelly. Roast rib of Scottish beef. Sauté of chicken with oranges, lemons, tomatoes and cinnamon. Grilled salmon steaks with parsley butter. Home-made sweets.*
STB Commended 4 Crowns
Credit cards: 1, 2, 3, 5, 6 + SWITCH
Proprietors: Grace Graham & David Taylor

ULLINISH LODGE HOTEL
Struan
Isle of Skye IV56 8FD
Tel: 01470 572214
Off A863 between Sligachan and Dunvegan.
Ullinish Lodge is an 18th century country house beautifully set overlooking the Cuillins and the shores of Loch Bracadale. It is ideally situated for walking and climbing, and there is brown trout fishing in the three lochs, salmon fishing in two rivers and rough shooting over 27,500 acres. John and Claudia Mulford are welcoming hosts. There is a large lounge with open fire and a pleasant restaurant where the menu changes daily and features a fine selection of Scottish produce. The hotel has a fine range of malt whiskies and a good selection of Scottish wines and liqueurs. German spoken.
Open Easter to 31 Oct
Rooms: 8 with private facilities
Bar Supper 6 – 8.45 pm Mon to Sat:
6.30 – 8.45 pm Sun (a)
Dinner 7 – 8 pm (or by arrangement) (c)
No smoking area in restaurant
Bed & Breakfast £20 – £40
Dinner B & B £38 – £58
Special Rates for 3+/7+ nights
• Home-made soups. Crêpe of local seafood. Skye king prawns. Waternish princess scallops with garlic butter. Roast Scottish fillet of beef. Highland venison in a red wine casserole. Cranachan. Clootie dumpling.
STB Commended 3 Crowns
Credit cards: 1, 3 + SWITCH
Proprietors: John & Claudia Mulford

South Queensferry

THE HAWES INN
Newhalls Road, South Queensferry
West Lothian EH30 9TA
Tel: 0131 331 1990
Fax: 0131 319 1120
At east end of the village, under the Forth Rail Bridge.
This fine historical building, with its marvellous view across the Firth of Forth, dates from the 16th century. It has literary connections with Sir Walter Scott and was immortalised by Robert Louis Stevenson in 'Kidnapped'. The Hawes Inn is full of character and almost a tourist attraction in its own right. A pleasant 20 minute drive from Edinburgh city centre and only five miles from Edinburgh Airport, it has long been a popular destination restaurant for the city cognoscenti before or after a stroll along the front at South Queensferry. There are eight bedrooms, a quality restaurant, an atmospheric bar with family room attached, and an extensive beer garden.
Open all year except Christmas Day + 1 Jan
Rooms: 8
Bar Meals 12 – 10 pm (a)
Dining Room/Restaurant Lunch 12 – 2 pm except Sat (a)
Dinner 6 – 10 pm (c)
Bed & Breakfast £27.50 – £50
Dinner B & B £35 – £67
Room Rate £34 – £55
Special Rates available
• Fresh mussels poached in white wine, orange, cream, leeks and herbs. Smoked seafood crêpes. Chargrilled steaks. Vegetarian strudel. Fillet of salmon baked with leeks, cream and stem ginger. Medallions of fillet steak with a red wine, onion and pickled walnut sauce. Rack of lamb with an Arran mustard and whisky sauce. Hot spiced Lanark pears in a rich butterscotch sauce.
STB Commended 1 Crown
Credit cards: 1, 2, 3, 5

by Spean Bridge

CORRIEGOUR LODGE HOTEL
Loch Lochy, by Spean Bridge
Inverness-shire PH34 4EB
Tel: 01397 712685
Fax: 01397 712696
Follow A82, 17 miles north of Fort William; 47 miles south of Inverness – between Spean Bridge and Invergarry.
Perhaps the finest location in "The Great Glen", with outstanding views over Loch Lochy, this former hunting lodge is the ideal retreat for a well deserved break. This grand old house has been tastefully restored to provide the atmosphere of yesteryear with the comfort of today. All bedrooms have en suite facilities and are individually furnished with antiques. The Loch View Conservatory offers guests a range of high quality cuisine – all home-made, using local produce. While enjoying a meal in this relaxing setting you can watch the boats sailing Loch Lochy on their way through the Caledonian Canal. The hotel has its own pontoon/jetty. A good place from which to explore the Highlands.
Open all year
Note: Nov to Feb open Fri Sat Sun only
Rooms: 9 with private facilities
Bistro Lunch 12 – 2.30 pm (a)
Restaurant Lunch for groups (min 10) by prior arrangement
Bistro Supper 6 – 9 pm (a)
Dinner 6.30 – 8.30 pm (c) 4 course menu
No dogs
No smoking in restaurant
Bed & Breakfast £28 – £40
Dinner B & B £47 – £59
Special Rates for 3+/7+ nights
• Home-made soup and pâté. Smoked haddock roulade with scallops. Rack of Highland hill lamb with rosemary and honey. Baked Loch Lochy trout stuffed with courgettes. Braised haunch of venison in red wine. Fillet of Aberdeen Angus beef en croûte. Poached salmon steak with lemon butter. Leek and yoghurt tart with fresh tomato sauce.
STB Highly Commended 3 Crowns
Credit cards: 1, 2, 3
Proprietors: Rod & Lorna Bunney

Credit Card Code		Meal Price Range	
1.	Access/Mastercard/Eurocard	(a)	under £10
2.	American Express	(b)	£10 – £15
3.	Visa	(c)	£15 – £20
4.	Carte Bleu	(d)	£20 – £25
5.	Diners Club	(e)	£25 – £30
6.	Mastercharge	(f)	over £30

OLD PINES

Gairlochy Road, Spean Bridge
Inverness-shire PH34 4EG
Tel: 01397 712324
Fax: 01397 712433

*From Spean Bridge take A82 to
Inverness. One mile north take B8004
next to Commando Memorial 300 yards
on right.*

The spectacular Commando Memorial
at Spean Bridge is a stopping place for
most people, not only for the
excellence of the sculpture but for the
fabulous views across the Great Glen
towards Aonach Mor and Ben Nevis. If
you have got this far, you are only 300
yards from the delightful Scandinavian-
style home of Bill and Sukie Barber
which nestles in a glade of pine trees.
A really friendly informal atmosphere
prevails and guests love it. Much
thought goes into the planning of the
daily menu and a four course dinner by
candlelight in the conservatory dining
room is a highlight in most people's
day.

*Open all year except 2 wks Nov
Rooms: 8 with private facilities
Food available 8 am – 9.30 pm except
Sun (a)
Dining Room/Restaurant Lunch 12 –
2.30 pm except Sun (c) – reservations
essential
Dinner 7 – 9.30 pm except Sun (c)
4 course menu – reservations essential
for non-residents
Unlicensed – guests welcome to take
own wine
No dogs indoors
Facilities for disabled visitors
No smoking throughout
Bed & Breakfast £25 – £30
Dinner B & B £45 – £50
Special Rates for 3+ nights*
• Home-smoked fish, shellfish. Broccoli
souffle with a lemon and chive sauce.
Chanterelle and cèpe stroganoff with
fresh pasta. Haunch of venison with
pineapple juice, thyme and juniper
berries. Leg of lamb stuffed with kidney
and five fresh herbs. Brown sugar
meringue with grapes and kiwi fruit.
Spiced plum and lemon flan. Home-made
breads and preserves. Scottish
farmhouse cheeses.
*STB Highly Commended 3 Crowns
Credit cards: 1, 3
Proprietor: Sukie Barber*

Stewarton

Location 193

CHAPELTOUN HOUSE HOTEL

nr Stewarton
Ayrshire KA3 3ED
Tel: 01560 482696
Fax: 01560 485100

*From Fenwick exit on A77 (Glasgow to
Ayr road), take B778 to Stewarton then
join B769 to Irvine. Chapeltoun is
2 miles along on right hand side.*

This beautiful country house retreat in
rolling Ayrshire countryside is all the
better for being a little off the beaten
track. Its secluded position makes it all
the more desirable a venue in which to
forget the outside world for a time. Built
in 1900 it features fine plasterwork and
friezes of thistles and roses to celebrate
the marriage of a Scottish industrialist
and his English wife. The splendid
panelled and timbered interior of
Chapeltoun induces a sense of
comfortable relaxation and that is what
this place is all about. Bedrooms are
spacious and beautifully appointed, and
the public rooms are sumptuously
furnished. Food is varied, interesting and
of high standard relying largely on the
excellence of the abundant local
produce, from what is one of the richest
farming areas in the country. The
proprietors are very much in evidence
supervising well-trained staff and
attending to the comfort and
convenience of their guests.

*Open all year
Rooms: 8 with private facilities
Bar Lunch 12 – 2 pm (b)
Dining Room/Restaurant Lunch 12.30 –
2 pm (c)
Dinner 7 – 9.15 pm (d)
No smoking in restaurant
Bed & Breakfast £47.50 – £89*
• Pan-fried noisettes of lamb with baby
vegetables and wild mushrooms in a
herb tartlet set on a green peppercorn
and redcurrant sauce. Ragoût of
monkfish tails in a tomato and basil
sauce served with a timbale of caraway
braised rice. Tournedos of beef fillet with
a pâté and mushroom duxelle wrapped in
puff pastry and set on a rich Madeira
essence.
*STB Highly Commended 4 Crowns
Credit cards: 1, 2, 3
Proprietors: Colin & Graeme McKenzie*

nr Stirling

Location 194

THE TOPPS FARM

Fintry Road, Denny
Stirlingshire FK6 5JF
Tel: 01324 822471

On B818 Denny – Fintry road, off M80.
This much commended working sheep
and cashmere goat farm is splendidly
sited in central Scotland within easy
reach of Edinburgh, Glasgow and Perth.
The huge picture windows in the modern
farmhouse give superb views out
towards the Fintry and Ochil Hills. A
popular restaurant complements the
guest house facilities. Jennifer and
Alistair Steel's home-cooking is highly
praised and covers many traditional
favourites as well as really interesting
and imaginative dishes. Alistair is in
charge in the kitchen at breakfast and
the 'Farmers Breakfast' is quite
something!

*Open all year
Rooms: 8 with private facilities
Dining Room/Restaurant Lunch 12.30 –
2 pm Sun Sat only (a) – reservation
essential
Dinner 7 – 9 pm (b)
No smoking throughout
Bed & Breakfast £18 – £30
Dinner B & B £40 – £42
Special Rates available*
• Breakfast – trout, oak-smoked
haddock, local haggis etc. Spring lamb
steaks sprinkled with wild garlic and
served with minted pears. Honey
poached salmon. Pheasant breast
'recipe no 7' (roasted and served with
garlic and cream sauce). Glenmorangie
gâteau – feather-light chocolate sponge
with a hint of the 'water of life'. Grilled
spiced peaches.
*STB Commended 3 Crowns
Credit cards: 1, 3
Proprietors: Jennifer & Alistair Steel*

Stonehaven

Location 195

TOLBOOTH RESTAURANT
Old Pier, Stonehaven Harbour
Stonehaven
Tel: 01569 762287

Off A90, onto A957 to Stonehaven, 16 miles south of Aberdeen.
The Tolbooth Restaurant is on the first floor of a 16th century building – the oldest in Stonehaven – which sits right on the harbourside. Inside a permanent exhibition of Royal Scottish Academy artists adorns the white-washed stone walls and Afghan rugs enhance the beautifully polished wooden floors. From this vantage point overlooking the harbour there are some very picturesque views. The restaurant specialises in fresh fish and seafood, imaginatively presented, and with some advance notice interesting vegetarian and meat dishes will also be provided. All vegetables and herbs for the kitchen are grown organically in the locality.
Open all year
Dining Room/Restaurant Lunch 12 – 2.30 pm Sun only (b)
Dinner 6.30 – 9 pm except Mon (d)
Closed Mon
• Marinated salmon served with a mild mustard and dill sauce. Finnan haddock with cream, coriander and tomatoes in a puff pastry case. Baked loin of lamb marinated in pistou and served on a meat glaze.
Credit cards: 1, 3
Proprietor: Moya Bothwell

Stranraer

Location 196

NORTH WEST CASTLE HOTEL
Portrodie
Stranraer DG9 8EH
Tel: 01776 704413
Fax: 01776 702646

Prestige Award Winner 1989

Seafront – opposite harbour.
The North West Castle is a long established family run hotel which sits in its own walled grounds overlooking the harbour. The original building dates from 1820 when it was the home of the Arctic explorer Sir John Ross. Now a superbly managed resort hotel it has a wide range of facilities on offer – indoor swimming pool, jacuzzi, multi-gym, saunas,

sunbeds, bowls, a curling rink (October to April), table tennis, darts, pool, snooker. Bedrooms and suites are very comfortable and delightfully decorated, well equipped with colour TV, radio, trouser press, hairdryer and coffee-making facilities. On the first floor and looking out over Loch Ryan is the elegant Regency Dining Room where gentle music from the grand piano adds to the atmosphere during dinner. Interesting à la carte and table d'hôte dinner menus utilise the best of local produce and at the weekends there is a buffet lunch served.
Open all year
Rooms: 71 with private facilities
Bar Lunch 12 – 2 pm (a)
Dining Room/Restaurant Lunch 12 – 2 pm (a)
Dinner 7 – 9 pm (c)
Bed & Breakfast £38 – £64
Dinner B & B £47 – £60 (min 2 nights stay)
• Poached fillet of lemon sole filled with prawn mousse, served with a creamed white wine sauce. Pan-fried noisettes of Scotch lamb with a fresh rosemary sauce. Honey roast breast of duck with an orange and ginger sauce.
STB Highly Commended 5 Crowns
Credit cards: 1, 3
Proprietor: H C McMillan

Strathcarron

Location 197

CARRON RESTAURANT
Cam-Allt, Strathcarron
Ross-shire IV54 8YX
Tel: 01520 722488

Lochcarron to Kyle of Lochalsh road.
This attractive little purpose-built restaurant sits just off the main road in a peaceful setting overlooking Loch Carron. There are hanging baskets and tubs of flowers outside the building and inside the restaurant is furnished in pine, with little wild flower posies on each table. Pictures by local artists are featured on the walls and are available for sale. Next door is the Carron Pottery which makes the hand-thrown crockery used in the restaurant. There is a good variety of food on the all day menu appealing to all tastes, ranging from home-baking and toasted sandwiches to chargrills supplemented by daily changing specialities highlighted on the blackboard, such as local Lochcarron prawns. The restaurant is well situated

to appreciate the spectacular sunsets across the loch in the evening.
Open 3 Apr to 28 Oct
Food available 10.30 am – 9.15 pm except Sun (a-c)
Closed Sun
Facilities for disabled visitors
No smoking throughout
• Home-made soup, pâté and desserts. Sea grown smoked trout with salad. Prime Scottish beef, lamb, venison, salmon and trout cooked on the chargrill. Lochcarron whole prawns.
Credit cards : 1, 2, 3
Proprietors : Seamus & Sarah Doyle

Strathlachlan

Location 198

INVER COTTAGE RESTAURANT
Strathlachlan, by Cairndow
Argyll PA27 8BU
Tel: 0136 986 396/275

B8000, 7 miles south of Strachur – signposted.
Overlooking Castle Lachlan on the shores of Loch Fyne this cottage exudes a bistro atmosphere but a coal/log fire and low ceilings remind you that cottage is perhaps a more appropriate word. The overall effect is relaxing and Tony and Gina Wignell like to keep it this way. The food is honest and wholesome with a definite bias towards local dishes.
Open Mar to 31 Oct (7 days)
Note: during Nov + Dec open Fri Sat Sun only
Bar Lunch 12 – 2.15 pm Mon to Sat: 12.30 – 2.15 pm Sun (a)
Dining Room/Restaurant Lunch 12 – 2.15 pm Mon to Sat: 12.30 – 2.15 pm Sun (b)
Bar Supper 6 – 9.15 pm Mon to Sat: 6.30 – 9.15 pm Sun (a)
Dinner 6 – 9.15 pm Mon to Sat: 6.30 – 9.15 pm Sun (c)
• Home-made soups. Avocado with prawns. Feuilleté of mushrooms.

Suprême of salmon with saffron sauce. Chargrilled fillet steak with peppercorn sauce. Steak and stout pie. Substantial sandwiches with home-made bread (lunchtime). Sticky toffee pudding.
Credit cards: 1, 3
Proprietors: Tony & Gina Wignell

Strathyre

Location 199
CREAGAN HOUSE
Restaurant with Accommodation
Strathyre
Perthshire FK18 8ND
Tel: 01877 384638
Fax: 01877 384638

On A84, ¼ mile north of Strathyre.
At the head of Loch Lubnaig, Strathyre forms part of the Queen Elizabeth Forest Park. In this lovely country setting is Creagan House, a family owned 17th century farmhouse which has been sympathetically restored and upgraded to provide five charming bedrooms. The Baronial Hall, with its grand fireplace, provides a unique setting in which to enjoy chef/proprietor Gordon Gunn's innovative and imaginative cooking. Each evening he presents two set price dinner menus offering a choice of Scottish dishes with classical French influences, and there is a fine wine list to complement your choice. The Gunns take great pleasure in welcoming guests to their home and their caring and friendly approach contributes to the overall enjoyment of the experience at Creagan House and makes it an ideal retreat.
Open 1 Jan to 28 Jan + 4 Mar to 31 Dec
Rooms: 5, 3 with private facilities
Dining Room/Restaurant Lunch at 1 pm Sun only (b)
Lunch parties on other days by arrangement
Dinner 7.30 – 8.30 pm (c-d)
Booking essential for all meals
No smoking in dining hall + bedrooms
Bed & Breakfast £24.50 – £42.50
Dinner B & B £40 – £63.50
Special Rates for 3+ nights
• Warm lobster and scallop pâté. Smokie in a pokie. Pigeon breast with goats cheese in a local honey dressing. Turbot and monkfish in lime and saffron sauce. Venison Breadalbane. Variations of traditional puddings.
STB Highly Commended 3 Crowns
Credit cards: 1, 2, 3
Proprietors: Gordon & Cherry Gunn

Strontian

Location 200
KILCAMB LODGE HOTEL
Strontian
North Argyll PH36 4HY
Tel: 01967 2257

On A861, 13 miles from Corran Ferry (A82, 15 miles south of Fort William).
Natural lawns sloping gently down to the waters edge with the Morvern Hills rising steeply in the background and 30 acres of secluded grounds right on the shores of Loch Sunart make a very pleasing setting for this charming old country house hotel. The Blakeway family are as delightful as is the location and their natural charm and friendliness makes guests feel specially welcome. Extensive upgrading and extension to the hotel has taken place to improve the facilities. There is a cosy bar area and an elegant sitting room and comfortable bedrooms. Flowers and china and other personal touches are evident throughout. The fine cuisine in the dining room has been recognised by the award of two AA Rosettes and the interesting menus take best advantage of the area's prime produce. All in all a very desirable place to tarry and enjoy the good things of life.
Open 1 Mar to 30 Nov
Rooms: 10 with private facilities
Light Lunch 12 – 2 pm
Dinner at 7.30 pm (d)
No smoking in dining room
Bed & Breakfast from £43
Dinner B & B from £68
Room Rate from £34
• Open ravioli of wild mushrooms. Confit of Barbary duck. Celery, almond and walnut soup. Roast saddle of venison with port and juniper sauce. Baked monkfish tails with tomato and mushroom sauce. Caramelised bread and butter pudding. Home-made profiteroles with strawberries.
STB Highly Commended 3 Crowns
Credit cards: 1, 3
Proprietors: Gordon, Ann & Peter Blakeway

Swinton

Location 201
THE WHEATSHEAF HOTEL & RESTAURANT
Main Street, Swinton
Berwickshire TD11 3NB
Tel: 01890 860 257

On B6461 Kelso-Berwick-upon-Tweed, 12 miles west of Berwick or a few miles east of A697.
The Wheatsheaf is a delightful old country inn which sits on the side of the green in the little village of Swinton. It is a popular hostelry for locals and one to which people travel from quite some distance to enjoy the good food. There is a lot of old world charm in the quaint bar with its black beams, game birds that have fallen into the hands of the taxidermist, appropriate furniture and considerable ambience. The restaurant menu is extensive and the food is exceptionally good, achieving Julie and Alan Reid's objective of providing the best of fresh local produce in a welcoming but unpretentious atmosphere – and representing excellent value for money. Over the past couple of years the bedroom accommodation has been upgraded, increasing the number of rooms with private facilities.
Open all year except Christmas + Boxing Days, last 2 wks Feb + last wk Oct
Rooms: 4, 3 with private facilities
Bar Lunch 12 – 2 pm except Mon (b)
Dining Room Lunch/Restaurant Lunch 12 – 2 pm except Mon (b)
Bar Supper 6 – 9.30 pm except Sun Mon (b)
Dinner 6 – 9.30 pm except Sun Mon (c)
Closed Sun evening + Mon
Facilities for disabled visitors
No smoking area in restaurant
Bed & Breakfast £30 – £45
• Slices of smoked salmon served on a warm cream and dill sauce. Tiger prawns sautéed in lime butter with ginger and spring onions. Vegetable and pine nut strogonoff. Medallions of Scotch beef fillet in an oyster mushroom and brandy sauce. Home-made honey and ginger ice-cream in a brandy snap basket with raspberry coulis. Iced praline soufflé on a warm dark chocolate sauce.
STB Commended 3 Crowns
Credit cards: 1, 3
Proprietors: Alan & Julie Reid

Tain

Location 202

MORANGIE HOUSE HOTEL
Morangie Road, Tain
Ross-shire IV19 1PY
Tel: 01862 892281

Just off A9 Inverness-Wick, on the outskirts of Tain.
Built for a Victorian sweet manufacturer this fine old Victorian mansion is set in its own beautifully kept grounds, close by the shores of the Dornoch Firth, on the northern outskirts of the Highland town of Tain, Scotland's oldest Royal Burgh. The hotel has been extensively modernised but still maintains the character of the building with its superb collection of Victorian stained glass windows. The hotel is very popular and the visitors book bears testimony to their satisfaction. The chefs are proud of their reputation in the district and strive to maintain it in the quality and variety of well presented meals. Efficient and friendly staff also make their contribution to the success of the hotel.
Open all year
Rooms: 13 with private facilities
Bar Lunch 12 – 2.30 pm (a)
Dining Room/Restaurant Lunch 12.30 – 2 pm (a)
Bar Supper 5 – 9.30 pm (a)
Dinner 7 – 9.30 pm (c)
Dogs by arrangement
Bed & Breakfast £33 – £50
Dinner B & B £50 – £60
Special Rates available
• Mussel and onion stew. Salmon steak poached in white wine served with a lobster and prawn sauce. Slices of prime Scottish fillet steak cooked in a port wine sauce. Local seafood and steaks.
STB Commended 4 Crowns
Credit cards: 1, 2, 3, 5, 6 + SWITCH
Proprietor: John Wynne

Tarbert

Location 203

THE COLUMBA HOTEL
East Pier Road, Tarbert
Argyll PA29 6UF
Tel: 01880 820808

On East Pier Road, ½ mile to the left around the harbour.
A family run hotel in a Listed Victorian building splendidly positioned on the loch side at the entrance to Tarbert Harbour where there is always lots of interest on the waterfront. There are fine views over Loch Fyne and the hills start at the back door. There are cosy bars usually with log fires burning and there is a sauna, mini gym and solarium. Restaurant menus place much emphasis on local produce with a leaning towards traditional Scottish dishes and imaginative preparation of other specialities. As the hotel so delightfully puts it "children and other pets are especially welcome".
Open all year except Christmas Day
Rooms: 10 with private facilities
Bar Lunch 12 – 2 pm (b)
Dining Room/Restaurant Lunch 12.30 – 2 pm Sun only (a)
Bar Supper 6 – 8.30 pm (b)
Dinner 7 – 9 pm (c)
No smoking in restaurant
Bed & Breakfast £25.95 – £32.95
Dinner B & B £29.95 – £44.95
Special winter Rates available
• Seared Loch Tarbert scallops with bacon and Scottish cheese sauce. Poached breast of chicken stuffed with haggis and served with malt whisky and onion sauce. Rosettes of Islay lamb with Gigha goats cheese and blueberry sauce.
STB Commended 3 Crowns
Credit cards: 1, 3
Proprietors: Gina & Bob Chicken

Tayvallich

Location 204

TAYVALLICH INN
Tayvallich
Argyll PA31 8PR
Tel: 01546 870282

On B8025 (via B841 [Crinan] off B816 at Cairnbaan).
Set in an idyllic position, Tayvallich is one of those places that generations of families return to year after year and the inn is very much the local hostelry as well as being renowned for its high standards of food. It is very popular with locals, yachtsmen and people from all over the country who having found it return again and again. The dining room is small and charming with a spectacular outlook to Tayvallich Bay, just across the narrow road from the inn. There is a friendly bistro-style atmosphere and the menus focus largely on the abundant fresh seafood available – scallops, prawns, crab, mussels and oysters – all locally supplied, but meat eaters and vegetarians are also given consideration. Children are welcome. The Tayvallich Inn is well known for its very high standard of food quality and presentation and so can be quite a busy place, so it is advisable to book to avoid disappointment.
Open all year
Note: closed Mon Nov to Mar
Bar Lunch 12 – 2 pm (a)
Bar Supper 6 – 8.30 pm (b)
Dinner 7 – 9 pm (d)
No smoking area in dining room
• Pan-fried Sound of Jura scallops. Baked goats cheese and roasted peppers. Loch Sween mussels marinière.
Credit cards: 1, 3
Proprietors: John & Pat Grafton

Thornhill

Dumfries

Location 205

TRIGONY HOUSE HOTEL
Closeburn, Thornhill
Dumfriesshire DG3 5EZ
Tel: 01848 31211

Off A76 south of Thornhill, 13 miles north of Dumfries.
Set in tranquil woodland gardens this attractive red sandstone country mansion provides a high standard of comfort, welcome and good food. Fine period furniture, interesting ornaments, original oak panelling and warm fires enhance the character of the house which has an air of sumptuous comfort. The dining room is a lovely bright elegant room overlooking the garden. It is clear from the construction of the menu that food is taken seriously, as indeed it is. Good use is made of local produce including salmon and venison and the emphasis in on good quality ingredients cooked without excess fuss. Frank and Mary Kerr take great pride in their hotel and look after their guests extremely well. Children over 10 years welcome.
Open all year except Christmas Day
Rooms: 9 with private facilities
Bar Lunch 12.30 – 2 pm (a)
Bar Supper 6.30 – 9 pm (a)

Dinner 7 – 8.30 pm (c)
No children under 10 years
Bed & Breakfast £28.50 – £37
Dinner B & B £44.50 – £53
Special Rates available Feb to Jun
• Noisettes of lamb with a wild rowan, port and rosemary gravy. Lemon sole fillets stuffed with smoked salmon mousse poached in white wine and lemon juice. Casserole of Border venison with orange and juniper berries, topped with a pastry fleuron.
STB Highly Commended 3 Crowns
Credit cards: 1, 3
Proprietors: Frank & Mary Kerr

Thornhill
by Stirling

Location 206
LION & UNICORN
Main Street, Thornhill
by Stirling FK8 3PJ
Tel: 01786 850204
Fax: 01786 850306

On A873, 9 miles west of Stirling, between Blair Drummond Safari Park and Aberfoyle.
The Lion & Unicorn is a picturesque old coaching inn which dates back to 1635. It is family run and friendly, very much an atmospheric 'local' with low ceilings, beams, stone walls and open log fires. Informal dining is available throughout the day both in the restaurant and bar. A good range of reasonably priced dishes featuring locally sourced seasonal produce is offered, displayed on a blackboard menu. Vegetarian options are also available. There is a selection of fine wines and an imaginative choice of malt, grain and blended whiskies. Dutch, French and German spoken.
Open all year
Rooms: 4
Bar Meals 12 – 10 pm (b)
Dining Room/Restaurant Meals 12 – 10 pm (c)
No smoking in restaurant
Bed & Breakfast £18.70 – £25
• Breast of local wood pigeon in lemon

sauce. West coast mussels in oatmeal, whisky and cream sauce. Rack of Perthshire lamb in apricot and rosemary glaze. Halibut in champagne and chive sauce. Breast of duck in Thornhill raspberry sauce. Venison in green peppercorn cream. Monkfish tails in whisky and crème fraîche.
Credit cards: 1, 2, 3, 5, 6
Proprietor: Walter & Ariane MacAulay

Tillicoultry

Location 207
HARVIESTOUN COUNTRY INN
Dollar Road, Tillicoultry
Clackmannanshire FK13 6PQ
Tel: 01259 752522
Fax: 01259 752523

Just off A91 on eastern edge of Tillicoultry.
Transformations and restorations sometimes do not succeed but this one comes off brilliantly. The original character of these old farm buildings form three sides of a spacious courtyard. In the past year this establishment has undergone some further improvements. Now behind that inviting warm stone frontage lies a delightful inn offering a good standard of en suite accommodation and a choice of dining styles. On the ground floor is the recently refurbished bar brasserie which has a lively and informal atmosphere, and for a finer touch to dining and comfort there is the elegant à la carte restaurant. The food is consistently reliable with a carefully balanced menu changing to reflect the best the seasons have to offer, imaginatively presented by Andy Morrison and his team.
Open all year
Rooms 10 with private facilities
Bar Lunch 12 – 2.30 pm (a)
Dining Room/Restaurant Lunch 12 – 2.30 pm except Sat (d)
Bar Supper 5 – 9.30 pm (b)
Dinner 7 – 9.30 pm (e)
Room Rate £39.99 – £49.99
Facilities for disabled visitors
No smoking area in restaurant
• Brace of quail boned and stuffed with a duxelle of woodland mushrooms on a rich game sauce. Calves liver collops lightly fried in hazelnut oil and served with a raspberry dressing. Marinated fruit kebab on a bed of rice pudding glazed with an Advocaat sabayon.
Credit cards: 1, 3
Proprietor: John Lapsley

Isle of
Tiree

Location 208
THE GLASSARY
Sandaig, Isle of Tiree
Argyll PA77 6XQ
Tel: 01879 220684

On west coast of island.
A restaurant and guest house situated on the picturesque west coast with views of the sandy shoreline and the Atlantic Ocean. The proprietors Mabel and Donnie Macarthur genuinely welcome their guests and strive to ensure their comfort while their son Iain is chef and prepares imaginative menus. The restaurant is a pine-lined converted byre and the well appointed guest house is all on one level with residents TV lounge and tea-coffee making facilities.
Open Easter to Oct
Rooms: 3
Restaurant Lunch 12 – 2 pm (a)
Dinner 7 – 8.30 pm (b-d)
Bed & Breakfast £18 – £20
Dinner B & B £28 – £32
• Grilled sirloin steak served on a bed of haggis, coated in whisky sauce. Strips of local lamb, pan-fried and flamed in brandy, pink peppercorns and cream. Poached fillet of lemon sole stuffed with prawns, served in a mushroom and white wine sauce. Pan-fried breast of chicken, flamed in Cointreau with peaches and fresh cream. Carrageen pudding – seaweed pudding prepared to traditional island recipe. Traditional bread and butter pudding laced with Drambuie.
No credit cards
Proprietors: Mabel & Donnie Macarthur

Tomintoul

Location 209

THE GORDON HOTEL
& CROMDALES RESTAURANT

The Square, Tomintoul
Banffshire AB37 9ET
Tel: 01807 580206
Fax: 01807 580488

On A939 c. 14 miles east of Grantown-on-Spey.

Tomintoul was founded by the fourth Duke of Gordon in 1776 and is the highest village in the Highlands, surrounded by the magnificent Cairngorm and Cromdale hills. On the square of the village sits The Gordon Hotel which was extensively renovated and modernised during 1994. Behind its somewhat austere old stone exterior the comfortable and stylish surroundings create a warm and welcoming atmosphere. Bedrooms are tastefully appointed and well equipped. The quality of cuisine in Cromdales Restaurant has already gained a fine reputation for the young and enthusiastic team, recognised by the award of an AA Rosette. Menus feature the best fresh ingredients such as Aberdeen Angus beef, Scottish lamb, game from surrounding estates, fresh fish and seafood and offer a good choice of dishes. The hotel has its own beats over four miles on the Rivers Avon and Livet for salmon and trout fishing, and can arrange a host of other outdoor activities such as golf, clay pigeon and game shooting, horse riding and pony trekking, mountain biking, hill-walking, skiing etc.

Open all year
Rooms: 29 with private facilities
Bar Lunch 12 – 2.30 pm (a)
Dinner 7 – 9 pm Mon to Fri: 7.30 – 9pm Sun (e) 5 course menu
Children over 12 years welcome in Cromdales Restaurant
No dogs
No smoking in restaurant
Dinner B & B from £55
Room Rate £35 – £79.50
• *Terrine of local seafood centred by monkfish and spinach, with a saffron dressing. Brochette of scallops on a bed of stewed asparagus. Roasted breast and stuffed leg of Guinea fowl on a ragoût of woodland mushrooms, with a light game jus flavoured by Madeira. Saddle of local venison on a red onion confit, with a hawthorn jelly flavoured game jus.*
STB Highly Commended 5 Crowns
Credit cards: 1, 2, 3 + SWITCH
Proprietor: David Abdy

Tongue

Location 210

THE BEN LOYAL HOTEL

Main Street, Tongue
Sutherland IV27 4XE
Tel: 01847 611216
Fax: 01847 611212

At junction of A838 and A836, midway between John o' Groats and Cape Wrath.

Standing in a splendid location overlooking the Kyle of Tongue, the peaks of 'The Queen of Scottish Mountains' and ruined Varrich Castle, this hotel seems to have been designed with the sole intention of enabling guests to enjoy these quite stunning panoramas from the comfortably furnished lounge to the beautifully appointed bedrooms with their pine furniture, pretty fabrics and four poster bed. But perhaps the best views of all can be had from the dining room. However you will find your loyalties torn between relishing the view and savouring the food. Only fresh local produce – much of it home-grown – is used in the preparation of traditional dishes presented in a modern way.

Open 24 Feb to 31 Dec except Christmas + Boxing Days
Rooms: 18, 9 with private facilities
Bar Lunch 12 – 2 pm Mon to Sat: 12.30 – 2 pm Sun (a)
Dining Room/Restaurant Lunch – by prior arrangement only (b)
Bar Supper 6 – 8.30 pm (8 pm winter) Mon to Sat : 6.30 – 8.30 pm Sun (8 pm winter) (a)
Dinner 7 – 8 pm (c)
Facilities for disabled visitors
Bed & Breakfast £17.50 – £30
Dinner B & B £32 – £48.50
Special Rates for 3+/7+ nights
• *Warm salad of wood pigeon with a cranberry vinaigrette. Poached suprême of Eriboll salmon on an avocado sauce. Breast of honey roasted duck with an orange and port wine gravy. Courgette and sweet potato bake.*
STB Highly Commended 3 Crowns
Credit cards: 1, 3, 6
Proprietors: Mel & Pauline Cook

Torridon

Location 211

LOCH TORRIDON HOTEL

Torridon, by Achnasheen
Ross-shire IV22 2EY
Tel: 01445 791242
Fax: 01445 791296

The only hotel on the A896 (do not turn off to Torridon village).

A stately and impressive country house in a delightful parkland setting extending down to the water's edge of Loch Torridon with pine covered mountain slopes towering up behind. The house is a former shooting lodge built by the first Earl of Lovelace in 1887 and many of the Victorian characteristics have been carefully restored and feature prominently, in particular the lovely ornate ceilings and wonderful rich wood panelling in the public rooms. Bedrooms are spacious and beautifully appointed, with every modern comfort. The food attracts much praise and shows imagination in planning and presentation, earning the hotel two AA Rosettes. In 1993 the hotel was designated best new AA hotel in Scotland.

Open all year but restricted service 3 Jan to 20 Feb
Rooms: 20 with private facilities
Bar Lunch: 12.30 – 2 pm (a)
Bar Supper: 6 – 9 pm (a)
Note: Bar Meals served in Ben Damph Lodge, 100 yds from main hotel
Dinner 7.15 – 8.30 pm (e)
Facilities for disabled visitors
No smoking in restaurant
Bed & Breakfast £40 – £90
Dinner B & B £40 – £110
Special Rates for 2+ nights
• *Arbroath smokie and smoked salmon bavarois on a cucumber and yoghurt dressing. Sautéed collops of monkfish*

tail with root ginger on a white wine and vegetable sauce. Roast saddle of venison on a bed of braised red cabbage and a game jus with cape gooseberries. STB Highly Commended 4 Crowns
Credit cards: 1, 3
Proprietors: David & Geraldine Gregory

Troon

Location 212
HIGHGROVE HOUSE
Old Loans Road
Troon KA10 7HL
Tel: 01292 312511
Fax: 01292 318228
Off A759 near Loans.
If there are three key words in Bill Costley's vocabulary they must be quality, freshness and value. His acquisition and transformation of Highgrove House was an immediate success as he introduced his formula of the pick of the market's produce, beautifully prepared and presented and at remarkably modest prices. Success was well earned and the popularity and appeal of Highgrove has continued unabated. Perched high on a hilltop just outside Troon, with fine views out over the Firth of Clyde to Arran, the location could not be better for those who want to play golf at some of the world's premier courses, sail or fish, wander round the country of Rabbie Burns – or just relax and enjoy the excellent food.
Open all year
Rooms: 9 with private facilities
Bar Lunch 12 – 2.30 pm (a)
Dinner 6 – 9.30 pm (c)
Bed & Breakfast from £55
Dinner B & B from £90
• *Warm salad of langoustines and red snapper with dill butter dressing. Steamed turbot with fresh asparagus, crab and orange mousseline.*
Credit cards: 1, 2, 3 + SWITCH
Proprietors: William & Catherine Costley

LOCHGREEN HOUSE
Monktonhill Road, Southwood
Troon KA10 7EN
Tel: 01292 313343
Fax: 01292 318661
A79 from Ayr, or A77 from Glasgow to roundabout near Prestwick Airport, take road for Troon (B749). Lochgreen is ½ mile on left.
Lochgreen House in Southwood near Troon is a magnificent mansion built in 1905 surrounded by 15 acres of beautiful woodlands, gardens and private tennis court, and situated in the heart of Ayrshire's Burns Country. The original oak and cherry wood panelling has been retained, as have the leaded and stained glass windows and original marble fireplaces. There is a sumptuously comfortable atmosphere throughout. The hotel is privately owned and managed by one of Scotland's top chefs, Bill Costley, and his wife Catherine, and it naturally follows that the food is superb, beautifully prepared and presented, and outstanding value for money. It is little wonder that guests come from far and near to sample it and it is therefore always wise to book in advance. This is a hotel with every facility for a relaxing and comfortable stay.
Open all year
Rooms: 7 with private facilities
Dining Room/Restaurant Lunch 12 – 2 pm (a)
Dinner 7 – 9 pm (d)
No dogs
Facilities for disabled visitors
No smoking in restaurant
Bed & Breakfast £52.50 – £90
Dinner B & B from £67.50
• *Warm quail and wild mushroom salad with toasted pine kernels and served with a crispy bacon and garlic dressing. Marinated rack of lamb with a tomato, spinach and mozzarella tart with a roasted garlic and rosemary sauce. Salmon and sole soufflé with fresh langoustine and crayfish and brandy sauce.*
Credit cards: 1, 2, 3 + SWITCH
Proprietors: William & Catherine Costley

MARINE HIGHLAND HOTEL
Troon
Ayrshire KA10 6HE
Tel: 01292 314444
Fax: 01292 316922
South end of Troon overlooking golf course and sea.
This magnificent four star hotel overlooks the 18th fairway of Royal Troon Championship Golf Course with breathtaking views across the Firth of Clyde to the Isle of Arran. An atmosphere of quiet elegance exists throughout the hotel combined with a standard of service and hospitality second to none. There are excellent leisure facilities within the Marine Leisure and Sports Club. A very special hotel which has admirably blended style and tradition with outstanding facilities, and where the quality of the food matches in every way the overall excellence of the hotel. For elegant dining there is the Fairways Restaurant with its daily and à la carte menus which feature a vast array of local and Scottish produce, or Crosbies Brasserie which offers a more informal style of dining with a varied selection of popular dishes.
Open all year
Rooms: 72 with private facilities
Crosbie's Brasserie open all day for meals and snacks
Bar Lunch 12 – 2.30 pm Mon to Sat: 12 – 5.30 pm Sun (a)
Dining Room/Restaurant Lunch 12.30 – 2 pm Mon to Sat: Buffet Sun 12.30 – 2.30 pm (b)
Afternoon Tea (Arran Lounge) 3 – 5 pm
Bar Supper 5.30 – 10 pm (b)
Dinner 7 – 10 pm (d) 4 course menu
Bed & Breakfast £88 – £105
Dinner B & B £55 – £80 (min 2 nights stay)
Special Rates & Breaks available throughout year
• *Fairways: crayfish soup laced with cream and brandy. Pan-fried scallops on a bed of shredded snow peas and smoked bacon. Roasted loin of marinaded lamb with a port wine and redcurrant essence. Escalope of Highland venison in a juniper berry sauce. Crosbie's Brasserie: grilled delice of Scotch salmon. Fresh mussels marinière. Prime Scotch sirloin steaks. STB Highly Commended 5 Crowns*
Credit cards: 1, 2, 3, 5, 6 + SWITCH, DELTA

Credit Card Code		Meal Price Range	
1.	Access/Mastercard/Eurocard	(a)	under £10
2.	American Express	(b)	£10 – £15
3.	Visa	(c)	£15 – £20
4.	Carte Bleu	(d)	£20 – £25
5.	Diners Club	(e)	£25 – £30
6.	Mastercharge	(f)	over £30

PIERSLAND HOUSE HOTEL
Craigend Road, Troon
Ayrshire KA10 6HD
Tel: 01292 314747
Fax: 01292 315613

South corner of Troon.
A very impressive Tudor style building built at the end of last century for Sir Alexander Walker grandson of Johnnie Walker founder of the famous Scotch whisky firm. It is located in four acres of garden including a Japanese garden and croquet lawns. Panelled walls and splendid beams distinguish the minstrel hall and reception area as do wood carvings, fireplaces and tapestry friezes. During 1994 four new cottage suites were added, each with its own lounge and twin bedroom with an array of modern facilities. The hotel is proud of its reputation for fine cuisine and the impressive restaurant menus show a well balanced selection of interesting dishes.
Open all year
Rooms: 23 with private facilities
Bar Lunch 12 – 2.30 pm (a)
Dining Room/Restaurant Lunch 12 – 2.30 pm (b)
Bar Supper 6 – 10 pm (a)
Dinner 7 – 9.30 pm (c)
Bed & Breakfast £47 – £60
Dinner B & B £64.50 – £76.95
Special Rates for 2+ nights Oct to Apr
• Beef and venison terrine with a redcurrant preserve. Sirloin steak topped with duxelle and asparagus on a Drambuie sauce. Poached fillet of salmon in a lemon and herb cream sauce. Roast saddle of lamb on a garlic croûton set on a sherry and pimento sauce.
STB Highly Commended 4 Crowns
Credit cards: 1, 2, 3, 5, 6 + SWITCH
Proprietor: J A Brown

Turnberry

Location 213
MALIN COURT HOTEL
Turnberry, Girvan
Ayrshire KA26 9PB
Tel: 01655 331457/8
Fax: 01655 331072

On A719 Ayr-Girvan, south of Maidens.
Malin Court is situated on the beautiful Ayrshire coast overlooking Turnberry's famous golf courses, Ailsa Craig, the Isle of Arran and Maidens Bay. It makes an ideal location for exploring the history and heritage of Burns Country and visiting the south west of Scotland. This modern hotel offers high standards of accommodation in its tastefully furnished and well appointed guest rooms. The Carrick Restaurant offers an interesting range of modern Scottish dishes, showing good combinations of ingredients presented with style. There are wonderful panoramic views from the restaurant and often during dinner guests can enjoy some spectacular sunsets over Arran.
Open all year
Rooms: 17 with private facilities
Dining Room/Restaurant Lunch 12.30 – 2 pm (b)
Supper/High Tea 5.30 – 6.45 pm (a)
Dinner 7.30 – 9 pm (c)
Bed & Breakfast £49.50 – £79.50
Dinner B & B £59.50 – £89.50
Special Rates for 7 nights
• Roulade of pork and venison wrapped in bacon, served on a tarragon and apple jus. Lamb cutlets coated in an Arran mustard and garlic crust on a pool of tomato coulis. Baked salmon fillets with a bed of cockles and samphire grass tossed in fresh chillies.
STB Highly Commended 4 Crowns
Credit cards: 1, 2, 3, 5, 6 + SWITCH

TURNBERRY HOTEL, GOLF COURSES & SPA
Turnberry
Ayrshire KA26 9LT
Tel: 01655 31000 • Telex: 777779
Fax: 01655 31706

Prestige Award Winner 1990

A77 – 17 miles south of Ayr.
Turnberry as one of Scotland's most exclusive hotels surpasses most superlatives with its world-renowned service and facilities. It is constantly winning awards and exemplifies the best of British hotel keeping in every department. A unique elevated situation overlooking the famous Turnberry golf courses ensures that it starts off on a pedestal. This is a hotel where elegance and gracious service are obvious throughout and especially so in the superb restaurants renowned for their food and where a meal looking out over Ailsa Craig and Arran becomes a memorable occasion. The magnificent spa is itself a winner of awards and the golf clubhouse incorporates a special restaurant offering a range of dishes for informal light dining, just right for hungry golfers. This is a superbly well managed hotel of the highest international standards offering the ultimate in comfort and cuisine. Accolades include RAC Five Star Hotel of the Year 1990, Caterer & Hotelkeeper's Hotel of the Year 1993, as well as five AA Red Stars and RAC Five Star Blue Ribbon Hotel 1994.
Open all year
Rooms: 132 with private facilities
Bar Meals (Clubhouse Restaurant) 11 am – 7 pm (a)
Lunch (Bay at Turnberry Restaurant) 12 – 2.30 pm (c)
Lunch (Hotel Restaurant) 1 – 2.30 pm Sun only (c)
Dinner (Hotel Restaurant) 7.30 – 10 pm (f)
Bed & Breakfast £77.50 – £210
Dinner B & B £115 – £249
• Grilled Atlantic sea bass served on a leek fondue with a saffron essence. Suprême of turbot poached in champagne, served in a sauce of crayfish, mussels and colloped mushrooms. Medallions of Galloway beef flared with Madeira, roast shallots, cèpes and chanterelles. Fillet of Ayrshire lamb oven-roasted with potatoes, onions and served with a rosemary sauce.
STB Deluxe 5 Crowns
Credit cards: 1, 2, 3, 5, 6 + SWITCH

Tyndrum

Location 214

THE CLIFTON COFFEE HOUSE & CRAFT CENTRE
Tyndrum
Perthshire FK20 8RY
Tel: 01838 400271
Fax: 01838 400330

On A85 just east of junction with A82.
What started off as a relatively simple self-service restaurant has, over the years, developed to a point where it has almost become a tourist attraction in its own right. A shopping complex selling crafts, books, woollens, gifts and food is augmented next door by the 'green welly' shop specialising in clothing for climbing, hill-walking and outdoor sports. But central to the whole is the popular self-service restaurant which offers a consistently good standard of home baking and home cooking of traditional Scottish meals and snacks with a seemingly endless choice. There are few travelling to, or from, Glencoe who will not stop off at the Clifton for a quick meal or snack.
Open 4 Mar to 4 Jan except Christmas + Boxing Days, 1 Jan
Meals + Snacks served all day 8.30 am – 5.30 pm (a-b)
No smoking area in restaurant
No dogs except guide dogs
• Fresh produce used to advantage, to produce a range of good food at affordable prices.
Credit cards: 1, 2, 3, 5, 6 + SWITCH, DELTA
Proprietors: L P Gosden,
D D, L V & I L Wilkie

Ullapool

Location 215

MOREFIELD MOTEL & MARINERS RESTAURANT
North Road, Ullapool
Ross-shire IV26 2TS
Tel: 01854 612161
Fax: 01854 612870

After c. 1 mile leaving village on North Road (A835), turn left immediately over the river bridge.
Ullapool lies on the shores of Loch Broom and is surrounded by some of the most beautiful scenery in Scotland. When the present owners of the Morefield took over in 1980, the property literally stood in the middle of a field in splendid isolation. However in the years since then Ullapool has been growing rapidly and now what was once a quaint little village pub with rooms has been engulfed by the encroaching dwelling houses. The Morefield has been described as an oasis in the middle of a sea of houses. The present partnership of David Smyrl and David Marsh set about to ensure that they would gain a good reputation as hoteliers and restaurateurs so people would seek them out even if the motel was no longer visible from the North Road! From the activity and bustling atmosphere in the busy lounge bar, they have obviously succeeded. The Mariners Restaurant is a split level room, with candles on the polished tables, and a very different picture from the bustle of the lounge bar. It has an atmosphere of intimate seclusion and the service is attentive but unhurried. The menus specialise in fresh fish and shellfish, but the meat-eater is not forgotten. Although the main focus of activity at the Morefield is the food, there is also good value for money basic motel accommodation.
Open all year except 25 to 27 Dec, 1 + 2 Jan
Rooms: 11 with private facilities
Bar Lunch 12 – 2 pm (a)
Bar Supper 5.30 – 9.30 pm (a)
Dinner (Mariners) 6 – 9.30 pm (c) – booking advisable
Facilities for disabled visitors
Bed & Breakfast £20 – £25
• Local mussels cooked with a garlic and wine cream sauce. Halibut cooked with a fish stock and finished with a citrus sauce. Salmon topped with prawns in a seafood sauce. Scallops cooked with leeks and shallots in a Pernod flavoured sauce. Lochinver sole brushed with herb butter and grilled. Sirloin steak topped with scallops and prawns in a garlic butter sauce.
STB Commended 3 Crowns
Credit cards: 1, 2, 3, 6 + SWITCH
Proprietors: David Smyrl & David Marsh

Uphall

Location 216

HOUSTOUN HOUSE HOTEL & RESTAURANT
Uphall
West Lothian EH52 6JS
Tel: 01506 853831
Fax: 01506 854220

Just off A89 Edinburgh-Bathgate at Uphall.
The core of this hotel is the early 16th century Tower House, of which the vaulted bar with its great open fireplace is the most striking reminder. Some of the traditionally furnished bedrooms in this part of the hotel have four poster beds. On the first floor are three adjacent dining rooms in what were the old drawing room, library and great hall. This arrangement not only provides flexibility but also creates an atmosphere of quietness and intimacy. Over the years the building has been adapted and extended to provide the comfortable hotel accommodation which is a feature today. There are 26 acres of grounds, and herbs and vegetables for the kitchen are grown in the garden. The well balanced menus change daily and food is both interesting and well presented. There is an extensive and carefully chosen wine list – and a fine range of malt whiskies.
Open all year
Rooms: 30 with private facilities
Bar Lunch 12 – 2 pm except Sun (b)
Dining Room/Restaurant Lunch 12.30 – 2 pm except Sat (c)
Dinner 7.30 – 9.30 pm (e) 4 course menu
No smoking dining room available
Bed & Breakfast £25 – £123
Dinner B & B £55 – £135.50
• Steamed escalopine of wild Scottish salmon on a cushion of creamed avocado, lined with a saffron cream. Roast saddle of tender lamb centred with a mixed herb and onion farce, coated with a pink peppercorn sauce. Grilled sirloin steak with roast mushrooms, masked with a garlic and chervil cream. Chocolate pyramid filled with milk chocolate mousse, with a tulip basket of praline parfait.
STB Commended 5 Crowns
Credit cards: 1, 2, 3, 5

Walkerburn

Location 217

TWEED VALLEY HOTEL
& RESTAURANT
Walkerburn
nr Peebles EH43 6AA
Tel: 01896 870636
Fax: 01896 870639

A72 at Walkerburn – 8 miles east of
Peebles and 10 miles west of
Galashiels. 32 miles south of Edinburgh.
The Tweed Valley Hotel sits in a slightly
elevated position with pleasing views
towards the hills and the River Tweed.
There is a lot of character in this
Edwardian building with its oak panelling
carvings and an ornate dining room
ceiling. It was built in 1906 by Henry
Ballantyne as a wedding present for his
son and has its own walled garden in
which are grown fresh herbs used in the
hotel kitchen. The hotel also has its own
smoker from which it produces some of
the succulent home-smoked items which
feature on the menus. A convenient base
for fishing, bird-watching, golf or other
outdoor pursuits and a comfortable place
to return to in the evening and enjoy a
leisurely dinner.
*Open all year except Christmas +
Boxing Days*
Rooms: 15 with private facilities
Snacks + Light Meals available all day
Bar Lunch 12 – 2 pm (a)
*Dining Room/Restaurant Lunch 12 –
2 pm (a-b)*
Bar Supper 6.30 – 9.30 pm (a)
Dinner 7 – 9.30 pm (c-d)
No smoking in restaurant
Bed & Breakfast £40 – £52
Dinner B & B £48.50 – £71
*• Home-smoked salmon with lemon juice
and poppy seeds. Roast Border beef with
Yorkshire pudding and gravy. Roast duck
with citrus sauce. Guinea fowl with
hawthorn sauce. Sautéed seafoods in
white wine and herb sauce served with
rice. Chargrilled steaks.*
STB Commended 4 Crowns
Credit cards: 1, 3 + SWITCH
Proprietors: Charles & Keith Miller

Whitebridge

Location 218

KNOCKIE LODGE
Whitebridge
Inverness-shire IV1 2UP
Tel: 01456 486276
Fax: 01456 486389

Prestige Award Winner 1990

On B862, 8 miles north of Fort
Augustus. 26 miles south of Inverness.
Originally built as a shooting lodge for
the Lovat family, Knockie Lodge is now
an outstanding country house hotel
which nestles in an idyllic setting
surrounded by trees and lochs. For
those who like to get away from it all
and enjoy real country house living there
are few equals to this the delightful
home of Ian and Brenda Milward.
Everything about it spells gracious living
at its best – comfortable beautifully
appointed bedrooms, elegant public
rooms, a reading/writing room and a
billiard room. Dinner is of an
exceptionally high standard, served in
the elegant dining room at polished
wood tables beautifully set out with

crystal and silver. The chef has been in
charge of the kitchen for more than eight
years and knows how to get the best out
of the prime raw materials available to
him and to present them with skill and
style. In all respects Knockie Lodge is a
very special experience.
Open 30 Apr to 22 Oct
Rooms: 10 with private facilities
*Bar Lunch 12.30 – 1.45 pm (a) for
residents only*
Dinner at 8 pm (e) 5 course set menu
*Note: dinner for non-residents by prior
arrangement only*
Restricted Licence
No smoking in dining room
Bed & Breakfast £47.50 – £70
*• Chicken and duck terrine served with
crisp warm rolls. Parsnip and fennel
soup. Scottish sirloin beef fillet wrapped
in bacon and herbs and served with a
red wine based sauce. Filo parcels of
salmon fillet with a sole mousseline and
cucumber and wine butter sauces. Bread
and butter pudding with apricot sauce.
Praline cream filled pancakes with
butterscotch sauce.*
STB Deluxe 3 Crowns
Credit cards: 1, 2, 3, 5, 6
Proprietors: Ian & Brenda Milward

Credit Card Code Range		Meal Price	
1.	Access/Mastercard/Eurocard	(a)	under £10
2.	American Express	(b)	£10 – £15
3.	Visa	(c)	£15 – £20
4.	Carte Bleu	(d)	£20 – £25
5.	Diners Club	(e)	£25 – £30
6.	Mastercharge	(f)	over £30

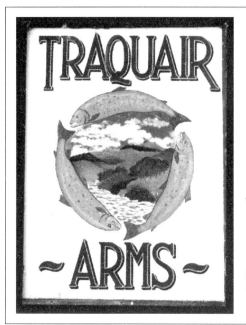

TRAQUAIR ARMS HOTEL

A traditional 19th Century Scottish Inn, just 30 minutes from Edinburgh and 10 from Peebles personally run by Hugh and Marian Anderson.

The very best of Scottish produce is used to prepare a wide range of meals served every day, from award winning Breakfasts to imaginative Dinners including Scottish High Teas with all home baked produce.

Borders Real Ales on hand-pumps in our relaxing Lounge complete with open log fires. Offering good value breaks in excellent en-suite accommodation all year round.

INNERLEITHEN, PEEBLESSHIRE EH44 6PD
TEL 01896-830229 • FAX 01896-830260

EGON RONAY "GOOD PUB GUIDE" • CAMRA "GOOD BEER GUIDE"
"BEER, BED & BREAKFAST" GUIDE

STB Commended

see entry page 117

Suppliers of fine wines

Are you interested in wine?
Join the *Waverley Wine Club*
and enjoy quality wines at
affordable prices!
Membership is free.

Waverley Wine Club

Fine wines direct to the public.

For full details and introductory offer, contact:-

Elaine Willis
Waverley Wine Club
Waverley Vintners
Crieff Road
Perth
PH1 2SL

Tel: 01738 629621 Ext 223

SCOTLAND'S COMMENDED
A selection of distinctive Country & Town House Hotels

Scotland's Commended is an Association of Country and Town House Hotels of distinction throughout Scotland, all of which are individually owned and managed. Each must attain high standards of ambience, environment and quality of food and service, set not only by the Association but also by The Scottish Tourist Board's Grading and Classification Scheme. The Hotels listed below have been awarded membership of the Taste of Scotland scheme. For telephone and fax numbers and to find out more about Scotland's Commended Members of the Taste of Scotland scheme refer to the page numbers shown.

To obtain a copy of the Scotland's Commended brochure or to gain free assistance with your itinerary, please telephone 0141 221 2300 or fax 0141 221 5443

RECIPE SECTION

Crusted Spring Lamb
set on a Potato Gâteau with Early Vegetables and a Clear Scented Stock

1994 Taste of Scotland Scotch Lamb Challenge Category 1: Second Place
Roddy Stewart, Sous Chef
Thainstone House Hotel (Simpsons Restaurant), Inverurie

Ingredients

1 lb loin of Scotch lamb
1 dessertspoon Arran mustard

Crust
1 dessertspoon basil, tarragon and parsley
1 clove garlic
2 oz white breadcrumbs
1 dessertspoon cracked buckwheat
1 tablespoon pine nuts
2 teaspoons olive oil
1 oz shallots

Sauce
18 fl oz clear chicken stock
2 yellow peppers
3 cloves garlic
2 oz onions
2 sprigs basil and tarragon
2 fl oz white wine
2 oz butter

Vegetables
6 red and yellow pear tomatoes
12 asparagus spears
12 broad beans
12 carrot flowers
12 button onions
12 chanterelles

Potato Cake
1 lb potatoes
1 egg yolk
seasoning
pinch of nutmeg
2 fl oz olive oil

(Serves four)

Method

Lamb
1. Bone out loin of lamb, remove all fat and sinews. Cut into 4 equal portions – seal in olive oil until golden brown – allow to cool.

Crust
2. Finely chop basil, parsley, tarragon and shallots. Place in food processor with pine nuts, cracked buckwheat, white breadcrumbs, garlic and olive oil and blend for 3 minutes. Spread Arran mustard on top of each portion, sprinkle with herb crust and press firmly into mustard.

Sauce
3. Brown lamb bones in oven. Place in clean pan with chicken stock, simmer for one hour. Pass into clean pan, reduce by half.

Purée yellow peppers, shallots and garlic in food processor with a little water. Blend for 3 minutes. Add to above stock with basil, white wine and tarragon. Simmer for 15 minutes then pass through chinois. Return to stove and bring to boil, reduce to correct consistency.

Vegetable Preparation
4. Blanch red and yellow pear tomatoes then cut in half. Clean, trim and blanch asparagus tips – refresh. Shell broad beans. Shape and cut carrot flowers. Trim chanterelles. Cook button onions.

Potato Gâteau
5. Cut potatoes into julienne, blanch, drain through fine strainer then cool slightly.

Add egg yolk, seasoning and nutmeg. Cook in 4 lightly greased rings until crisp and golden brown on both sides.

Final Preparation
6. Roast lamb in hot oven GM5\195°C\385°F for approximately 7 minutes until lamb is pink. Glaze crust under the grill until crisp. Heat all vegetables in a little water and butter – check seasoning. Place potato gâteau in centre of plate, cut lamb in two, place on top of gâteau. Finish each plate with vegetable garnish scattered all over. Bring sauce to first boil, finish with hard butter, pour sauce around and sprinkle with a few drops of olive oil.

Roast Scotch Lamb Loin

with Garlic Confit, Spinach, Wild Mushrooms and Hasselback Potatoes

1994 Taste of Scotland Scotch Lamb Challenge Category 1: Third Place

John Rutter, Sous Chef
Atrium Restaurant, Edinburgh

Ingredients

2 boned racks of lamb
(marinated in confit oil)
4 bulbs of garlic
¼ pint olive oil
4 oz breadcrumbs
8 oz wild mushrooms
6 oz spinach
3 baking potatoes
2 garlic cloves
4 small shallots
2 sticks celery
2 oz basil

olive oil (from confit)
1 onion
1 carrot
¼ bottle of red wine
1 pint stock
1 sprig tarragon
2 oz parsley
pinch of dry mushrooms
salt and pepper

(Serves four)

Method

1. Peel garlics and cover with olive oil. Cover pan with tin foil and cook at GM1½\150°C\300°F for one hour.

2. Bone racks of lamb. Cut excess sinew and fat.

3. When confit is cooked, cool, then pour oil over lamb. (Marinate for 10 days).

4. Slice potatoes ½ inch thick. Add salt, pepper and nutmeg. Dice garlic finely and add olive oil.

5. Stack potatoes and bake at GM6\200°C\400°F for 45 minutes.

6. Prepare mushrooms, slice quite thick.

7. Rinse spinach and allow to drain. Mix with diced shallots, torn basil and season.

8. Purée garlic confit in processor.

9. Sweat lamb trimmings. Add celery and shallots. When brown add red wine and reduce. Add stock and simmer for 30 minutes.

10. Seal lamb, grill for 10 minutes. Allow to rest. Coat with garlic confit then breadcrumbs. Grill till brown.

11. Toss mushrooms in hot pan and season. Add parsley. Push into pastry ring to give height.

12. Dress spinach, place on top of mushrooms.

13. Put hassleback potatoes opposite mushrooms and spinach.

14. Cut end off lamb loin. Cut loin in half, put on top of potatoes.

15. Pass jus, correct seasoning. Add parsley and tarragon and pour on plate.

Roast Rack of Perthshire Lamb

flavoured with Rosemary and garnished with West Coast Langoustines, set on a Garden Chive Butter Sauce

1994 Taste of Scotland Scotch Lamb Challenge Category 2: Second Place

John Rae, Head Chef
Piersland House Hotel, Troon

Ingredients

4 lb best end lamb
2 sprigs fresh rosemary or ½ oz dried
1 lb langoustines
1 lb butter
½ oz fresh chives
1 onion
8 oz carrots
8 oz courgettes
2 lb potatoes
3 lb turnip
2 oz oil
2 glasses white wine

(Serves four)

Method

1. Pre-heat sauté pan.

2. Trim best ends, spike with rosemary and season.

3. Seal and brown off meat. Cook in oil until pink.

4. Reduce stock made from bone, pass and season.

5. Prepare langoustines, chop chives.

6. Prepare vegetables and potatoes.

7. Reduce white wine stock by half, add chives, add butter.

8. Quickly fry off langoustines in butter.

9. Carve lamb.

10. Present on main course plate with langoustines and chive butter sauce. Accompanied by vegetables and potatoes.

Casserole of Scotch Lamb
with Leeks, Roast Shallots and Pesto Potatoes

1994 Taste of Scotland Scotch Lamb Challenge Category 1: Second Place
Martin Howard Russell, Head Chef
Borthwick Castle Hotel, North Middleton, near Edinburgh

Ingredients

2 lb cubed lamb
2 onions
4 oz flour
6 oz tomato paste
3 oz black olives
6 fl oz olive oil
sprig thyme
sprig rosemary

4 teaspoons red pesto
4 teaspoons pesto
4 leeks
8 shallots
4 baking potatoes
4 oz caster sugar
salt and pepper to taste

(Serves four)

Method

1. Cut the meat from the leg of lamb into even sized cubes (about 1 inch square), taking care to remove all excess fat and gristle. Season well.

2. Heat the oil in a thick based pan and seal the meat. Place lid on pan and cook for about 5 minutes until the meat has "sweated" out some of its natural juices. Place the meat and juices into a strainer, collect the juices and save for later use.

3. Heat the rest of the olive oil in the cleaned pan. Slice and cook the onions in the oil until brown; re-fry the lamb until brown, add the tomato paste, herbs and flour. Stir well to completely combine the ingredients into roux.

4. "Boil" the roux and slowly add the lamb juices, mixing well all the time, to avoid forming of lumps. Add the olives. Cook the lamb over a slow heat, stirring occasionally, so as not to burn the sauce.

5. Peel and wash the potatoes, cut into large pieces and cook in salted water. When tender, strain off the water, mash the potatoes into a smooth purée. Check the seasoning and add the pesto. Mix well and store in a warm place.

6. Peel the shallots, fry in oil and sprinkle with caster sugar; place in the oven to cook at GM6\205°C\400°F for 15 minutes. Wash and cut the leeks into large chunks, blanch in boiling salted water. Strain.

7. To serve, place a quenelle of pesto potatoes at the top of the plate; arrange the leeks to one side, top with caramelised shallots; spoon the lamb casserole onto the plates and serve.

Warm Lobster and Scallop Pâté
served with a Champagne Sauce

Gordon A Gunn, Chef/Proprietor
Creagan House, Strathyre

Ingredients

12 oz scallops
1 egg
3 oz double cream
12 oz (lightly) cooked lobster
8 oz crab meat

Sauce

5 fl oz stock (made from lobster shells)
5 fl oz champagne
2 oz chopped shallots
1 clove chopped garlic
5 fl oz double cream
1 tablespoon chopped parsley

(Serves eight)

Method

1. Purée raw scallops in a blender with a pinch of salt. Add egg, then cream.

2. Transfer to a bowl, add lobster and crab.

3. Line terrine with cling film. Cook in a bain marie at GM½\120°C\250°F for about 1-1½ hours then cool.

For the Sauce

4. Reduce champagne, shallots, stock and garlic to 3 fl oz. Add cream – thicken – add parsley.

5. Turn out pâté. Slice in thickish slices, sauté in clarified butter.

6. Place on warm plate, pour sauce round and garnish with a whole langoustine.

Haggis Filo Pastry Parcel
laced with Cream and Malt on a Purée of Turnip

Tony Kersley, Executive Chef
Invercreran Country House Hotel, Appin

Ingredients

1 lb bung of good quality haggis
1 pack of filo pastry
1 nip of malt whisky
¼ pint double cream
1 medium size turnip
coriander for garnish

(Serves four)

Method

1. Unfold filo pastry. Use one sheet per portion. Fold the sheet until it ends up being a quarter of its original size. Brush on a little olive oil.

2. Divide your haggis into 4 and place portions into centre of each pastry.

3. Lace the haggis with the malt and cream.

4. Fold each corner of the pastry into the centre enclosing the filling.

5. Place into a medium hot oven GM4\180°C\350°F for 25-30 minutes until golden brown.

6. Cook and purée the turnip with a little butter and seasoning.

7. Place or pipe the purée of turnip onto the plate and arrange the filo pastry neatly with it. Garnish with a sprig of coriander.

Princess Scallops with Saffron

Christopher Trotter, Chef
The Grange Inn, St Andrews

Ingredients

40 princess scallops
sprig parsley
sprig thyme
bay leaf
8 peppercorns
5 fl oz dry white wine
5 fl oz fish stock
packet of saffron
2½ fl oz double cream
lots of chopped parsley
seasoning

(Serves eight)

Method

1. Wash the scallops in water and discard any open or broken ones.

2. Put the herbs and peppercorns in a pan which has a lid and add the wine and scallops.

3. Steam until they open.

4. Remove scallops and keep warm, but do not allow to dry out.

5. Add the fish stock to the pan and bring to a rapid boil. Reduce the liquid by half. Add the cream and reduce to a thin cream. Add the saffron, season.

6. Put the scallops into 4 warm soup plates. Sprinkle with parsley and strain the sauce over. Serve with lots of crusty bread.

Carsgore Finnan Pancake

Smoked Orkney Cheese and Finnan Haddock blended together and presented on a Rough, Brown Pancake, Garnished with Lemon Dill

The Muirs Inn, Kinross

Ingredients

8-10 oz Finnan haddock fillet
4 oz smoked Orkney cheese
8 oz rough brown flour
5 size 6 eggs
1 pint semi-skimmed milk
2 oz unsalted butter
4 oz cracked wheat
8 sprigs lemon dill
salt and pepper

(Serves four)

Method

Pancake

1. Using two of the size 6 eggs, crack into a large mixing bowl. Add ½ pint milk, beat together then add brown flour until a stiff consistency is achieved. Fold in half of the cracked wheat and season to taste. Divide mixture into 4 equal measures and proceed to cook 4 individual pancakes in the normal fashion.

Finnan Soufflé

2. Using the other ½ pint of milk poach the haddock fillets until cooked. Allow to cool and flake the fish. Add to the cooking liquor grated cheese, 3 beaten eggs and allow to cook slowly folding all the time. Add the flaked fish until a light mousse is formed. Season to taste.

Presentation

3. Pre-heat 4 plates. Place a pancake on each, spoon a little of the soufflé at the side. Grill slightly to colour and decorate with dill.

Steamed Escalopes of Salmon
with Elderflower Wine

Colin Drummond, Head Chef
Channings

Ingredients

4 x 5 oz escalopes of salmon – cut on the slant from a salmon fillet
1 pint chicken stock
2 oz unsalted butter
1 wine glass full of elderflower wine – or commercial elderflower presse will work just as well
1 oz finely diced celery

For garnish

sprigs of elderflower or flat leaf parsley

(Serves four)

Method

1. Butter the pan and sprinkle with the diced celery.

2. Lay in the escalopes and season with plenty of black pepper.

3. Gently add the elderflower wine and chicken stock (a good clear chicken stock is essential).

4. The liquor should barely quarter cover the fish. Reserve any excess stock.

5. Place a round of buttered greaseproof paper over the fish and place in a medium to hot oven GM5-6\195°C\385°F for 7-10 minutes or until the salmon is firm to the touch.

6. Remove the escalopes directly onto serving plates.

7. The cooking liquor should now be of a syrupy consistency.

8. A further ladleful of the reserved chicken stock should be added, then altogether brought to the boil.

9. Whisk the butter to form the consistency of a thin sauce, and pour over the fish.

10. Serve immediately, garnished with sprigs of elderflower or flat leaf parsley.

11. Serve with new potatoes.

Borthaugh Vegetable Layer Bake

Doreen L Maybury
Whitchester Christian Guest House & Retreat Centre, Borthaugh, nr Hawick

Ingredients

3 medium sized parsnips
3 medium leeks
2 medium onions
4 oz pinhead oatmeal

(Serves four)

Method

1. Peel and cut parsnips into small pieces and boil or pressure cook until tender and mash. Retain the stock to moisten the mixture if needed.

2. Trim off the tough green ends of the leeks but leave 4-5 inches of the darker leaves.

3. Split down their length and clean carefully to ensure there is no soil left around which gives an unpleasant gritty result.

4. Slice into ¼ inch rings and sauté in a little butter until tender.

5. Mix with the mashed parsnip and season.

6. Skin, slice and sweat onions in a saucepan with a little oil until transparent.

7. Add oatmeal and add more oil and fry until the oatmeal is slightly browned.

8. Starting with the parsnip and leek mixture layer the two mixtures into your dishes. If additional flavour is desired a layer of grated cheddar can be inserted but not too much or it will spoil the other flavours. Finish with the oatmeal layer. If you prefer you can finish with a cheese or potato on top but do try it first without. Bake at GM5\195°C\375°F for 20 minutes or until top is crisp and well coloured but not burnt.

This bake uses traditional Scottish vegetables to create a moist dish full of flavour and reminiscent of white or mealy pudding.

Aberdeen Angus Fillet of Beef
with Braised Oxtail, Pomme Purée and Red Wine

David R Bates, Head Chef
Sunlaws House Hotel, Heiton, Kelso

Ingredients

1 lb oxtail
salt and pepper
2 oz butter
2 oz diced shallots
1 oz diced carrots
1 oz diced celery

1 oz mushrooms
1½ pints red wine
¾ pint meat stock
1 bouquet garni
4 X 6 oz Angus beef fillets
1 lb mashed potatoes

(Serves four)

Method

1. Pre-heat the oven to GM4/180°C/350°F.

2. Trim the oxtails of fat and sinew, cut into pieces, season and brown in half the butter on top of the stove.

3. Add the shallots, carrots, celery, mushrooms and red wine, boil and reduce the volume by half.

4. Add the meat stock and bouquet garni, bring back to the boil, skim off the scum that rises to the top, then braise in the oven for 2 hours.

5. Remove the oxtail and flake the meat, skim the stock, pass through and sieve.

6. Fry the beef fillets in the remaining butter for 3 minutes on each side, set aside on a wire rack for several minutes.

7. To serve, place the mashed potatoes in the centre of 4 warm plates, place the beef fillets on top. Carefully place the flaked oxtail on top (this can be done in a biscuit cutter for a neat shape). Spoon the seasoned sauce around the mashed potatoes.

Salmon and Filo Parcel

Colin Potter, Head Chef
The Lang Bar & Restaurant, Perth

Ingredients

6 X 3-4 oz escalopes of salmon
1 pink grapefruit
2 limes
3 oz prawns
1 oz parsley
2 lemons
12 sheets filo pastry
2 oz melted butter

(Serves six)

Method

1. Fillet and zest the lemons and limes. Fillet the grapefruit.

2. For each portion, lay out one sheet of filo pastry, grease thoroughly with melted butter then cover with a second sheet of pastry.

3. Place the salmon on the pastry, then arrange the prawns, lemon and lime zest, and the grapefruit fillets on top with parsley butter.

4. Fold into the width of the salmon and carefully roll up.

5. Place on a greased baking sheet and bake in a hot oven GM7\215°C\420°F for 20-25 minutes.

Shortbread Biscuits Crowned by Seasonal Berries
and Blackcurrant Meringue with Vanilla and Butterscotch Sauce

Paul Baron, Head Chef
James Hardy, Pastry Chef
Greywalls Hotel, Gullane

Ingredients

Shortbread Biscuits

4½ oz plain flour
3 oz hard unsalted butter
1½ oz icing sugar

Meringue

3 egg whites
6 oz caster sugar
2 fl oz water
2 fl oz blackcurrant sauce
8 oz seasonal fruits (strawberries, raspberries,
blueberries, blackcurrants)

Vanilla & Butterscotch Sauce

4 egg yolks
3 oz sugar
1 vanilla pod split lengthways
½ pint milk
1½ oz butter
1½ oz soft brown sugar
1½ oz golden syrup

(Serves four)

Method

For Shortbread

1. Blend flour, butter, icing sugar in mixer until bound together.

2. Roll out paste to ¼ inch thick and cut rounds with a 3 inch cutter.

3. Bake on GM7\220°C\425°F for 5 minutes. Leave to rest.

4. Put 6 oz caster sugar, 2 fl oz water in a copper pan and cook the sugar to 121°C\248°F.

5. Whilst sugar is cooking whisk the egg whites to form stiff peaks. Slowly pour sugar onto whites, beat until cold. Fold in 1 fl oz of blackcurrant juice.

For the Sauce

6. Cream yolks and sugar in a bowl.

7. In a saucepan bring milk and vanilla pod to boil. Pour onto yolks and sugar, whisk in butter, soft brown sugar and syrup and cook out to 105°C\225°F. Quickly cool over a bowl of ice.

8. Mix the berries with 1 fl oz of blackcurrant juice. Place a tablespoon of berries onto each biscuit, pipe meringue on top with a star nozzle, and bake for 4 minutes until browned. Arrange each biscuit in the centre of hot plates and border with the sauce. Garnish with a sprig of fresh mint and icing sugar.

Biscuits for Cheese

Anita Steffen
Cuilmore Cottage, Kinloch Rannoch

Ingredients

4 oz grated smoked Orkney cheese
4 oz butter
4 oz plain flour
teaspoon mix of salt, pepper, mustard powder

(Serves eight)

Method

1. Process the ingredients until mixed using the "pulse" button on food processor. Chill in plastic bag for 15 minutes then roll out very thinly and cut into shapes. Bake at GM4\180°C\350°F for 8 – 10 minutes until golden, and cool.

Tomato & Olive Spread

Anita Steffen
Cuilmore Cottage, Kinloch Rannoch

Ingredients

½ lb softened butter
1 large clove garlic (chopped)
small tin of anchovy fillets
4 oz of green olives (stoned)
5 sun-dried tomato halves
2 tablespoons capers
chopped parsley
5 chopped lovage leaves

(Serves eight to ten)

Method

1. Put all ingredients in food processor and "pulse" until evenly mixed. This mixture may be kept in refrigerator for 1 month.

2. This spread is served as a delicious accompaniment to home-made bread or rolls and butter served with dinner at Cuilmore.

Layers of Hazelnut and Heather Honey Wafers, Light Pear Mousse Garnished with Pearls of Apple
and Served on a Pool of Vanilla and Calvados Syrup

Shirley Smith, Chef
Balbirnie House Hotel, Markinch, by Glenrothes

--- Ingredients ---

Wafers
4½ oz unsalted butter
5 oz icing sugar
4½ oz soft flour
2 oz ground hazelnuts
1 teaspoon heather honey

Mousse
4 ripe pears, cooked and pureed
4 egg yolks
2 oz sugar
4 sheets gelatine soaked in cold water
7 fl oz milk
1 teaspoon vanilla flavouring
½ pint whipped cream
1 teaspoon Pear William liqueur (optional)
1 teaspoon lemon juice

Syrup
½ pint water
3½ oz brown sugar
1 vanilla pod
¼ pint white wine
¼ pint Calvados
pinch of cinnamon
1 lemon, squeezed
2 whole apples

(Serves six)

--- Method ---

Mousse

1. Cream the egg yolks with the sugar.

2. Boil the milk and vanilla, whisk into creamed egg and sugar. Replace into a clean pot and place on a low heat. Stir continuously until it thickens (do not boil) and remove from heat.

3. Squeeze excess water off soaked gelatine and stir into mix until dissolved. Add pear purée, lemon juice, Pear William and strain. Cool the mixture until it reaches the consistency of half whipped cream (almost setting).

4. Then gently fold through whipped cream into the mixture.

5. Pipe the mousse into ½ inch deep and 3 inch wide moulds and place in the refrigerator to set for approximately 1 hour.

Wafers

6. Mix all ingredients except egg whites to a smooth paste in a blender then add egg whites and blend for a further 30 seconds.

7. Lightly oil a baking tray. Using a 3 inch round template, spread the mixture evenly using a palette knife and bake in an oven GM4\180°C\350°F until edges of the biscuits are tinged a light golden brown colour.

8. Remove from the baking tray with a palette knife while still warm and cool on a wire tray.

Syrup

9. Peel apples using a medium sized parisienne scoop. Cut out 36 balls of apple and soak with lemon juice.

10. In a small pan add all ingredients for syrup and bring to the boil. Lightly blanch apples in syrup and then remove and cool. Continue to reduce syrup to a thick pouring consistency. Remove from heat, split vanilla pod, scrape and add to syrup. Strain and cool.

Serve

11. Pour syrup on plate. Garnish with apples round the plate and layer alternately the wafers and mousse. Finish with a wafer on top in the centre of the plate.

Henderson's Muesli

Henderson's Salad Table, Edinburgh

Ingredients

4 oz breakfast oatflakes
2 oz hazelnuts
¼ lemon
1 medium apple (approx 5 oz)
1 small orange (approx 3 oz)
1 oz raisins and/or sultanas
8 fl oz natural yoghurt
4 fl oz cream
4 fl oz dried fruit juice
(juice left from soaking dried fruit –
alternatively orange juice can be used)

(Serves four)

Method

1. In food processor, grate hazelnuts, whole orange, whole apple and lemon.

2. Add the remaining ingredients and mix thoroughly, ensuring that the orange and lemon rind is evenly distributed.

3. Decorate with fresh fruit and wheatgerm to serve.

Crisp Honey Wafer Biscuits layered with Raspberries
on a Rhubarb Ginger Sauce

Billy Campbell, Executive Chef
The Balmoral Hotel, Edinburgh

Ingredients

Honey Wafers

2 tablespoons unsalted butter, softened
1½ oz icing sugar, sifted
2 tablespoons clear honey
1½ oz plain flour, sifted
1 egg white
8 fl oz double cream
12 oz fresh raspberries, or wild strawberries
pinch of ginger
icing sugar for sifting

Rhubarb Sauce

12 oz fresh rhubarb, trimmed, skinned and sliced
2 fl oz water

Caramelised Lime Rinds

zest of 2 limes
6 oz granulated sugar
4 fl oz water

(Serves four)

Method
---

1. To prepare lime zest blanch twice. Mix sugar and water and bring to boil. When dissolved add lime zest and continue to cook until caramelised. Transfer to an oiled tray and separate with a fork and cool.

2. Combine rhubarb, sugar and water. Cover and simmer for 5 minutes. Uncover and continue to cook for a further 10 minutes or until tender. Purée in a food blender, strain and refrigerate until serving time.

3. In a bowl cream butter then add icing sugar, honey, flour, egg white and ginger one at a time until bound together.

4. Spoon teaspoons full of mixture on to an ungreased or non stick baking sheet and spread out with the back of a spoon to 3 inches diameter.

5. Ensure that there is a division between each of them and bake in oven GM7\215°C\420°F for approximately 3 minutes or until golden brown.

6. Let baking tray cool and continue process until mixture is finished. There should be approximately 24 wafers.

7. Whip cream and sort out raspberries or hull strawberries.

Presentation

8. Sift icing sugar over 4 wafers. Spread out a further 12 wafers and spread or pipe on cream. Cover each cream covered wafer with raspberries.

9. Place a spoonful of rhubarb sauce on to a chilled plate.

10. Stack 3 of the wafers on top of each other and place on to centre of plate. Top with icing sugar coated wafer.

11. Garnish round plate with raspberries and caramelised lime zest.

The 1996 Taste of Scotland Guide

is scheduled to be published in November 1995.

To reserve a copy at a special post inclusive price, just complete the coupon below indicating your method of payment and send it to:

> Taste of Scotland (Guide Sales)
> 33 Melville Street
> Edinburgh EH3 7JF

You will be placed on the priority list to receive the Guide as soon as it is published. For your convenience, we accept ACCESS and VISA

--✂

To: Taste of Scotland (Guide Sales), 33 Melville Street, Edinburgh EH3 7JF

Please send _____ copy/copies of
the Taste of Scotland 1996 Guide and debit my ACCESS/MASTERCARD/VISA (please delete as appropriate)

Card No. ⬜⬜⬜⬜⬜⬜⬜⬜⬜⬜⬜⬜⬜⬜⬜⬜⬜⬜⬜

Expiry Date   Month _____ Year _____

Account Name: _____

Signature _____

Please ✓ appropriate amount:

To addresses	in UK	£5.50
	in Europe	£7.00
	in North America (Airmail)	£9.00

Note: cheques in £ sterling also accepted

NAME: _____

ADDRESS: _____

_____

_____

POST CODE: _____ COUNTRY: _____

Bʟᴏᴄᴋ Cᴀᴘɪᴛᴀʟs, Pʟᴇᴀsᴇ

• Post inclusive prices to other countries availabile on request •

Taste of Scotland Guide

Taste of Scotland welcomes your recommendations on restaurants and hotels you have visited which you feel merit inclusion but are as yet not listed in the Taste of Scotland Guide.

Send to: Taste of Scotland, 33 Melville Street, Edinburgh EH3 7JF

THE MACALLAN TASTE OF SCOTLAND AWARDS 1995

I nominate_____(Establishment)
for a Macallan Taste of Scotland Award for the following category:
(Please tick one category only)

☐ Hotel of the Year   ☐ Country House Hotel of the Year   ☐ Restaurant of the Year

☐ Special Merit for ....   ☐ Personality of the Year ....

Name _____

Address _____

_____

_____

Date of visit _____

Meal (if appropriate) _____

Closing date for entries: 31 August 1995

-- ✂

Send to: Taste of Scotland, 33 Melville Street, Edinburgh EH3 7JF

THE MACALLAN TASTE OF SCOTLAND AWARDS 1995

I nominate_____(Establishment)
for a Macallan Taste of Scotland Award for the following category:
(Please tick one category only)

☐ Hotel of the Year   ☐ Country House Hotel of the Year   ☐ Restaurant of the Year

☐ Special Merit for ....   ☐ Personality of the Year ....

Name _____

Address _____

_____

_____

Date of visit _____

Meal (if appropriate) _____

Closing date for entries: 31 August 1995

Comments on meals in places listed in

The Taste of Scotland Guide are welcomed.

Send to Taste of Scotland, 33 Melville Street, Edinburgh EH3 7JF

95
O
E

Establishment visited _____

Date of visit _____ Meal(s) taken _____

Comments _____

_____

_____

_____

_____

_____

_____

Name_____

Address_____

_____

_____

✂ --

Comments on meals in places listed in

The Taste of Scotland Guide are welcomed.

Send to Taste of Scotland, 33 Melville Street, Edinburgh EH3 7JF

95
O
E

Establishment visited _____

Date of visit _____ Meal(s) taken _____

Comments _____

_____

_____

_____

_____

_____

_____

Name_____

Address_____

_____

_____

Send to: Taste of Scotland, 33 Melville Street, Edinburgh EH3 7JF

THE MACALLAN TASTE OF SCOTLAND AWARDS 1995

I nominate_____(Establishment)
for a Macallan Taste of Scotland Award for the following category:
(Please tick one category only)

☐ Hotel of the Year ☐ Country House Hotel of the Year ☐ Restaurant of the Year

☐ Special Merit for .... ☐ Personality of the Year ....

Name _____

Address _____

_____

_____

Date of visit _____

Meal (if appropriate) _____

Closing date for entries: 31 August 1995

- -

Send to: Taste of Scotland, 33 Melville Street, Edinburgh EH3 7JF

THE MACALLAN TASTE OF SCOTLAND AWARDS 1995

I nominate_____(Establishment)
for a Macallan Taste of Scotland Award for the following category:
(Please tick one category only)

☐ Hotel of the Year ☐ Country House Hotel of the Year ☐ Restaurant of the Year

☐ Special Merit for .... ☐ Personality of the Year ....

Name _____

Address _____

_____

_____

Date of visit _____

Meal (if appropriate) _____

Closing date for entries: 31 August 1995

Comments on meals in places listed in

The Taste of Scotland Guide are welcomed.

Send to Taste of Scotland, 33 Melville Street, Edinburgh EH3 7JF

95
O
E

Establishment visited _____

Date of visit _____Meal(s) taken_____

Comments _____

_____

_____

_____

_____

_____

_____

Name_____

Address_____

_____

_____

✂ -

Comments on meals in places listed in

The Taste of Scotland Guide are welcomed.

Send to Taste of Scotland, 33 Melville Street, Edinburgh EH3 7JF

95
O
E

Establishment visited _____

Date of visit _____Meal(s) taken_____

Comments _____

_____

_____

_____

_____

_____

_____

Name_____

Address_____

_____

_____

Index – 1995

** New Member

Taste of Scotland Guide 1995

EDITOR

NANCY K CAMPBELL BA

PUBLISHED BY

TASTE OF SCOTLAND SCHEME LTD,

A NON-PROFIT MAKING COMPANY LIMITED BY GUARANTEE TRADING AS TASTE OF SCOTLAND

DESIGN, ILLUSTRATION & TYPESETTING

DAVID FRAME CREATIVE

EDINBURGH

PRINTED BY

MACKENZIE & STORRIE LTD

LEITH, EDINBURGH

FRONT COVER PHOTOGRAPH

BONNINGTON LINN, THE FALLS OF CLYDE

BACK COVER

VIEW ACROSS RIVER TAY FROM FIFE

THE TERRACE AT THE SHERATON GRAND HOTEL, EDINBURGH

COLOUR PHOTOGRAPHY

COURTESY OF

ALEX GILLESPIE PHOTOGRAPHY, FORT WILLIAM

AYRSHIRE TOURIST BOARD

BUTE & COWAL TOURIST BOARD

CLYDE VALLEY TOURIST BOARD

DUMFRIES & GALLOWAY TOURIST BOARD

DUNDEE TOURIST BOARD

EDINBURGH TOURIST BOARD

FORTH VALLEY TOURIST BOARD

GRAMPIAN HIGHLAND & ABERDEEN TOURISM

GREATER GLASGOW TOURIST BOARD

INVERNESS, LOCH NESS & NAIRN TOURIST BOARD

ISLE OF ARRAN TOURIST BOARD

JAMES GARDINER ASSOCIATES/MIDLOTHIAN TOURISM ASSOCIATION

MORAY TOURIST BOARD/ANNE BURGESS

PERTHSHIRE TOURIST BOARD

SCOTTISH BORDERS TOURIST BOARD

SHERATON GRAND HOTEL, EDINBURGH

WESTERN ISLES TOURIST BOARD

TASTE OF SCOTLAND SCHEME LTD.

33 MELVILLE STREET

EDINBURGH EH3 7JF

TEL: 0131 220 1900

FAX: 0131 220 6102

ISBN 1 871445 06 X